JOURNEYS IN

Math 8

RALPH D. CONNELLY
JACK W. LESAGE
JEFFERY D. MARTIN
THOMAS O'SHEA
J. NORMAN C. SHARP
R. HUGH BEATTIE
FRED BILOUS
WILLIAM C. BOBER
BRIAN BRIGHT
DALE R. DROST
JACK A. HOPE
RALPH LEE
STELLA TOSSELL

Ginn and Company
Educational Publishers

ISBN 0-7702-1433-9
C98204

EDITORS
Barry Scully
Janet Scully
Shirley Miller
Mary Agnes Challoner

COMPUTER MATERIAL
Gemini Education Group, Inc.

Printed and bound in Canada
ABCDEFG 89876

Authors and Consultants

RALPH D. CONNELLY
Associate Professor
College of Education
Brock University
St. Catharines, Ontario

JEFFERY D. MARTIN
Mathematics Head
Etobicoke Collegiate
Etobicoke, Ontario

J. NORMAN C. SHARP
Former Mathematics Coordinator
Etobicoke Board of Education
Etobicoke, Ontario

FRED BILOUS
Vice Principal
Hedges Junior High School
Winnipeg, Manitoba

BRIAN BRIGHT
Principal
St. Francis School
Halifax, Nova Scotia

JACK A. HOPE
Associate Professor
Department of Curriculum Studies
University of Saskatchewan
Saskatoon, Saskatchewan

STELLA TOSSELL
Mathematics Consultant
Ginn and Company
Former Mathematics Consultant
North York Board of Education
North York, Ontario

JACK W. LESAGE
Assistant Head of Mathematics
Eastview Secondary School
Barrie, Ontario

THOMAS O'SHEA
Assistant Professor
Faculty of Education
Simon Fraser University
Burnaby, British Columbia

R. HUGH BEATTIE
Mathematics Coordinator
North York Board of Education
North York, Ontario

WILLIAM C. BOBER
Mathematics Coordinator
Edmonton Separate School Board
Edmonton, Alberta

DALE R. DROST
Consultant in
Mathematics Education
Fredericton, New Brunswick

RALPH LEE
Teacher, Grades 7, 8, 9
Vernon Barford Junior High School
Edmonton, Alberta

Contents

1/Whole Numbers

Astronomers study the universe—planets, stars, constellations,...They use numbers to catalogue the celestial bodies for easy reference.

Get Set

1. Add mentally. Look for sums of 10.
   a. $6 + 5 + 4 + 5 + 9$
   b. $3 + 8 + 6 + 7 + 2$
   c. $5 + 1 + 8 + 9 + 3 + 5 + 7$
   d. $2 + 5 + 6 + 8 + 3 + 4 + 7 + 5$

2. Copy and complete by adding.

   a.
78	49	
97	77	
33	58	

   b.
187	212	505	
324	197	483	

3. Copy and complete.

   a.
33		74
	49	
47		137

   b.
42	61		152
	29		
		86	300

4. Multiply the number by 1001.
   a. 123   b. 204   c. 189   d. 675

5. Divide.
   a. $2 \overline{)\ 285\ 714}$ b. $3 \overline{)\ 428\ 571}$
   c. $\dfrac{571\ 428}{4}$ d. $\dfrac{714\ 285}{5}$
   e. $857\ 142 \div 6$ f. $999\ 999 \div 7$

6. Round to the nearest hundred.
   a. 917   b. 3491   c. 19 546

7. Round to the nearest thousand.
   a. 7500   b. 68 912   c. 714 283

8. Can the number be divided by 2 exactly?
   a. 416   b. 87   c. 520

9. Can the number be divided by 3 exactly?
   a. 312   b. 76   c. 503

10. Which numbers have only 2 factors?
    a. 13   b. 31   c. 12   d. 17
    e. 42   f. 28   g. 23   h. 19

11. Find the area of the square.
    a.   b.   c.
    10 cm   8 cm   3 cm

12. Which number is the exponent?
    a. 5^3 b. 7^4 c. 8^9

13. Find the product.
    a. 2×2 b. $2 \times 2 \times 2$
    c. $3 \times 3 \times 3$ d. $3 \times 3 \times 3 \times 3$

14. Does the division give a quotient of 1?
    a. $\dfrac{25}{5}$ b. $\dfrac{5}{5}$ c. $\dfrac{5 \times 5}{5 \times 5}$ d. $\dfrac{5 \times 5 \times 5}{5 \times 5}$

15. Which number does not appear to belong? Explain.
    a. 2, 4, 7, 8, 10, 12
    b. 10, 20, 30, 35, 40
    c. 1, 3, 5, 7, 10, 11

16. Write three possible numbers to complete the pattern.
    a. 1, 4, 7, ☐, ☐, ☐
    b. 1, 2, 4, ☐, ☐, ☐
    c. 160, 80, 40, ☐, ☐, ☐

17. Evaluate mentally.
    a. $46 + 34 + 82$
    b. $241 - 139$
    c. $37 \times 56 \times 0 \times 7$

Numbers in Our World

Computers are being used more and more in our world. Efficient use requires that people, places, and products be represented by numbers.

Gail lives in Ottawa, Canada. Her grandmother lives in Lyon, France. To call her grandmother directly, Gail dials

	Country code	Routing code	Local number
011	33	7	417 90318

If Gail needs operator assistance, she dials 01 instead of 011, followed by the remaining eleven digits.

Country	City	Country Code	Routing Code	Digits in local number
France	Lyon	33	7	8
	Rouen	33	35	8
Greece	Athens	30	1	7 or 8
	Rodos	30	241	7 or 8
Israel	Ako	972	4	6–8
	Holon	972	3	6–8
Italy	Naples	39	81	5–10
	Venice	39	41	5–10
Japan	Gifu	81	582	8 or 9
	Osaka	81	6	8 or 9

WORKING TOGETHER

1. Which country and city will you reach if you dial the number?

   a. 011   39   81   70592

   b. 011   81   6   10751833

   c. 01   972   3   513482

   d. 01   30   1   1050946

   e. 011   33   35   77419246

   f. 01   39   41   465283

2. At Brennan's Meat Market 50 numbers are recycled. When the market opened 16 was showing, and when the market closed 31 was showing. How many customers might have been served that day?

   CUSTOMERS PLEASE TAKE A NUMBER.

   31

1. What is the greatest number of digits that may be used to call someone here?

   a. Ako, Israel   **b.** Venice, Italy

   c. Rodos, Greece

2. What is the least number of digits needed to call someone in this place?

   a. Naples, Italy   **b.** Osaka, Japan

   c. Holon, Israel

3. The ninth digit of every Social Insurance Number (SIN) is a check digit. The first eight digits of Ellen's SIN are 424 748 38.

   a. Find the sum of the 1st, 3rd, 5th, and 7th digits.

   b. Find each product.
   2 × 2nd digit, 2 × 4th digit
   2 × 6th digit, 2 × 8th digit

   c. Find the sum of the digits in the products from part **b**.

   d. Add the results from part **a** and part **c**.

   e. Take the ones digit of the result from part **d** and subtract it from 10. This difference is the check digit.

   f. Write the complete nine-digit SIN.

4. Use the method of exercise 3. Calculate the check digit.

   a. 624 759 86 ☐   **b.** 238 147 32 ☐

   c. 481 549 26 ☐   **d.** 534 626 18 ☐

5. Is the Social Insurance Number valid?

   a. 422 312 652   **b.** 235 816 473

6. Which digit cannot serve as a check digit? Explain.

7. Make a valid SIN that has 8 as its check digit.

8. Computer programmers may use a secret code to protect a program from being copied. Using all five symbols B, T, *, #, !, once each, how many different codes that begin and end with a letter are possible?

9. An overseas phone call to Rodos, Greece, used 14 digits.

   a. Was this a direct or operator-assisted call?

   b. What number might have been dialled?

Freshness expiry dates use two letters for the month and two digits for the day.

1. Which two letters would you use for each month in coding freshness expiry dates?

2. Which letters would you use in two-letter codes to represent each province and territory?

3. What other two-letter codes do you know?

Try This

3

Estimating Results

The chart shows the paid attendance for three events at the stadium in B.C. Place.

Event	Attendance
Football	59 126
Baseball	32 435
Concert	15 445

- About how many people attended the two sports events?

  Estimate. Use numbers that can be added quickly in your head.

  $$
  \begin{array}{rcr}
  59\ 126 & \to & 60\ 000 \\
  +\ 32\ 435 & \to & +\ 32\ 000 \\
  \hline
   & & 92\ 000
  \end{array}
  $$

  About 92 000 people attended the sports events.

- The attendance for all three events was more than 7 times the attendance at the concert. About how many people attended in all?

  Estimate. Use numbers that can be multiplied quickly in your head.

  $$
  \begin{array}{rcr}
  15\ 445 & \to & 15\ 000 \\
  \times\ 7 & \to & \times\ 7 \\
  \hline
   & & 105\ 000
  \end{array}
  $$

  About 105 000 people attended in all.

- About how many more people attended the football game than the concert?

  Estimate. Use numbers that can be subtracted quickly in your head.

  $$
  \begin{array}{rcr}
  59\ 126 & \to & 60\ 000 \\
  -\ 15\ 445 & \to & -\ 15\ 000 \\
  \hline
   & & 45\ 000
  \end{array}
  $$

  About 45 000 more people attended the football game.

- The attendance for 3 recent home football games was 123 798. About how many people attended per game?

  Estimate. Use numbers that can be divided quickly in your head.

  $$
  3\,\overline{)\,123\ 798} \quad \to \quad 3\,\overline{)\,120\ 000}^{\ 40\ 000}
  $$

  About 40 000 people attended per game.

WORKING TOGETHER

Estimate.

a. $\begin{array}{r} 4828 \\ +\ 3746 \\ \hline \end{array}$ **b.** $\begin{array}{r} 59\ 478 \\ -\ 34\ 351 \\ \hline \end{array}$ **c.** $\begin{array}{r} 40\ 782 \\ \times\ 9 \\ \hline \end{array}$ **d.** $7\,\overline{)\,47\ 954}$ **e.** $\dfrac{3874}{8}$

1. Choose the best estimate.

15 000	60 000	70 000
30 000	80 000	100 000

a. 74 378
  + 13 413

b. 65 074
  + 32 109

c. 89 101
  − 9 817

d. 47 412
  − 15 807

e. 15 062
  + 17 193

f. 70 106
  − 12 040

2. Choose the best estimate.

4 000	15 000	12 000
10 000	9 000	20 000

a. 2217
  × 7

b. 2756
  × 3

c. 5 ⟌ 92 471

d. $\frac{29\ 875}{8}$

e. 1875
  × 6

f. 42 418 ÷ 4

3. About how many times greater was the attendance at B.C. Place?

   a. at the football game than at the concert

   b. at the baseball game than at the concert

4. a. Estimate the combined area of the four largest islands in Canada.

Island	Area (km²)
Baffin	507 451
Victoria	217 290
Ellesmere	196 236
Newfoundland	108 860

   b. About how many times larger is Baffin Island than Newfoundland?

   c. Make other size comparisons.

5. a. Estimate the total area covered by the oceans.

Ocean	Area (km²)
Pacific	166 241 000
Atlantic	86 557 000
Indian	73 427 000
Arctic	9 485 000

   b. Estimate the difference in area between the Pacific and the Atlantic.

   c. The total area of the earth is about three times the area of the Pacific Ocean. What is the area of the earth?

   d. Make other size comparisons.

Try This

When estimating sums, some numbers may be ignored.

1. Which numbers could you ignore when estimating the sum?

a. 17 533
     71
   8 579
  + 24 105

b. 94 161
     875
     107
  + 12 074

c. 49 070
   8 947
     75
  + 202

2. Estimate each sum in exercise 1.

3. a. Which populations could you ignore?

Community	Population
Arnprior	6 111
North York	559 521
Oshawa	117 519
Parry Sound	5 501
Sudbury	91 829

   b. Estimate the total population.

Adding and Subtracting

At one time there were many more
whales in our oceans than there are now.

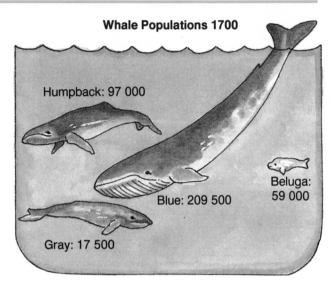

Whale Populations 1700

Humpback: 97 000

Beluga: 59 000

Blue: 209 500

Gray: 17 500

- What was the total population of
these species of whale in 1700?

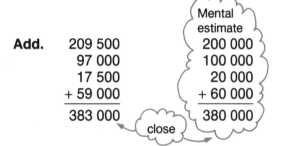

Add.		Mental estimate
	209 500	200 000
	97 000	100 000
	17 500	20 000
	+ 59 000	+ 60 000
	383 000	380 000

close

The total population of these species was 383 000.

- Today the total population of these four species has
dropped to 62 700. How much has the
population decreased?

Subtract.		Mental estimate
	383 000	380 000
	− 62 700	− 60 000
	320 300	320 000

close

The population has decreased by 320 300 whales.

WORKING TOGETHER

1. What was the combined population?

   a. blue whales and gray whales

   b. humpback, beluga, and gray whales

2. What was the difference in the
   populations of the beluga and the gray
   whales?

3. Find the result.

   a. 22 107
          + 97 412

   b. 4589
          − 2170

   c. 42 483
          + 51 407

   d. 9104
          − 8203

1. Add.

 a. 5436 **b.** 1843 **c.** 297
   9274   754   9135
   + 3865   + 87   + 92

 d. 148 + 795 + 42 **e.** 71 425 + 2053

2. Add only if the sum is greater than 1200.

 a. 553 **b.** 448 **c.** 309
   194   612   483
  + 176   + 349   + 728

 d. 605 + 312 + 79 **e.** 583 + 94 + 812

3. Subtract.

 a. 9384 **b.** 4652 **c.** 25 634
  − 5278   − 2546   − 18 942

 d. 8412 − 2301 **e.** 7943 − 5872

4. Subtract if difference is less than 4000.

 a. 8193 **b.** 9605 **c.** 48 109
  − 2585   − 8483   − 46 876

 d. 7053 − 5161 **e.** 6872 − 985

5.

Whale species	Population	
	Past	Present
Bowhead	20 900	2 300
Fin	494 000	98 700
Sei	199 500	75 200

 a. What are the total whale populations for the past and for the present?

 b. Which species had the greatest decrease in population?

6. The chart shows recent costs of controlling pollution in North America.

Type	Cost ($billions)
air pollution	393
water pollution	228
solid waste pollution	22
land reclamation	19
noise	11
toxic wastes	11

 a. Would $600 billion be enough to spend to control pollution?

 b. What is the approximate total cost?

7.

Corporation	Sales ($) in a recent year
Bell Canada	5 264 739 000
Canadian Pacific	8 150 000 000
Chrysler Canada	2 570 160 000
Hudson's Bay Co.	3 435 209 000
Imperial Oil Ltd.	6 623 000 000
Noranda Mines	2 484 690 000

 a. List the corporations in order of sales, greatest to least.

 b. Estimate the total sales for the top 3.

8. Three darts hit the target. List the different possible point totals.

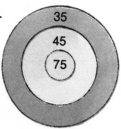

Use short division.

a. 7) 518 **b.** 5) 3450 **c.** 8) 17 424 **d.** 9) 205 875 **e.** 6) 745 806

Multiplying and Dividing

- Jupiter is the largest planet in our solar system.
  Its diameter is about 11 times that of Earth.
  The diameter of Earth is about 12 680 km (kilometres).
  What is the diameter of Jupiter?

Multiply.

$$
\begin{array}{r}
12\ 680 \\
\times\ 11 \\
\hline
12\ 680 \\
126\ 80 \\
\hline
139\ 480
\end{array}
$$

(close)

$$
\begin{array}{r}
13\ 000 \\
\times\ 10 \\
\hline
130\ 000
\end{array}
$$

The diameter of Jupiter is about 139 480 km.

- Jupiter is about 588 810 000 km from Earth.
  It took Voyager 1 19 months to reach Jupiter.
  About how far did Voyager 1 travel each month?

Divide.

$$
\begin{array}{r}
30\ 990\ 000 \\
19\,\overline{)\,588\ 810\ 000} \\
57 \\
\hline
188 \\
171 \\
\hline
171 \\
171 \\
\hline
0
\end{array}
$$

(close)

$$
\begin{array}{r}
30\ 000\ 000 \\
20\,\overline{)\,600\ 000\ 000}
\end{array}
$$

Voyager 1 travelled about 30 990 000 km each month.

WORKING TOGETHER

1. Choose the best estimate.

6 000	120 000	800
60 000	20 000	2 000
90	1 000	12 000

   a. $\begin{array}{r} 210 \\ \times\ 28 \end{array}$ **b.** $\begin{array}{r} 380 \\ \times\ 47 \end{array}$ **c.** $\begin{array}{r} 605 \\ \times\ 21 \end{array}$

   d. $12\,\overline{)\,8279}$ **e.** $102\,\overline{)\,8924}$

2. The diameter of our sun is about 10 times the diameter of Jupiter. What is the diameter of the sun?

3. The diameter of Earth's moon is 3456 km. About how many times greater is Earth's diameter than the diameter of its moon?

APPLICATIONS AND EXERCISES

1. Multiply.
   a. 725
      × 64

   b. 634
      × 18

   c. 916
      × 34

   d. 1209
      × 45

   e. 3147
      × 63

   f. 7009
      × 86

2. Multiply only if the product is greater than 30 000.
   a. 6950
      × 4

   b. 8126
      × 5

   c. 6043
      × 6

   d. 394
      × 82

   e. 316
      × 83

   f. 431
      × 79

3. Divide.
   a. 96) 2592
   b. 27) 2565
   c. 72) 27 792
   d. 58) 124 294

4. Divide only if the quotient is greater than 150.
   a. 626) 28 796
   b. 33) 6336
   c. 82) 37 884
   d. 39) 16 497

5. a. Multiply each number in the box by 1.
   b. Divide each number by 1.
   c. State rules for multiplying and dividing by 1.

748	1092	47 126
3805	635	90 173

6. Copy and complete. Use a calculator to check.
   a. $75 \times 97 = 97 \times \square$
   b. $48 \times 77 = 77 \times \square$
   c. $292 \times 65 = 65 \times \square$
   d. $493 \times 86 = 86 \times \square$

7. a. State a rule illustrated in exercise 6.
   b. Does this rule also work for addition, subtraction, and division?

8. A fruit grower has 37 rows of pear trees each containing 29 trees. He estimates each tree will yield 25 baskets of pears. About how many baskets are needed?

9. Estimate the monthly sales of each company.

Sales for a recent year	
Company	Sales ($)
Alcan Aluminum	5 132 160 000
C.N.R.	3 294 360 000
INCO Ltd.	2 915 040 000
Ontario Hydro	2 568 120 000
Provigo Inc.	2 314 452 000

10. The Pioneer 10 spacecraft covered about 4 552 600 000 km in 11 a (years). About what distance was covered each year?

KEEPING SHARP

1. Multiply mentally.
   a. 689×10
   b. 621×10
   c. 963×100
   d. 89×1000
   e. $136 \times 10\ 000$
   f. $206 \times 10\ 000$

2. State a rule for multiplying by 10, 100, 1000, ...

3. Divide mentally.
   a. $670 \div 10$
   b. $1720 \div 10$
   c. $1900 \div 100$
   d. $2000 \div 1000$
   e. $4000 \div 1000$
   f. $20\ 000 \div 10\ 000$

4. State a rule for dividing by 10, 100, 1000, ...

9

Divisibility Tests

At Lake Street Public School, 282 students register to play intramural volleyball.
Each volleyball team has 6 players.
Is each student on a team?

Divide.

$$\begin{array}{r} 4\ 7\ \text{R0} \\ 6\ )\overline{2\ 8\,\substack{4}2} \end{array}$$ The division is exact.

The 282 students make up 47 teams with 0 students left. Each student is on a team.

If the remainder is 0 when dividing a number by 6, the number is **divisible** by 6.

This chart shows tests that can be used to determine if a whole number is divisible by 2, 3, 4, 5, 8, 9, or 10.

Divisor	Divisibility test	
2 5 10	Is the last digit	{ an even number? 0 or 5? 0?
3 9	Is the sum of the digits	{ divisible by 3? divisible by 9?
4 8	Is the number formed by the last	{ two digits divisible by 4? three digits divisible by 8?

WORKING TOGETHER

1. For each divisibility test in the chart, give a three-digit number that works.

2. Examine the last digit in 5784.
   a. Is the last digit an even number?
   b. Is 5784 divisible by 2?
   c. Is the last digit a 0 or 5?
   d. Is 5784 divisible by 5?
   e. Is 5784 divisible by 10?

3. Add the digits in 5784.
   a. Is the sum divisible by 3? by 9?
   b. Is 5784 divisible by 3? by 9?

4. Examine the last digits in 5784.
   a. Are the last two digits divisible by 4?
   b. Are the last three digits divisible by 8?
   c. Is 5784 divisible by 4? by 8?

APPLICATIONS AND EXERCISES

1. Is the number divisible by 2?

    a. 21 588   **b.** 29 505   **c.** 4950

    d. 83 761   **e.** 58 420   **f.** 35 116

2. Which numbers in exercise 1 are divisible?

    a. by 5   **b.** by 10

3. Is the number divisible by 4?

    a. 57 396   **b.** 29 124   **c.** 30 562

    d. 18 920   **e.** 73 518   **f.** 14 440

4. Which numbers in exercise 3 are divisible by 8?

5. Find all possible digits for □ that would make the number divisible by 3.

    a. 41 78□   **b.** 10 83□   **c.** 22 10□

    d. □753   **e.** 8□99   **f.** 74 □15

6. A baseball team uses 9 players on the field. Will each of the 379 girls and boys who register for a play day be on the field?

7. The modern Olympic Games began in 1896. They are held in years divisible by 4. Is the year an Olympic year?

    a. 1928   **b.** 1952   **c.** 1962   **d.** 1978

8.

1 797	19 284	43 706
47 250	12 458	89 448

    a. Which numbers are divisible by 2?

    b. Which numbers are divisible by 3?

    c. Which numbers are divisible by both 2 and 3?

    d. Which numbers are divisible by 6?

    e. Copy and complete.
A whole number is divisible by 6 if it is divisible by ⬚ and ⬚.

9. Does the division have a remainder 0?

    a. 27 520 ÷ 5   **b.** 58 624 ÷ 2

    c. 15 085 ÷ 3   **d.** 94 313 ÷ 9

    e. 48 138 ÷ 6   **f.** 10 942 ÷ 4

    g. 73 651 ÷ 8   **h.** 86 185 ÷ 10

10. The second digit of a three-digit number is 7. The number is divisible by 3 and 5. Find all the numbers it could possibly be.

11. Carlos wants to cut this fabric into rectangular pieces measuring 5 cm by 6 cm (centimetres). Can he do it without any waste?

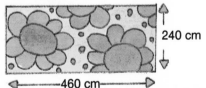

240 cm

◄————460 cm————►

What do the keys of your calculator, other than the numbered keys, do?

1. List each key and its function. Experiment using simple numbers with any key whose function is not clear.

2. Give an example to show the correct use of each key.

3. Which keys can perform the same function as ⊟ ?

Prime and Composite Numbers

The many colors on a television screen are produced by projecting three basic colors of light—red, blue, and green. When these three colors are blended, other colors result.

In mathematics, all whole numbers greater than 1 are formed from basic numbers called **prime numbers**. When various prime numbers are multiplied, the other numbers result.

A prime number has exactly two distinct **factors**, itself and 1.

A **composite number** has more than two distinct factors.

11 is a prime number. Its only factors are 11 and 1.

10 is a composite number. Its factors are 1, 2, 5, and 10.

The number 1 is neither a prime number nor a composite number.
A composite number can be expressed as a product of prime factors.

Method One Making a Factor Tree Express 60 as a product of prime factors. 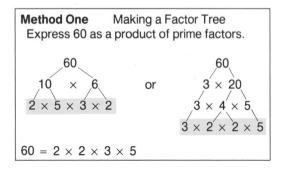 $60 = 2 \times 2 \times 3 \times 5$	**Method Two** Dividing by Prime Factors Express 60 as a product of prime factors. $60 \div 2 = 30$ $2 \overline{)60}$ $30 \div 2 = 15$ $2 \overline{)30}$ $15 \div 3 = 5$ or $3 \overline{)15}$ 5 $60 = 2 \times 2 \times 3 \times 5$

As a product of prime factors, 60 is $2 \times 2 \times 3 \times 5$.

WORKING TOGETHER

1. Is the number a prime number?
   - **a.** 7
   - **b.** 10
   - **c.** 13
   - **d.** 3
   - **e.** 18
   - **f.** 29
   - **g.** 25
   - **h.** 41

2. Is the number a composite number?
   - **a.** 33
   - **b.** 23
   - **c.** 12
   - **d.** 20

3. Find the smallest prime factor.
   - **a.** 18
   - **b.** 45
   - **c.** 30
   - **d.** 111

4. Write each number in exercise 3 as the product of prime factors.

1. List the first ten prime numbers.

2. Find the prime factors.

   a. 16   **b.** 12   **c.** 10   **d.** 24

   e. 25   **f.** 28   **g.** 40   **h.** 42

   i. 54   **j.** 100   **k.** 315   **l.** 924

3. Express the number as the product of its prime factors.

   a. 15   **b.** 27   **c.** 48   **d.** 30

   e. 36   **f.** 78   **g.** 96   **h.** 205

   i. 414   **j.** 420   **k.** 693   **l.** 2625

4. Is the statement true?

   a. 4 is the smallest composite number.

   b. 1 is not a composite number.

   c. 1 is a prime number.

   d. 2 is the only even prime number.

   e. 13 is the largest prime number.

   f. 99 is a prime number.

5. Find all the factors of the number.

   a. 12   **b.** 20   **c.** 27   **d.** 30

   e. 45   **f.** 52   **g.** 56   **h.** 65

6. Teresa swam a number of lengths of a pool. The coach told her that she swam 500 m (metres). Find the lengths possible for the pool. Which length is most likely the actual length?

7. Louis is asked to arrange 40 chairs in rows of equal length. How many chairs can be put in each row?

8. The mass of a beaker is 20 g (grams). A number of identical ball bearings are placed in the beaker. The new mass is 284 g. How many ball bearings can there be in the beaker?

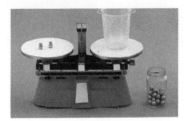

9. Find the sum of the 11 smallest prime numbers. Write the sum as the product of prime factors.

10. One way 33 can be written as a sum of three different prime numbers is
    $$33 = 5 + 11 + 17.$$
    List other possible ways.

11. An even number less than 100 is divisible by 3 and by 7. Which numbers have these properties?

12. Reversing the digits of a prime number may result in a prime number. For example, 17 is a prime and so is 71. Find three other such pairs of prime numbers.

Try This

A **perfect number** is one that can be expressed as the sum of all its factors, excluding itself.

6 is a perfect number.   6 = 1 + 2 + 3

Find another perfect number.

1. Stores sometimes obtain a telephone number that can be spelled out to give two words associated with their product.
   For example, PET SHOP has the telephone number 738-7476.
   Give the telephone number associated with each of these stores.
   a. MAX MILK   b. SNO BLOW
   c. TOP DISC   d. RECORDS

2. Choose the best estimate.

70 000		60 000
50 000	110 000	30 000
90 000		80 000

   a.   57 384   b.   32 715   c.   84 320
       + 46 092   + 37 444   + 11 819

   d. 4889 × 5   e. 16 451 × 3

3. Choose the best estimate.

50 000		40 000
	60 000	
70 000		30 000

   a.   83 750   b.   59 683   c.   104 736
       − 47 064   − 8 561   − 62 842

   d. 4) 158 260   e. 9) 257 048

4. Copy and complete the Magic Squares.

   a.
		868
	1085	1953
		434

   b.
2868	146	
	1530	

   Magic Sum: 4590

5. Multiply.
   a.   485   b.   8500   c.   384
       × 92   × 54   × 107

6. Divide.
   a. 29) 986   b. 89) 45 034
   c. 8164 ÷ 26   d. 61 584 ÷ 48

7. Multiply only if the product is greater than 20 000.
   a.   962   b.   635   c.   660
       × 25   × 26   × 37

8. Divide if the quotient is less than 200.
   a. 22) 3256   b. $\frac{29\,631}{83}$ c. 47) 6486

9. Sebastian can read 205 words per minute. How many words can he read in half an hour?

10. Total attendance at Donway Junior High for 21 school days in November was 19 467. What was daily attendance?

11. Which numbers are divisible by 2?
    a. 16 217   b. 18 612   c. 624 119
    d. 10 002   e. 5850   f. 111 111 111

12. Which numbers in exercise 11 are divisible by these numbers?
    a. 3   b. 6   c. 9   d. 5

13. Which numbers are prime?
    a. 13   b. 26   c. 37   d. 45

14. Find the prime factors.
    a. 10   b. 18   c. 25   d. 124

14

Permutations

Permutation means changing around.

A permutation of letters is called an **anagram**.

spot…tops…pots…stop…

1. Choose a three-letter word and write each anagram.

2. Choose a four-letter word and write each anagram.

3. Choose a five- and a six-letter word and write each anagram.

The permutation of some numbers creates special numbers.

71 is a permutation of the digits in the number 17.

71 and 17 are prime numbers.

71 and 17 are a **permuprime pair**.

031, 310, 301, and 013 are permutations of the digits in the number 103.

031, 013, and 103 are prime numbers.

031, 013, and 103 form a **permuprime set**.

4. Find as many permuprime pairs as you can.

5. Find as many permuprime sets as you can.

196 is a permutation of the digits in the number 169.

196 and 169 are squares.

196 and 169 are **permusquare pairs**.

$$196 = 14^2$$
$$169 = 13^2$$

6. Find as many permusquare pairs as you can.

7. Find as many permucube pairs as you can.

Exponents

Laura is studying bacteria through a powerful microscope. Each hour she observes that the number of bacteria is double that of the previous hour. How many bacteria will there be after 5 h?

Hours	Number of bacteria
0	1
1	2
2	2×2
3	$2 \times 2 \times 2$
4	$2 \times 2 \times 2 \times 2$
5	$2 \times 2 \times 2 \times 2 \times 2$

There will be $2 \times 2 \times 2 \times 2 \times 2$, or 32, bacteria.

$\underbrace{2 \times 2 \times 2 \times 2 \times 2}_{\text{5 factors}}$ can be expressed as 2^5. exponent base

2^5 is a **power**. It can be read as "two to the fifth" or "two to the exponent five."

- Express the product $3^5 \times 3^3$ as a single power.

$$3^5 \times 3^3$$
$$= 3 \times 3 \times 3 \times 3 \times 3 \times 3 \times 3 \times 3$$
$$= 3^8$$

What shortcut simplifies the product of two powers with the same base?

- Express the quotient $\frac{3^5}{3^3}$ as a single power.

$$\frac{3^5}{3^3} = \frac{3 \times 3 \times 3 \times 3 \times 3}{3 \times 3 \times 3}$$
$$= 3 \times 3$$
$$= 3^2$$

What shortcut simplifies the quotient of two powers with the same base?

WORKING TOGETHER

1. Copy and complete.

   a. $10 \times 10 \times 10 = 10^{\square}$

   b. $7 \times 7 \times 7 \times 7 = 7^{\square}$

   c. $2 \times 2 \times 2 \times 2 \times 2 \times 2 = \square^6$

2. Express as a power.

   a. $6 \times 6 \times 6$ b. $9 \times 9 \times 9 \times 9$

3. Express as a product. Evaluate.

   a. 5^2 b. 7^3 c. 3^3 d. 2^6

4. Express as a single power.

   a. $2^3 \times 2^2$ b. $5^2 \times 5^2$ c. $10^4 \times 10^1$

   d. $\frac{4^3}{4^1}$ e. $\frac{10^6}{10^4}$ f. $\frac{2^8}{2^5}$

APPLICATIONS AND EXERCISES

1. Express as a power.
   a. $2 \times 2 \times 2$ b. $5 \times 5 \times 5 \times 5$
   c. $3 \times 3 \times 3 \times 3 \times 3 \times 3$
   d. $10 \times 10 \times 10 \times 10 \times 10 \times 10 \times 10$

2. Express as a single power.
   a. $2^4 \times 2^3$ b. $5^3 \times 5^3$ c. $7^6 \times 7^2$
   d. $3^8 \times 3^3$ e. $8^9 \times 8^{10}$ f. $6^4 \times 6^2$
   g. $15^2 \times 15^2$ h. $10^6 \times 10^1$

3. Express as a product. Evaluate.
   a. 7^2 b. 3^4 c. 5^3 d. 15^2
   e. 2^4 f. 4^4 g. 10^5 h. 9^3

4. Which number is greatest?
   a. 100^4, 1000^3, $10\ 000^2$
   b. 1^{16}, 2^8, 4^5, 8^2

5. The value of 12^2 is 144. Reversing the digits of 12 gives $21^2 = 441$.
   a. Compare the digits of 144 and 441.
   b. Find two other two-digit numbers with the same feature.

6. Express as a single power. Evaluate.
   a. $\frac{3^7}{3^4}$ b. $\frac{5^6}{5^3}$ c. $\frac{10^6}{10^5}$ d. $3^2 \times 3^3$
   e. $\frac{11^5}{11^2}$ f. $\frac{6^6}{6^4}$ g. $\frac{2^8}{2^4}$ h. $10^4 \times 10^5$

7. Amplifiers are used to increase the signal strength of undersea telephone cables. The first amplifier strengthens the signal 10^6 times. The second one strengthens the signal 10^6 times again. To what power has the original signal been strengthened?

8. Each galaxy contains about 10^{11} stars. There are about 10^{11} galaxies in the universe. Approximately how many stars are there in all?

9. Express as a power with base 10.
   a. 1 000 000   b. 10 000 000 000
   c. 100 000 000   d. 1 000 000 000 000

10. Express as a power with base 2.
    a. 8   b. 32   c. 16   d. 128

All computers, whether microcomputers, minicomputers, or mainframe computers, work in the same general way.

INPUT $\longrightarrow$ PROCESSING $\longrightarrow$ OUTPUT

INPUT	PROCESSING	OUTPUT
They receive information, which might be in the form of numbers, words, pictures, or sounds.	They store, then process the information by following a list of given instructions (a **program**).	They show the results. The program being used tells the computer how to display the results.

1. Describe the activity in terms of input, processing, and output.
   a. doing a geography project   b. making a pizza
   c. taking a photograph   d. controlling a computerized robot

17

Principal Square Roots

The gymnast performs his floor exercises on a square mat. The area of the mat is 144 m². How long is each side of the mat?

What number when multiplied by itself gives 144?

$144 = 12 \times 12$

Each side of the mat is 12 m long.

12 is the **principal square root** of 144.

principal ———→ square root symbol $\sqrt{144} = \sqrt{12 \times 12}$
$= 12$

$\sqrt{144}$ is read as "the principal square root of 144" and often simply "the square root of 144."

Evaluate $\sqrt{49}$.

$\sqrt{49} = \sqrt{7 \times 7}$
$= 7$

Check. $7 \times 7 = 49$. ✓

Find the principal square root of 576.

$\sqrt{576} = \sqrt{2 \times 2 \times 2 \times 2 \times 2 \times 2 \times 3 \times 3}$
$= 2 \times 2 \times 2 \times 3$
$= 24$

Check. $24 \times 24 = 576$ ✓

The principal square root of 576 is 24.

WORKING TOGETHER

1. Express as the square of a number.
   a. 25 b. 36 c. 64 d. 100

2. Find the principal square root of each number in exercise 1.

3. Write as the product of prime factors.
   a. 196 b. 324 c. 441 d. 676

4. Find the principal square root of each number in exercise 3.

APPLICATIONS AND EXERCISES

1. Evaluate.

    a. $\sqrt{4}$ b. $\sqrt{81}$ c. $\sqrt{16}$

    d. $\sqrt{121}$ e. $\sqrt{17^2}$ f. $\sqrt{400}$

    g. $\sqrt{169}$ h. $\sqrt{0}$ i. $\sqrt{23^2}$

2. Square mats are used in karate and judo. Find the length of a side of the mat.

    a.
    Area:
    64 m²
    karate

    b.
    Area:
    256 m²
    judo

3. Evaluate.

    a. $\sqrt{3 \times 3 \times 7 \times 7}$

    b. $\sqrt{2 \times 2 \times 11 \times 11}$

    c. $\sqrt{2 \times 2 \times 3 \times 3 \times 5 \times 5}$

    d. $\sqrt{5 \times 5 \times 7 \times 7 \times 11 \times 11}$

4. Find the principal square root.

    a. 484   b. 529   c. 625

    d. 324   e. 961   f. 1089

    g. 1764   h. 4356   i. 5625

5. A block of land is divided into 20 equal square lots. The area of the block is 2880 m². Find the length of a side of each lot.

6. Find two numbers for which the principal square root of the number is the same as the number.

7. a. Find $\sqrt{100}$ and $\sqrt{324}$.

    b. Use the results to find $\sqrt{32\,400}$.

    c. Find $\sqrt{3\,240\,000}$.

    d. Find $\sqrt{324\,000\,000}$.

8. Evaluate.

    a. $\sqrt{4900}$ b. $\sqrt{3600}$ c. $\sqrt{10\,000}$

    d. $\sqrt{90\,000}$ e. $\sqrt{14\,400}$ f. $\sqrt{40\,000}$

9. Mr. Sugden's farm equipment shed has a square base that covers an area of 729 m². How far is the shed from the front of his property?

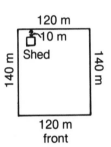

10. To estimate the number of seconds it takes a freely falling object to fall a certain distance, divide the distance (in metres) by 5. Then find the principal square root of the quotient.
About how many seconds would it take a freely falling object to fall the distance?

    a. 45 m   b. 125 m   c. 2000 m   d. 8820

19

Patterns and Sequences

Astronomers and solar scientists have studied sunspot activity since the fifteenth century. In our century they have observed sunspot activity reaching a maximum during each of these years.

1909　1920　1931　1942　1953　1964　1975　1986
　　+11　　+11　　+11　　+11　　+11　　+11　　+11

The list suggests a pattern. The pattern can be useful in summarizing
"Beginning in 1909 and each eleven years thereafter, sunspot activity has reached a maximum."

and making predictions
"We can expect maximum sunspot activity again in 1997."

WORKING TOGETHER

1. Predict the next three years when high sunspot activity may occur.

2. The numbers 1, 3, 6, 10, and 15 are **triangular numbers**.

　1　　3　　　6　　　　10　　　　15

State the next triangular number and illustrate.

3. List the next seven triangular numbers.

4. Use the sequence of triangular numbers.
   a. Copy and complete.
      1st number + 3rd number = □
      2nd number + 4th number = □
      3rd number + 5th number = □
   b. Predict the next three sums.

5. Use the sequence of triangular numbers.
   a. Copy and complete.
      1st number + 2nd number = □
      2nd number + 3rd number = □
      3rd number + 4th number = □
   b. What type of number is each sum in part **a**?
   c. Predict the next three sums.

6. Use the sequence of triangular numbers.
   a. Copy and complete.
      2nd number − 1st number = □
      3rd number − 2nd number = □
      4th number − 3rd number = □
   b. Study the pattern in part **a**. What shortcut can be used to find each difference?
   c. Predict the difference between the 10th and 9th triangular numbers.

1. The dot patterns show the first four **square numbers**.

   a. Draw dot patterns to show the next two square numbers.

   b. List the first ten square numbers.

   c. Find the 13th square number.

2. Use the sequence of square numbers.

   a. Copy and complete.
      2nd number − 1st number = ☐
      3rd number − 2nd number = ☐
      4th number − 3rd number = ☐

   b. Study the pattern. What shortcut can be used to find each difference?

   c. Predict the difference between the 12th and 11th square numbers.

3. Use the sequence of odd numbers.

   a. Copy and complete.
      1 + 3 = ☐
      1 + 3 + 5 = ☐
      1 + 3 + 5 + 7 = ☐

   b. Study the pattern. What shortcut can be used to find each sum?

   c. Predict the sum of the first ten odd numbers.

4. The distance between the earth and the moon changes. The table shows the dates when the moon was close to the earth in a recent year.

Month	Feb.	Mar.	Apr.	May
Day	8	8	5	3

For the same year, predict what the next three dates would be.

5. Describe the pattern. Then list the next three numbers in the sequence.

   a. 5, 7, 11, 19   b. 1, 4, 9, 16

   c. 1, 5, 11, 19   d. 2, 3, 5, 7, 11

   e. 1, 5, 14, 30   f. 0, 1, 1, 2, 3, 5

6. In some families each person buys one birthday present for each other person.

   a. How many presents are bought in a two-person family?

   b. How many presents are bought in a three-person family?

   c. How many presents are bought in a four-person family?

   d. What shortcut can be used to find the number of presents bought in a ten-person family? How many presents are bought?

1. Add mentally. Look for sums of 100.

   a. 64 + 72 + 41 + 36 + 28

   b. 47 + 19 + 53 + 62 + 81

   c. 27 + 33 + 87 + 13 + 40

2. Add mentally. Look for sums of 50.

   a. 16 + 33 + 28 + 17 + 22

   b. 14 + 38 + 36 + 12 + 42 + 58

   c. 27 + 31 + 23 + 40 + 19

Order of Operations

Rosita uses a combination lock on her school locker.

By following the intructions on the tag, she is able to open the lock every time.

Mathematics has rules to follow when several operations are performed. Everyone gets the same result by following the rules.

Rules for the Order of Operations
1. Perform operations inside parentheses.
2. Evaluate powers.
3. Multiply and divide from left to right.
4. Add and subtract from left to right.

Evaluate. $3 \times 19 - (5 + 3^3)$

$3 \times 19 - (5 + 3^3)$
$= 3 \times 19 - (5 + 27)$
$= 3 \times 19 - 32$
$= 57 - 32$
$= 25$

Evaluate. $\dfrac{46 - 3 \times 2}{10 - 40 \div 8}$

$\dfrac{46 - 3 \times 2}{10 - 40 \div 8}$
$= (46 - 3 \times 2) \div (10 - 40 \div 8)$
$= (46 - 6) \div (10 - 5)$
$= 40 \div 5$
$= 8$

WORKING TOGETHER

1. Evaluate.

   a. $18 \div 3 + 3$ **b.** $20 - 5 \times 2$

   c. $10 - 5 + 1$ **d.** $3^2 - 2^3$

2. Study the expression $4^2 - 3 \times 5 + 10$.

   a. Which part is evaluated first?

   b. Which part is evaluated next?

   c. Evaluate the expression.

3. **a.** State an order in which the expression $\dfrac{(6 + 5) \times 2 + 5}{5 - 4 \div 2}$ may be evaluated.

   b. Evaluate the expression.

4. Copy and use parentheses to make the statement true.

   a. $\dfrac{19 + 3 \times 2}{7 \times 2 - 10} = 11$ **b.** $\dfrac{2^2 + 3 + 3^2}{14 - 3^2} = 8$

1. Evaluate.

a. $6 - (2 + 2)$ **b.** $6 \div 3 \times 2$

c. $24 + 8 - 6$ **d.** $12 \div 3 + 6 \div 3$

e. $6 \div 2 \times 0 + 8$ **f.** $(6 + 8) \div 2 + 5$

g. $5 + 21 \div 7 - 7$

h. $25 + 10 - 4^2 \times 2$

i. $40 \div 2 \times 2^2 - 2$

j. $6^2 - 12 \div 3 \times 4$

k. $12 \div (6 - 3) \times 4$

l. $50 - 10 \times (3 + 2)$

2. Find the value.

a. $\dfrac{3 + 7 \times 3}{4 + 8}$ **b.** $\dfrac{13 \times 5 - 2}{22 \div 11 + 5}$

c. $\dfrac{3^3 - 2^2 + 5}{12 \div 3}$ **d.** $\dfrac{(5 + 4) \times 3}{5^2 + 2}$

e. $\dfrac{2^2 + 4^3}{6 \times 2 - 8}$ **f.** $\dfrac{(32 - 17) \div 3}{10^2 \div 20}$

3. To develop a roll of film, Foto Mart charges $9 while Quick Photo charges $7. Which number sentence represents the difference in developing charges if 3 rolls are to be developed?

   i. $3 + 9 - 7 = 5$

   ii. $3 \times 9 - 7 = 20$

   iii. $3 \times (9 - 7) = 6$

   iv. $3 \times (9 + 7) = 48$

4. The table shows the seating capacity and ticket prices for a concert.

Level	Capacity	Price
Balcony	928	$15.00
Mezzanine	670	$22.00
Orchestra	1095	$25.00

If the concert is sold out, what is the total income?

5. Copy and use parentheses to make the statement true.

a. $16 - 4 + 6 = 6$

b. $84 - 28 \div 4 \times 7 = 2$

c. $4^2 + 5 \div 3 + 4 = 3$

d. $\dfrac{8 + 2 \times 9 \div 3}{10 + 4 \div 2} = 2$

e. $\dfrac{6^2 \div 3 - 1}{1 + 5 \times 3} = 1$

6. Evaluate.

a. $22 \times 9 - 14 \times 9$

b. $22 \times 11 + 18 \times 11$

c. $11 \times (22 + 18)$ **d.** $9 \times (22 - 14)$

7. a. Which expressions in exercise 6 can you do mentally?

b. Rewrite $16 \times 89 + 16 \times 11$ as an expression that can be evaluated mentally. Evaluate it.

Try This

The expression $(4 + 4 + 4) \div 4$ has value 3.

1. Write an expression for each of the other numbers from 1 to 10.
Use only four 4s, and any of the symbols $+, -, \times, \div, \sqrt{\ }$, and parentheses in each expression.

2. Which numbers from 1 to 10 can you represent using only four 3s?

Shortcuts in Computation

Some people have astounding abilities for mental calculations.

Mrs. Shakuntala Devi multiplied

7 686 369 774 870 by 2 465 099 745 779

correctly in 28 s.

These examples show some ways to group or write numbers to make mental calculations easier.

Evaluate   19 + 52 + 28.

$$19 + 52 + 28$$
$$= 19 + (52 + 28)$$
$$= 19 + 80$$
$$= 99$$

> Group into multiples of 10.

Evaluate   6 × 14 × 5.

$$6 \times 14 \times 5$$
$$= (6 \times 5) \times 14$$
$$= 30 \times 14$$
$$= 420$$

Evaluate   72 × 102.

Since 102 = 100 + 2
$$72 \times 102$$
$$= 72 \times (100 + 2)$$
$$= 72 \times 100 + 72 \times 2$$
$$= 7200 + 144$$
$$= 7344$$

> Write as a multiple of 10 and a single digit.

Evaluate   19 × 43.

Since 19 = 20 − 1
$$19 \times 43$$
$$= (20 - 1) \times 43$$
$$= 20 \times 43 - 1 \times 43$$
$$= 860 - 43$$
$$= 817$$

WORKING TOGETHER

1. Which numbers could be grouped to make mental calculations easier?

   a. 43 + 76 + 224   b. 11 × 18 × 5

   c. 79 + 82 + 21   d. 15 × 7 × 6

2. Try to evaluate the expressions in exercise 1 mentally.

3. Try to evaluate mentally.

   a. 25 × 71 × 4   b. 31 × 45 × 0

   c. 11 + 45 + 49   d. 48 × 101

   e. 92 − 58 − 32   f. 99 × 8

APPLICATIONS AND EXERCISES

1. Evaluate mentally.
   a. 231 + 75 + 25
   b. 15 + 98 + 285
   c. 19 + 26 + 41
   d. 187 + 76 + 23
   e. 17 + 22 + 33 + 28

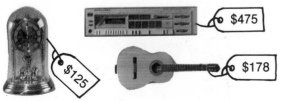

2. a. Terri added the costs of the items mentally. Which items did she probably group together?
   b. What is the total cost?

3. Evaluate mentally.
   a. 87 × 25 × 4
   b. 39 × 2 × 500
   c. 89 × 47 × 0 × 70
   d. 50 × 126 × 2
   e. 40 × 65 × 5
   f. 5 × 346 × 2

4. Each interlocking stone has a mass of about 5 kg. The stones are delivered on a pallet containing 8 layers with 13 stones to a layer. Calculate the total mass of the stones on a pallet.

5. Each interlocking stone costs $0.29. What is the cost of the pallet of stones in exercise 4?

6.

1	12	10
15	2	4
8	5	3

   a. Multiply the numbers in each row.
   b. Multiply the numbers in each column.
   c. What do you notice?
   d. Create a different square that has the same property.
   e. How many such squares can you make?

7. 16 120 people attended each of four concerts. If tickets sold for $25 each, what was the total ticket revenue?

8. Evaluate. Look for a shortcut.
   a. 36 × 21
   b. 63 × 101
   c. 51 × 26
   d. 81 × 81
   e. 109 × 55
   f. 99 × 101

9. Evaluate. Look for a shortcut.
   a. 42 × 39
   b. 32 × 79
   c. 55 × 98
   d. 69 × 61
   e. 97 × 43
   f. 99 × 49

10. Hans purchased 18 boxes of disks at $19 a box. If he returned 2 boxes, how much did he spend on disks?

1. Choose a whole number from 1 to 9.
   Multiply this number by 9.
   Multiply the product by 12 345 679.
   Describe the pattern in the answer.

2. Repeat for different numbers from 1 to 9.

3. Repeat for whole numbers from 10 to 18.

Try This

25

1. Express as a single power.

   a. $2^3 \times 2^4$ **b.** $3^7 \times 3^4$

   c. $10^3 \times 10^3$ **d.** $7^6 \div 7^4$

   e. $5^{15} \div 5^3$ **f.** $6^9 \div 6^8$

   g. $2^2 \times 2^3$ **h.** $10^8 \div 10^1$

   i. $13^5 \div 13^1$ **j.** $\dfrac{4^9}{4^5}$

   k. $\dfrac{10^8}{10^6}$ **l.** $\dfrac{2^7}{2^3}$

2. Express as a single power, then evaluate.

   a. $5^5 \div 5^2$ **b.** $10^7 \div 10^3$ **c.** $2^2 \times 2^4$

   d. $\dfrac{6^3}{6^1}$ **e.** $3^2 \times 3^2$ **f.** $\dfrac{7^8}{7^7}$

3. Find the length of a side of each square.

   a.
   36 cm²

   b.
   100 cm²

   c.
   81 cm²

4. Evaluate.

   a. $\sqrt{121}$ **b.** $\sqrt{900}$ **c.** $\sqrt{196}$

   d. $\sqrt{19^2}$ **e.** $\sqrt{441}$ **f.** $\sqrt{2500}$

   g. $\sqrt{1225}$ **h.** $\sqrt{1764}$ **i.** $\sqrt{3025}$

5. The surface area of the walls of a shower is 40 000 cm². The walls are tiled using 625 square tiles. Find the length of a side of a tile.

6. Describe the pattern and then list the next two numbers in the sequence.

   a. 1, 3, 7, 15   **b.** 2, 5, 10, 17

   c. 1, 3, 7, 13   **d.** 2, 4, 8, 16

   e. 1, 2, 6, 24   **f.** 2, 3, 6, 18

7. Is the statement true?

   a. $5 \times 74 \times 20 = 5 \times 20 \times 74$

   b. $48 \div (6 \div 2) = (48 \div 6) \div 2$

   c. $4781 + 2342 = 2342 + 4781$

   d. $64 \div 8 = 8 \div 64$

   e. $123 \times 456 \times 789 \times 0 = 0$

   f. $3785 \times 1 = 3786$

   g. $3785 + 0 = 0$

   h. $3785 + 0 = 3785$

   i. $3785 \times 1 = 3785$

   j. $5 \times 307 = (5 \times 30) + (5 \times 7)$

8. Evaluate.

   a. $4 \times 9 - 3$ **b.** $4 \times (9 - 3)$

   c. $3 + 5^2$ **d.** $3^2 + 5$

   e. $(3 + 5)^2$ **f.** $17 - 4^2 \div 2$

   g. $\dfrac{3 + 6 \times 5}{2^2 + 7}$ **h.** $\dfrac{4 \times 3 + 8}{6^2 - 4^2}$

   i. $\dfrac{(28 + 3 \times 4) \div (2 \times 10)}{(5 + 7) \div 6}$

   j. $\dfrac{8^2 + 5^2 + 1}{11 - 10 \div 5}$

9. Evaluate. Look for a shortcut.

   a. $25 \times 17 \times 4$ **b.** $38 + 265 + 62$

   c. 199×63 **d.** 51×49

   e. 31×17 **f.** 54×102

   g. 98×76 **h.** 49×25

   i. $(56 + 44) \times 36 \times 0$

Order of Operations

Wendy and Laura entered 6 + 5 × 12 into their calculators.

Wendy's calculator displayed 132 while Laura's displayed 66.
Which girl has the correct display?

Different calculators follow different rules in problems that mix addition or subtraction with multiplication or division.
Wendy's calculator performs the operations in the order they are entered.
Laura's calculator performs the operations according to the rules for the order of operations on page 22.

Laura's answer, 66, is the correct one.

Test your calculator. What does 6 + 5 × 12 display as the answer?

132   OR   66

To obtain the correct result   Your calculator is like Laura's.
you must follow the rules for
the order of operations.

To calculate 6 + 5 × 12 correctly   Display

Enter [c] [5] [×] [12] [+] [6] [=]   66

---

1. Evaluate using your calculator.
   a. 49 + 200 ÷ 25   **b.** (521 − 185) ÷ 12   **c.** 75 × (18 ÷ 9 + 4)
   d. 28 + 34 × 51 − 197   **e.** 33 + 47 × 53 − 315   **f.** 74 + (19 × 27 − 94) − 25
   g. 412 − 58 + 12 × 61   **h.** 38 × 95 + 45 × 22   **i.** 72 × 16 − 63 × 15

2. Stefan bought stereo equipment by paying $198 cash plus 52 weekly payments of $15. How much did he pay for the equipment?

3. For a concert, 9275 people bought $35 tickets and 7450 people bought $25 tickets. What was the total income from ticket sales?

Communications

Computers cannot think by themselves. People must tell them exactly what to do and when to do it. A list of instructions for a computer is a **program**. A computer can follow the instructions in a program, one step at a time, if they are written in a computer language such as Pascal or COBOL.

1. Name some computer languages that you have used or heard of.

A person who writes the detailed instructions for a computer to follow is a **programmer**. Anyone can use a computer without having to know a special language. Experts write programs to do certain tasks and store them on disks, tapes, or cartridges. Such programs are called **software**.

2. Name some software that you have used or heard of.

Store managers in Vancouver, Calgary, and Montreal used to telephone their weekly sales records to Beth Sellers at the head office in Windsor. Now daily figures from each store's computer go directly to the computer at head office.

Peter Valence, confined to a wheelchair, found it difficult to continue his work as an accountant. Then his microcomputer was hooked up to the office computer and Peter finds that he can do most of his work at home.

3. Discuss the advantages and any disadvantages that might occur in the situations above.

4. In what other situations might it be useful to communicate by computer?

Two people can communicate using their computers if special software is used, and if a **modem** is connected to each computer. A modem is a piece of equipment that lets you send or receive information on your computer over ordinary telephone lines.

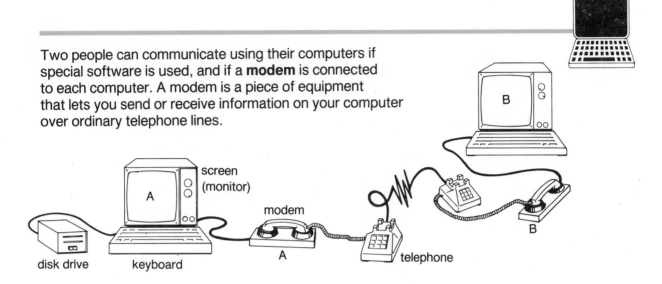

screen (monitor)

modem

disk drive   keyboard   A   telephone

When computer A "talks" to computer B:
- The information from computer A is sent to modem A, where it is changed (**mod**ulated) into sound patterns.
- The sound travels along the wires to modem B, where it is changed (**dem**odulated) back into computer code.
- The code goes to computer B and is displayed on the screen.

When computer B "talks" to computer A, the process is reversed.

> **Modem** means **mod**ulator-**dem**odulator.

Computer-linked communication is also used for collecting, storing, and sharing information among many people. For example, the computer terminal in a local bank is connected by telephone lines to the large mainframe computer at the bank's head office. The large computer controls hundreds of terminals across the country, and also may control the automated teller machines. Many computers that are linked together to share information are said to form a **network**.

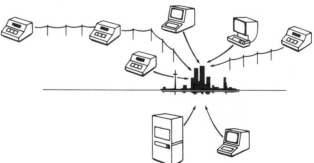

5. Discuss how people might be able to do all their banking at home in the future.

How to Solve a Problem

Problem: Last year Walt, Gail, and Malcolm sold lemonade at their school's annual spring carnival. They collected only enough money to pay for the lemonade, cups, and ice. If they sold lemonade again this year, could they make a profit? How much profit could they make?

First **think** of questions to ask about the situation.

—How much lemonade did we sell last year?
—How much can we probably sell this year?
—What is the cost of the ingredients?
—What is the cost of the cups?
—What is the cost of the ice?
—How much should we charge per cup?
—How much will people pay per cup?

Walt, Gail, and Malcolm thought they needed more information before they could decide what to do next.

At the local supermarket they found the following information.

Lemonade:
frozen concentrate: makes 1.4 L, $0.59/can
　　　　　　　　　　 makes 1.78 L, $0.89/can

crystals: makes 2 L, $1.29/package
　　　　　　makes 5 L, $2.99/package

Cups:
51 cups—185 mL size—$0.99/package

Ice:　　　　　　　　　$1.10/bag

Gail suggested they save on the ice by making it in ice-cube trays at home.

Next, use the information to **plan and do** a solution.

The students thought they could sell at least 10 L of lemonade.

Which container of lemonade would be the best buy to make about 10 L?

 　1.4 L/can, need about 7 cans, cost $4.13
　　　1.78 L/can, need about 6 cans, cost $5.34
　　　2 L/package, need 5 packages, cost $6.45
　　　5 L/package, need 2 packages, cost $5.98

The small can is the best buy.

How many cups are needed for 10 L?
1 cup holds 185 mL.
51 cups hold 9435 mL.
54 cups hold 9990 mL.

$$10\ L\ =\ 10\ 000\ mL$$

Walt, Gail, and Malcolm made this table to help them decide what to charge.

Money Paid		Money Collected		Profit
10 L lemonade	$4.13	54 cups @ 15¢	$ 8.10	$ 8.10 − 6.11 = $ 1.99
2 packages cups	+ 1.98	20¢	$10.80	$10.80 − 6.11 = $ 4.69
Total	$6.11	25¢	$13.50	$13.50 − 6.11 = $ 7.39
		30¢	$16.20	$16.20 − 6.11 = $10.09
	$0.11	35¢	$18.90	$18.90 − 6.11 = $12.79
Cost per cup	54) $6.11	40¢	$21.60	$21.60 − 6.11 = $15.49

Then **look back**. Walt, Gail, and Malcolm discussed their work
and what people might pay for a cup of lemonade.
If they charged too much, no one would buy.
They agreed to charge 30¢/cup and they would make about $10 profit.

To help you solve problems, use this as a guide.

Think: Do you understand what the problem is about? Restate it in your own words.
What is the important information in the problem?
Ask yourself questions. What assumptions are you making?

Plan and do. Have you solved a similar problem? How did you do it?
What strategies might help you solve the problem—drawing a diagram, looking for a pattern,
guessing and testing? Use a strategy.
Are you getting closer to solving the problem?

Look back. Does your solution make sense? Check it and explain it.
Can you solve the problem differently or in fewer steps?
Are other solutions possible? What other problems can be created?
What if the situation changes?

WORKING TOGETHER

1. How would this affect the amount of lemonade Walt, Gail, and Malcolm sell?

   a. number of people at carnival

   b. weather **c.** advertising

2. What questions might you want answered if you wanted to start a lawn-mowing or a snow-shovelling business?

Tell how you would solve the problem. Use **Think, Plan and do**, and then **Look back**.

1. How could you determine accurately the measurement?

   a. the thickness of a piece of paper

   b. the mass of a dog

   c. the amount of space a box occupies

2. How would you estimate?

   a. the speed of a flying bird

   b. the height of a mountain

   c. the number of times you blink per hour

   d. the number of penguins on a large iceberg

3. What is the worth of your height in quarters?

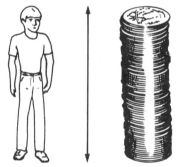

4. How many beans are there in 1 tonne?

5. What numbers must there be on the other sides of the cubes of the desk calendar to show all the dates from 01 to 31?

6. Which question is being asked in the problem? Solve the problem.

   On a cob of sweet corn Marty counted 17 rows and 23 kernels in one row. On a cob of field corn he counted 22 rows and 36 kernels in one row. About how many more kernels were there on one type than the other?

   a. What was the average number of kernels on a corn cob?

   b. How many more kernels were there on the cob of field corn?

   c. What was the total number of kernels on both cobs?

   d. What is the difference in the number of kernels?

Each problem may require some unusual kinds of thinking. Check the assumptions you are making. Then solve.

7. How can you turn a glass upside down without spilling any water?

8. Ken and Justin played five games of checkers. They each won the same number of games and there were no ties. How is this possible?

9. How can nine marbles be put into five cups so that each cup has a different number of marbles?

10. How can you get a ping-pong ball out of a hole that is 1 m deep? The diameter of the hole is 10 mm greater than the diameter of the ball.

Chapter Checkup

1. The table shows the recent provincial circulation for Sunday newspapers.

Province	Circulation
Alberta	411 448
British Columbia	418 618
Manitoba	267 477
New Brunswick	84 444
Newfoundland	58 065
Nova Scotia	8 638
Ontario	1 816 474
Prince Edward Island	
Quebec	1 222 629
Saskatchewan	

   a. Estimate the total circulation for the Western provinces.

   b. Estimate the total circulation for the Atlantic provinces.

   c. Estimate the difference in circulation between Ontario and Quebec.

   d. About how many times greater is the circulation in Newfoundland than in Nova Scotia?

2. Find the result.

   a.
   ```
      12 367
     758 107
   +      88
   ```
   b. 409 + 1827 + 95

   c. 2004 − 1369   d. 19 107 − 7829

   e. 835 × 94   f. 319 × 67

   g. 43) 2752   h. 14 958 ÷ 18

3. Is the number divisible by 3? by 9?

   a. 417   b. 2853   c. 40 389

   d. 29 538   c. 79 866   f. 93 612

4. Can a piece of wood 1946 cm long be cut into 8 equal lengths without waste?

5. Find the prime factorization.

   a. 75   b. 44   c. 81   d. 100

6. Express as a power.

   a. $5 \times 5 \times 5$

   b. $7 \times 7 \times 7 \times 7 \times 7 \times 7$

   c. $10 \times 10 \times 10 \times 10$

   d. $2 \times 2 \times 2 \times 2 \times 2$

7. Express as a single power. Then evaluate.

   a. $4^6 \div 4^3$ b. $10^9 \div 10^5$ c. $9^7 \div 9^5$

   d. $5^1 \times 5^3$ e. $2^3 \times 2^3$ f. $3^2 \times 3^3$

8. Evaluate.

   a. $\sqrt{16}$ b. $\sqrt{169}$ c. $\sqrt{324}$

   d. $\sqrt{24^2}$ e. $\sqrt{2500}$ f. $\sqrt{784}$

9. Describe the pattern, and then give the next two numbers in the sequence.

   a. 1, 2, 4, 7   b. 1, 4, 9, 16

   c. 1, 8, 27, 64   d. 5, 11, 19, 29

10. Here are the first five rows of **Pascal's triangle**.

```
            1
          1   2   1
        1   3   3   1
      1   4   6   4   1
    1   5  10  10   5   1
```

   a. Describe how the third row is obtained from the second row.

   b. Give the sixth row of Pascal's triangle.

11. Evaluate.

   a. $24 \div 6 + 2$ b. $5 + 7 \times 3$

   c. $16 - 12 \div 4$ d. $5^2 + 8 - 3$

   e. $5^2 + 8 \times 3$ f. $6 + 30 \div 5 - 2$

   g. $9 \times 4 \div 2 + 5$ h. $(12^2 - 14) \div 26$

   i. $18 + 3 \times 4 - 2^4 \div (3 + 1)$

2/Decimals

A skilled machinist grinds metal to obtain accurate thicknesses and lengths. Decimal numbers are used to describe these measures.

Get Set

1. Express as a power of 10.
   a. 100   **b.** 1000   **c.** 10 000
   d. 100 000   **e.** 1 000 000

2. Express in standard form.
   a. $(4 \times 100\,000) + (7 \times 10\,000) +$ (8×1000)
   b. $(6 \times 10\,000) + (2 \times 100) + (4 \times 10)$

3. Copy and use > or < to make a true statement.
   a. 909 ◯ 990   **b.** 327 ◯ 723
   c. 1010 ◯ 1001   **d.** 94 517 ◯ 94 571

4. Arrange in increasing order.
   7528   7512   7583   7575

5. Round to the nearest hundred.
   a. 623   **b.** 1492
   c. 37 835   **d.** 659
   e. 1752   **f.** 62 972

6. Evaluate.
   a. 3296 + 1049   **b.** 4176 − 1387
   c. 193 + 79 + 87   **d.** 9825 ÷ 5
   e. 708 × 48   **f.** 2156 ÷ 22

7. Evaluate.
   a. $137.19 + $245.17
   b. $975.28 − $163.45
   c. $845.21 + $65.88
   d. $277.62 − $9.85
   e. $108.55 + $3420.62 + $47.75

8. Multiply or divide mentally.
   a. 795 × 100   **b.** 874 × 1000
   c. 9800 ÷ 10   **d.** 8200 ÷ 100
   e. 18 090 × 10   **f.** $1000 \overline{)\,36\,000}$

9. Is the statement true?
   a. When you multiply a number by 10, 100, or 1000, the product is greater than the number.
   b. When you divide a number by 10, 100, or 1000, the product is less than the number.

10. Multiply or divide mentally.
    a. 40 × 15   **b.** 30 × 9
    c. 72 ÷ 9   **d.** 150 ÷ 5
    e. 180 × 5   **f.** 2000 ÷ 40

11. Name each number as factor, product, dividend, divisor, or quotient.
    a. 16 × 20 = 320   **b.** 35 ÷ 5 = 7
    c. $\begin{array}{r} 120 \\ \times\,3 \\ \hline 360 \end{array}$ **d.** $12\overline{)576}\;^{48}$

12. State the unit price.
    a. 4 apples sell for $2
    b. 6 chairs sell for $624
    c. 8 glasses sell for $24

13. How many digits are shown after the decimal point?
    a. 2.176   **b.** 4.0085
    c. 14.07   **d.** 512.7

Place Value

The bee hummingbird has a mass of 1.742 g.
In one day it can beat its wings about 5 600 000 times.

A place value chart helps us understand the
meaning of each digit in these numbers.

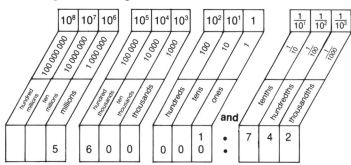

1.742 is read
standard form
one and seven hundred forty-two thousandths.

5 600 000 is read
five million six hundred thousand.

1.742

$= (1 \times 1) + (7 \times \frac{1}{10}) + (4 \times \frac{1}{100}) + (2 \times \frac{1}{1000})$

5 600 000

$= (5 \times 1\ 000\ 000) + (6 \times 100\ 000)$

expanded form

$= (1 \times 1) + (7 \times \frac{1}{10^1}) + (4 \times \frac{1}{10^2}) + (2 \times \frac{1}{10^3})$

$= (5 \times 10^6) + (6 \times 10^5)$

expanded form using powers of 10

The 7 in 1.742 has a value of 7 tenths.

The 5 in 5 600 000 has a value of 5 millions.

WORKING TOGETHER

1. What is the value of 5?

  a. 15.82   **b.** 751 000   **c.** 37.15

  d. 0.105   **e.** 1 205 792   **f.** 5.648

2. Express in expanded form.

  a. 26.15   **b.** 318.102   **c.** 17 051

3. Express in expanded form using powers
of 10.

  a. 687.0001 **b.** 18 407 000 **c.** 0.643

4. Express in standard form.

  a. eight million four hundred fifty
thousand twenty-one

  b. thirty-three and seven tenths

  c. twenty-six hundredths

  d. $(8 \times 1000) + (3 \times 10) + (6 \times \frac{1}{100}) + (1 \times \frac{1}{1000})$

  e. $(3 \times 10^6) + (4 \times 10^2) + (2 \times 1) + (7 \times \frac{1}{10^1})$

1. What is the value of the 2?

    a. 2.45   **b.** 43.12   **c.** 98 421.3

    d. 983.562   **e.** 0.024   **f.** 1289.5

2. Write the number in words.

    a. 3.41   **b.** 92 105   **c.** 0.739

3. Express in standard form.

    a. four million eight hundred two

    b. three hundred and sixteen hundredths

    c. eight hundred thousand five and three hundredths

    d. $(3 \times 10^7) + (5 \times 10^6) + (4 \times 10^5)$

4. Express the number in standard form.

    a. The area of Monaco is one and forty-nine hundredths square kilometres.

    b. Over sixteen million three hundred thirty-four thousand passengers pass through Kennedy Airport in a year.

5. Time Period of Revolution About the Sun in Earth Years

Jupiter	11.862	Pluto	248.43
Mars	1.881	Saturn	29.458
Mercury	0.241	Uranus	84.013
Neptune	164.794	Venus	0.6156

    Express the period of revolution for each planet in expanded form.

6.

    5.8175 m   4.812 m   5.099 m   5.12 m   6.009 m

    a. Which pipe would seem to be measured more accurately?

    b. Express in expanded form only those pipe lengths that are between 5 m and 6 m long.

7. Express the number in expanded form using powers of 10.

    a. Normal body temperature is 36.9°C (degrees Celsius).

    b. The population of Asia is about 2 696 082 000.

    c. Ben Johnson ran the 100 m in 9.95 s.

8. Express in standard form.

    a. $9 \times \frac{1}{10^3}$ **b.** $6 \times \frac{1}{10^5}$ **c.** 3×10^6

    d. 4×10^9 **e.** 5×10^3 **f.** $7 \times \frac{1}{10^4}$

9. Which measurement would seem to be more accurate?

    a. A nail is 3.2 cm long.
    A nail is 3.18 cm long.

    b. A cat's mass is 5.07 kg (kilograms).
    A cat's mass is 5.1 kg.

    c. A car's odometer reads 30 976.0 km.
    A car's odometer reads 30 976 km.

Try This

Copy and insert a decimal point to make a reasonable statement.

1. The highest average wind speed in Canada is 252 km/h at Churchill, Manitoba.

2. The longest underwater vehicular tunnel in Canada was built under the St. Lawrence River. The tunnel is 161 km long.

3. On the average, each Canadian consumes 354 kg of beef a year.

Comparing and Ordering

Which girl threw the javelin farther, Erin or Roula?

Javelin Throw Results	
Beth	29.58 m
Erin	29.46 m
Malak	29.12 m
Roula	29.83 m

The numbers representing the throwing distances are shown on a number line.

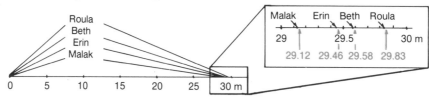

29.83 is to the right of 29.46. Therefore 29.83 > 29.46.

The numbers can be compared also by comparing the digits from left to right.

Erin: 2 9 . 4 6
same

Roula: 2 9 . 8 3

8 is greater than 4, so 29.83 > 29.46

Roula threw the javelin farther than Erin.

The chart gives the javelin throw results listed in order from greatest distance to least.

Roula	29.83 m
Beth	29.58 m
Erin	29.46 m
Malak	29.12 m

WORKING TOGETHER

1. Copy and complete the number line.

   a.
      3.5 ☐ ☐ ☐ ☐ ☐ 4.1 ☐ ☐

   b.
      0.57 0.58 ☐ ☐ ☐ ☐ ☐

2. What number is indicated by the letter?

   0 ↑ 0.1 ↑ 0.2 ↑ 0.3↑ ↑0.4
     A   B   C   D E

3. Copy and use > or < to make true statements.

   a. 8.73 ○ 8.78   b. 0.09 ○ 0.90
   c. 22.75 ○ 21.75   d. 0.214 ○ 0.412

4. Arrange the numbers in increasing order.
   5.20   2.05   2.55   5.02

5. Arrange the numbers in decreasing order.
   10.19   9.86   10.21   9.99

38

APPLICATIONS AND EXERCISES

1. Copy and complete the number line.

a.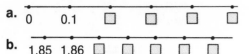

b.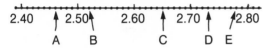

2. What number is indicated by the letter?

2.40   2.50   2.60   2.70   2.80
    A   B   C   D   E

3. The mass of a regulation size baseball is between 141.74 g and 155.92 g. Is the baseball of regulation size?

a. 141.75 g   **b.** 155.94 g   **c.** 148.64 g

d. 141.71 g   **e.** 141.04 g   **f.** 155.89 g

4. Copy and use >, <, or = to make a true statement.

a. 9.0135 ○ 9.135   **b.** 29.16 ○ 29.159

c. 7.0 ○ 7.00   **d.** 16.062 ○ 16.1

e. 4.21 ○ 4.19   **f.** 12.64 ○ 12.63

g. 7.853 ○ 7.863   **h.** 1.42 ○ 1.50

i. 8.216 ○ 8.126   **j.** 3.469 ○ 3.4690

5. For proper engine performance, the spark plug gap on a certain car must be between 0.84 mm and 0.97 mm. Does the gap meet the specifications?

a. 0.848 mm   **b.** 0.876 mm   **c.** 0.837 mm

d. 0.951 mm   **e.** 0.98 mm   **f.** 0.972 mm

6. Arrange in order from greatest to least.

a. 6.2, 5.9, 6.32

b. 9.3, 8.57, 8.286, 8.09

c. 4.7, 6.39, 6.385, 5.86, 4.939

d. 12.041, 12.102, 12.075, 12.203, 12.125

7. The table shows the annual growth rate of population for several nations.

Nation	Annual Growth Rate (%)
Algeria	3.08
Canada	1.01
France	0.53
Kenya	4.13

a. Which nation has the smallest rate?

b. The annual growth rate in population for the world is 1.7%. Which nations in the chart are above the world rate?

c. Arrange the countries so that their growth rates are in decreasing order.

8. The times of two Olympic races are given. Arrange them in increasing order.

a.

Runner	Time(s)
Brown	10.26
Graddy	10.19
Johnson	10.22
Lewis	9.99
Sharpe	10.35

b.

Country	Time
Australia	2:59.70
Britain	2:59.13
Canada	3:02.82
Italy	3:01.44
United States	2:57.91

Try This

Use tracing paper to copy. Join the points in decreasing order. Connect the last point and the first point to complete the design.

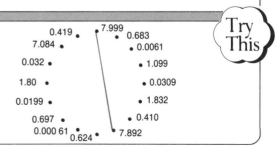

Rounding

Carlo measures the distances that
Adam, Eric, and Greg throw the shot put.

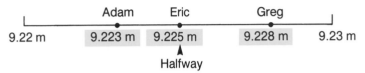

	Adam	Eric		Greg	

9.22 m   9.223 m   9.225 m   9.228 m   9.23 m

Halfway

The distances are to be accurate to the nearest
hundredth of a metre.

Carlo rounds 9.223 m to 9.22 m since 9.223 m is less than
halfway between 9.22 m and 9.23 m.

He rounds 9.228 m to 9.23 m since 9.228 is more than
halfway between 9.22 m and 9.23 m.

He rounds 9.225 m to 9.23 m since 9.225 m is exactly halfway
between 9.22 m and 9.23 m.

Carlo could use this method to round.

Round to the nearest hundredth of a metre.

- Find the rounding place.

- Look at the digit to its right.

- Compare this digit to 5.

- Write the rounded number.

9.2②3

The digit is less
than 5. Keep
the circled digit
as is.

9.22 m

9.2②8

The digit is greater
than 5. Add 1
to the circled
digit.

9.23 m

9.2②5

The digit is 5.
Add 1 to the
circled digit.

9.23 m

WORKING TOGETHER

1. Which numbers round to 6.0?

   6.0 6.1   6.3   6.5 6.6   6.9 7.0

2. Which numbers in exercise 1 round to 7.0?

3. Does the number round to 60?

   a. 59.8   b. 60.7   c. 59.48
   d. 59.5   e. 60.5   f. 60.3

4. Round to three decimal places.

   a. 1.5729   b. 0.0096   c. 4.8054

5. Round the number to the nearest tenth.

   a. 26.25   b. 9.33   c. 52.08

APPLICATIONS AND EXERCISES

1. Round to the nearest whole number.
   - **a.** 7.2
   - **b.** 2.9
   - **c.** 17.3
   - **d.** 6.24
   - **e.** 8.34
   - **f.** 6.78

2. Round to the nearest hundredth.
   - **a.** 5.0261
   - **b.** 16.965
   - **c.** 0.083
   - **d.** 1.234
   - **e.** 6.666
   - **f.** 5.104

3. Round to one decimal place.
   - **a.** 28.62
   - **b.** 13.24
   - **c.** 0.561
   - **d.** 9.51
   - **e.** 0.08
   - **f.** 109.83

4. Round to the nearest dollar.
   - **a.** $1.38
   - **b.** $26.55
   - **c.** $120.98
   - **d.** $0.67
   - **e.** $15.86
   - **f.** $5.25

5. Find to the nearest centimetre.
   - **a.** the width of this book
   - **b.** your hand span

6. A horse and rider cover the following distances in a three-day event.

Event	Distance (km)
Endurance	18.25
Steeplechase	4.14
Roads and tracks	15.75
Cross-country	7.95

   - **a.** Round each distance to the nearest tenth of a kilometre.
   - **b.** What distance was covered in 3 d?

7.

Mean Annual Precipitation (mm)	
Prince Albert, Sask.	124.5
Prince Rupert, B.C.	2428.0
Resolute, N.W.T.	136.4
St. John's, Nfld.	1511.5
Thunder Bay, Ont.	738.5
Winnipeg, Man.	535.2

   - **a.** Round the amount of precipitation to the nearest millimetre.
   - **b.** Order the cities from greatest annual precipitation to least.

8. Copy and complete.

		Rounded to the nearest		
		one	tenth	hundredth
a.	23.524			
b.	8.609			
c.	0.815			
d.	15.033			
e.	19.965			

9. Which decimal numbers become 16.1 when rounded to the nearest tenth?

10. **a.** Why are populations of towns and cities often given as rounded numbers?
    - **b.** Why is the paid attendance at a baseball game not rounded?

Evaluate 15^2.

15 lies between 10 and 20.

$15^2 = 10 \times 20 + 5^2$
$\quad = 200 + 25$
$\quad = 225$

Try This

1. Use the shortcut to evaluate.
   - **a.** 25^2
   - **b.** 45^2
   - **c.** 95^2
   - **d.** 35^2
   - **e.** 65^2
   - **f.** 85^2
   - **g.** 75^2
   - **h.** 55^2

2. Try squaring a three-digit number ending in 5. Does the shortcut still work?

41

Adding and Subtracting

McClung School is buying the video equipment as a package. How much does the school save by buying the entire package?

Save. $$$
Entire
Package $1999

Add.

$469.95	$500
499.99	500
+ 1225.00	+ 1200
$2194.94 ← (close) →	$2200

If purchased separately, the equipment would cost $2194.94.

Subtract.

$2194.94	$2200
− 1999.00	− 2000
$195.94 ← (close) →	$200

The school would save $195.94.

WORKING TOGETHER

1. Calculate the total cost of the purchase.

a.
```
16.50
7.25
9.89
10.49
18.75
```

b.
```
8.02
2.98
1.29
3.75
0.84
```

c.
```
41.82
26.14
79.50
23.67
50.25
```

2. Evaluate.

a. 9.1 + 7.13 + 12.2   **b.** 16.43 − 9.74

c. 42.45 + 1.01 + 18   **d.** 24.7 − 1.38

3. a. What is the cost of the video cassette recorder and the camera?

b. What is the cost of the camera and the television set?

4. Find the length of A.

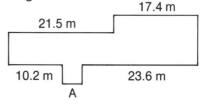

APPLICATIONS AND EXERCISES

1. Evaluate.

    a.   17.635   **b.**   53.12   **c.**   2.033
        + 6.728   + 74.39   + 0.582

    d.   10.84   **e.**   1.072   **f.**   62.5
        − 7.19   − 0.859   − 3.928

2. Find the result.

    a. 7 + 0.24 + 3.18   **b.** 483.17 − 17.82

    c. 85 − 19.46   **d.** 199.35 + 100.08

    e. 24.3 + 12   **f.** 619.257 − 17.1654

    g. 5.083 − 1.904   **h.** 15.8 + 0.03 + 9.3

3. The stated diameter of a five pin bowling ball is 12.7 cm. The manufacturer is allowed to produce balls whose diameters are within 0.033 cm of that diameter. What are the largest and smallest diameters allowed?

4. **a.** What is the cost of the three least expensive items?

    b. Calculate the change if a $50 bill is used to pay for the items in part **a**.

    c. How much more expensive is the monitor than the total cost of the other four items?

$19.75 $99.99 $10.99 $16.50 $29.95

5. Add only if the sum is less than 1000.

    a. 375.7 + 738.21

    b. 312.07 + 579.99

    c. 701.1 + 183.04 + 312.17

    d. 241.2 + 307.4 + 111.9

6. Subtract only those with differences over 300.

    a. 527.1 − 386.8

    b. 976.14 − 359.38

    c. 846.3 − 151.72

    d. 612.4 − 395.2

7. The rise and tread lengths of uniform stairs are shown. Find h and w.

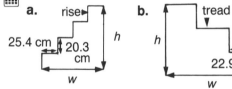

    a. rise   **b.**   tread

    25.4 cm   20.3 cm h h 30.5 cm   22.9 cm

    w w

8. Copy and complete. Use a calculator to check.

    a. 7.51 + 4.28 = ☐ + 7.51

    b. 2.17 + 11.73 = 11.73 + ☐

    c. 10.14 + 6.3 + 9.04 = 6.3 + ☐ + 9.04

9. **a.** State a rule that is illustrated in exercise 8.

    b. Does this rule also work for subtraction, multiplication, and division?

Evaluate.

    1. 5^2 **3.** 3^3 **5.** 2^5 **7.** $4^2 \times 4^1$ **9.** $2^2 \times 2^2$ **11.** $6^5 \div 6^3$

    2. $10^8 \div 10^4$ **4.** $2^3 + 4^3$ **6.** $5^3 - 3^4$ **8.** $10^5 + 10^2$ **10.** $10^4 \times 10^3$ **12.** $7^{12} \div 7^9$

Multiplying and Dividing by 1000, 100, 10, 0.1, 0.01, 0.001,....

Trina uses a calculator to multiply and divide 2.54 by 10, 100, 1000, 10 000,....
She sees a pattern in the products and in the quotients.

$2.54 \times 10\ 000 = 25\ 400.$
$2.54 \times 1\ 000 = 2\ 540.$
$2.54 \times 100 = 254.$
$2.54 \times 10 = 25.4$

- The products are greater than 2.54.

$2.54 \div 10\ 000 = 0.000\ 254$
$2.54 \div 1\ 000 = 0.002\ 54$
$2.54 \div 100 = 0.025\ 4$
$2.54 \div 10 = 0.254$

- The quotients are less than 2.54.

Trina multiplies and divides 2.54 by 0.1, 0.01, 0.001, 0.001,....
She sees a pattern similar to those above.

$2.54 \times 0.1 = 0.254$
$2.54 \times 0.01 = 0.025\ 4$
$2.54 \times 0.001 = 0.002\ 54$
$2.54 \times 0.0001 = 0.000\ 254$

- The products are less than 2.54.

$2.54 \div 0.1 = 25.4$
$2.54 \div 0.01 = 254.$
$2.54 \div 0.001 = 2\ 540.$
$2.54 \div 0.0001 = 25\ 400.$

- The quotients are greater than 2.54.

WORKING TOGETHER

1. Evaluate.

   a. $35.4 \times 10\ 000$
   35.4×1000
   35.4×100
   35.4×10

   b. $35.4 \div 10\ 000$
   $35.4 \div 1000$
   $35.4 \div 100$
   $35.4 \div 10$

2. A number is multiplied by 10, 100, 1000, 10 000,....

   a. Which direction does the decimal point move?

   b. What determines the number of places the decimal point moves?

3. Repeat exercise 2 for division by 10, 100, 1000, 10 000,....

4. Evaluate.

   a. 35.4×0.0001
   35.4×0.001
   35.4×0.01
   35.4×0.1

   b. $35.4 \div 0.0001$
   $35.4 \div 0.001$
   $35.4 \div 0.01$
   $35.4 \div 0.1$

5. A number is multiplied by 0.1, 0.01, 0.001,....

   a. Which direction does the decimal point move?

   b. What determines the number of places the decimal point moves?

6. Repeat exercise 5 for division by 0.1, 0.01, 0.001,....

APPLICATIONS AND EXERCISES

1. Copy the result and insert the decimal point in the proper place.
   a. $47 \div 10 = 47$
   b. $6.48 \times 10 = 648$
   c. $0.416 \times 100 = 416$
   d. $1.92 \div 0.1 = 192$
   e. $0.495 \div 0.01 = 495$

2. Copy and complete.
   a. $345 = 34.5 \times \square$
   b. $27.8 = 0.278 \times \square$
   c. $72\,000 = 7.2 \times \square$
   d. $12.17 = \square \times 0.1$ e. $1.43 = \square \times 0.01$

3. Is the result greater that 12.1?
   a. 12.1×1000 b. $12.1 \div 1000$
   c. 12.1×0.001 d. $12.1 \div 0.001$
   e. 12.1×0.1 f. $12.1 \div 0.1$
   g. $12.1 \times 10\,000$ h. $12.1 \div 10\,000$

4. Which products in exercise 3 are less than 0.121?

5. Evaluate.
   a. $41.32 \div 100$ b. $217.5 \div 1000$
   c. 1000×5.08 d. $47.3 \div 0.1$
   e. $84 \div 0.0001$ f. 0.73×0.001

6. Which gives the smallest product? the largest product?
   a. 8.72×0.001 b. 8.72×100
   c. 8.72×10 d. 8.72×0.1
   e. 8.72×0.01 f. 8.72×1000
   g. $8.72 \times 10\,000$ h. 8.72×1

7. Which gives the smallest quotient? the largest quotient?
   a. $4.59 \div 0.1$ b. $4.59 \div 100$
   c. $4.59 \div 0.001$ d. $4.59 \div 1000$
   e. $4.59 \div 10$ f. $4.59 \div 0.01$

8. Your body produces about one billion red blood cells each day. A red blood cell measures about 0.01 mm across.
   a. How many red blood cells are produced in a year?
   b. If the yearly production of red blood cells were placed in a line, how long would the line be in kilometres?

9. One Canadian dollar can be exchanged for $0.71 American. How much American money would you receive for the following Canadian dollars?
   a. 100   b. 1000   c. 10 000
   d. 100 000   e. 1 million   f. 100 million

Enter 860 813 in your calculator.
Can you make the calculator reverse the digits of this number to display 318 068 in ten steps or less?

A step uses one operation with a one- or two-digit number. The operation may be addition, subtraction, multiplication, or division. The number may be a whole number or a decimal.

1. Reverse the digits of the numbers in ten steps or less.
   a. 478 506   b. 924 523   c. 123 456

1. Express in standard form.
   a. two hundred five and fifty-seven thousandths
   b. seventy-eight hundredths
   c. $(2 \times 10^3) + (8 \times 10^2) + (7 \times 1) + (3 \times \frac{1}{10})$
   d. $(5 \times \frac{1}{10^2}) + (2 \times \frac{1}{10^3})$

2. Express in expanded form using powers of 10.
   a. 407 852   b. 159.3   c. 200.05
   d. 0.106   e. 0.4077   f. 3900.08

3. Copy and use >, <, or = to make a true statement.
   a. 15.67 ○ 51.76   b. 21.85 ○ 21.582
   c. 0.78 ○ 0.780   d. 7.49 ○ 7.50
   e. 258.4 ○ 248.5   f. 11.18 ○ 11.08

4. Arrange in increasing order.
   a. 5.07, 0.75, 7.50, 5.75
   b. 243.8, 297.1, 237.9, 274.1
   c. 0.085, 0.508, 0.058, 0.805
   d. 15.93, 1.593, 1593, 159.3

5. When inflated, the mass of a regulation size basketball is between 0.6 kg and 0.65 kg. Is the basketball of regulation size?
   a. 0.63 kg   b. 0.649 kg
   c. 0.655 kg   d. 0.605 kg

6. Round to the nearest cent.
   a. $15.788   b. $12.266   c. $20.015
   d. $32.211   e. $500.999   f. $147.382

7. Copy and complete.

		Rounded to the nearest		
		one	tenth	hundredth
a.	7.863			
b.	20.577			
c.	0.749			
d.	6.326			

8. Which numbers become 7.003 when rounded to the nearest thousandth?

9. Evaluate.
   a.   5.24   b.   7.5   c.   0.282
      + 0.86   − 3.26   + 3.999

   d.   9.08   e.   900.01   f.   19.41
      − 4.0035   +   0.092   − 2.47

   g. 379.72 − 158.93   h. 2.84 + 0.135

10. Three Grade 8 classes collected money for the cancer campaign. Mr. Mulkewich's class collected $38.25. Mrs. Da Souza's class, $29.35, and Miss Roberts' class, $30.07.
    a. Find the total amount collected.
    b. Which class collected the most?
    c. The goal was to collect $100. Did the Grade 8 classes reach their goal? How much over or under were they?

11. Calculate.
    a. 8.95 × 100   b. 6.07 × 0.1
    c. 7.05 ÷ 0.1   d. 0.038 ÷ 0.001
    e. 50.72 × 0.001   f. 45.16 ÷ 10 000

12. A sheet of paper is 0.006 35 mm thick. How high is a stack of 1000 sheets?

Precision and Accuracy

Any measurement is an **approximation**.

How good the approximation is depends on the precision of the measurement.

The **precision** of the measurement depends on the unit of measurement
and the measuring instrument.

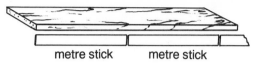

metre stick   metre stick

The wood is approximately 2 m long.

The wood is approximately 220 cm long or 2.2 m long.

The approximate measure of the length of the wood is more precise in the second example.

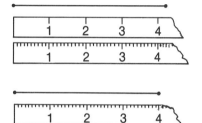

The measurement recorded as 4 cm means the length has been measured to the nearest centimetre. The measurement indicates the length is between 3.5 cm (lower bound) and 4.5 cm (upper bound).

The measurement recorded as 4.0 cm indicates a length between 3.95 cm and 4.05 cm. The length has been measured to the nearest tenth of a centimetre.

> 4 cm has one significant digit.
> 4.0 cm has two significant digits.

Digits that help show the precision of a measurement are **significant digits**.

When calculations are made with approximations, the result
is expressed to the same number of significant digits as
in the approximation having the least number of significant digits.

$$4 \text{ cm} \times 1.9 \text{ cm} \doteq 8 \text{ cm}^2$$

one significant digit   two significant digits   7.6 rounded to one significant digit

---

1. Measure the dimensions.

   a. to the nearest centimetre

   b. to the nearest tenth of a centimetre

2. For each part above, multiply the lower bound, then the upper bound, to give the range for the area. Then find the approximate result using the rule for significant digits.

Estimating Products and Quotients

Sharon delivers 768 papers in one month. She earns $0.13 profit on each paper. About how much profit does she earn in a month?

In one month Doug earns $89.76 not including tips. His profit is $0.11 on each paper. About how many papers does he deliver in a month?

Estimate using numbers that can be multiplied easily in your head.

$$\begin{array}{ccc} 768 & \rightarrow & 768 \\ \times\,0.13 & \rightarrow & \times\,0.1 \\ \hline & & 76.8 \end{array}$$

Estimate using numbers that can be divided easily in your head.

$$0.11\,\overline{)\,89.76} \quad \rightarrow \quad 0.1\,\overline{)\,89.76} \xrightarrow{\;897.6\;}$$

Sharon's profit is about $76.80.

Doug delivers about 898 papers.

Sometimes both numbers are rounded to estimate.

$$\begin{array}{ccc} 28.6 & \rightarrow & 30 \\ \times\,8.85 & \rightarrow & \times\,9 \\ \hline & & 270 \end{array}$$

$$8.3\,\overline{)\,74.5} \quad \rightarrow \quad 8\,\overline{)\,72}\xrightarrow{\;9\;}$$

WORKING TOGETHER

1. Is the estimate of Sharon's profit above or below her actual profit? Explain.

2. Estimate Sharon's profit for the number of papers delivered.

   a. 629   **b.** 735   **c.** 587   **d.** 805

3. Is the estimate of the number of papers that Doug delivers above or below the actual number he delivers? Explain.

4. Estimate the number of papers Doug delivers for these earnings.

   a. $75.24   **b.** $59.40   **c.** $64.35

5. Choose the best estimate.

   a. 186.3 ÷ 5.3 | 20   40   60 |

   b. 75.17 × 7.8 | 600   800   1000 |

   c. 91.23 × 95 | 10 000   15 000   20 000 |

APPLICATIONS AND EXERCISES

1. Is the product greater than 150? Estimate.
   a. 225 × 0.83   b. 1493 × 0.09
   c. 1751 × 0.14   d. 15 122 × 0.0083
   e. 150 × 1.013   f. 150 × 0.987

2. Estimate.
   a. 533 × 0.088   b. 917 × 0.0079
   c. 845.2 × 0.89   d. 12.13 × 0.0014
   e. 6759 × 0.032   f. 5.34 × 0.000 92

3. Is the quotient less than 150? Estimate.
   a. 49 ÷ 0.087   b. 5.12 ÷ 0.0026
   c. 1.53 ÷ 0.93   d. 1.58 ÷ 0.098
   e. 15.7 ÷ 0.0014   f. 15.1 ÷ 0.97

4. Estimate.
   a. 293 ÷ 0.0092   b. 1258 ÷ 0.088
   c. 45.27 ÷ 0.0027   d. 751.6 ÷ 0.893
   e. 64 108 ÷ 0.132   f. 8.105 ÷ 0.252

5. Choose the best estimate.

10 000	15 000	25 000
	200 000	
35 000	50 000	100 000

   a. 157.54 × 98.3   b. 3581 × 9.58
   c. 112.36 × 97.8   d. 181.4 × 962.5
   e. 9935.7 ÷ 0.98   f. 34 796 ÷ 1.9

6. The fuel tank of one of the world's largest trucks holds 5904.6 L of diesel fuel. Diesel fuel costs 45.3¢/L. Estimate the cost to fill the tank.

7. Mount Waialeale, in Hawaii, has an average annual rainfall of 116.84 cm. Estimate the average daily rainfall.

8. The population of North America is about 366 628 000. The population of Asia is about 7.5 times that of North America. Estimate the population of Asia.

9. The special edition of a newspaper sold for $1.25 a copy. 295 136 copies of the special edition were sold. Estimate the revenue.

10. The longest insect has a body 7.62 cm long and antennae 19.05 cm long. Estimate the length of the insect.

11.

Animal	Speed (m/s)
Garden snail	0.013
Giant tortoise	0.075
Spider	0.52
Sloth	0.067

   a. Estimate the distance travelled in 1 h.
   b. Estimate the time to travel the length of your classroom.

Try This

Mr. Williams has driven his truck 78 295 km. For even wear of the 5 tires, they were rotated regularly so that they all travelled the same distance. About how many kilometres was each tire used?

Multiplying

Ms. Tselios works 37.5 h/week in a machine shop. She earns $12.25/h. How much does she earn each week?

An estimate of the product can be used to determine the placement of the decimal point.

$$
\begin{array}{r}
12 \\
\times\ 40 \\
\hline
480.
\end{array}
$$

$$
\begin{array}{r}
12.25 \\
\times\ 37.5 \\
\hline
6125 \\
8575 \\
3675 \\
\hline
459.375
\end{array}
$$

Ms. Tselios earns $459.38 each week.

Another way to place the decimal point is to count decimal places.

$$
\begin{array}{r}
12.\ \boxed{25} \\
\times\ 37.\ \boxed{5} \\
\hline
459.\ \boxed{375}
\end{array}
\qquad
\begin{array}{l}
\longrightarrow\quad 2\ \text{decimal places} \\
\longrightarrow\quad 1\ \text{decimal place} \\
\longrightarrow\quad 3\ \text{decimal places}
\end{array}
$$

When decimal numbers are multiplied, the number of decimal places in the product is the same as the total number of decimal places in the factors.

WORKING TOGETHER

1. Choose the correct product for the expression.

   a. 5.25×0.9 | 0.4725   4.725   47.25 |

   b. 19.7×11.6 | 228.52   2285.2   22852 |

   c. 7.52×8.5 | 6.392   63.92   639.2 |

2. How many decimal places are there in the product?

   a. 2.87×0.4 **b.** 33.2×5

   c. 3.14×0.07 **d.** 493×0.009

   e. 187.3×4.8 **f.** 0.12×0.97

3. Copy. Then place the decimal point in the product.

   a.
   $$
   \begin{array}{r}
   6.5 \\
   \times\ 0.47 \\
   \hline
   3055
   \end{array}
   $$
   b.
   $$
   \begin{array}{r}
   8.7 \\
   \times\ 7.9 \\
   \hline
   6873
   \end{array}
   $$
   c.
   $$
   \begin{array}{r}
   14.83 \\
   \times\ 0.17 \\
   \hline
   25\ 211
   \end{array}
   $$

4. Calculate.

   a. 33.2×5 **b.** 493×0.009

   c. 3.14×0.07 **d.** 0.12×0.97

   e. $(1.5)^2$ **f.** $(0.2)^3$

1. Copy. Then place the decimal point in the product.

   a. 13
       × 0.8
       ────
       104

   b. 6.21
       × 7.4
       ─────
       45954

   c. 28.5
       × 1.77
       ─────
       50445

   d. 209.6
       × 4.26
       ──────
       892896

   e. 151
       × 0.92
       ─────
       13892

   f. 5.84
       × 27.5
       ──────
       160600

2. Multiply if the product is greater than 50.

   a. 11.8
       × 6.4

   b. 65
       × 0.25

   c. 10.84
       × 0.95

   d. 11.76
       × 7.47

   e. 7.07
       × 6.71

   f. 65.8
       × 32.6

3. Calculate.

   a. $(1.3)^2$
   b. $(2.6)^2$
   c. $(0.98)^2$
   d. $(8.75)^2$
   e. $(6.5)^2$
   f. $(14.4)^2$

4. Joanna is paid $3.85/h. Find her earnings for the following hours of work.

   a. 20 h
   b. 35 h
   c. 38.5 h
   d. 17 h
   e. 19.5 h
   f. 37.5 h

5. Employees are paid 1.5 times their regular rate for any overtime they work. Copy and complete the chart.

	a.	b.	c.	d.
Regular rate ($/h)	4.00	3.92	5.60	4.75
Overtime rate ($/h)				

6. The Deutsche Mark (DM) is the main currency used in West Germany. 1 Deutsche Mark can be exchanged for $1.76 Canadian. Convert the amounts in the table to Canadian dollars.

FINANCIAL STATEMENT	
Total Assets	56.42 billion DM
Total Customers' Deposits	24.87 billion DM
Loans to Customers Outstanding	33.51 billion DM
Capital and Reserves	1.79 billion DM

7. The table shows the times and fuel consumption for flights from Montreal to Vancouver.

Type of Plane	Flight length (h)	Fuel Consumption (L/h)
747	4.1	12 161
DC-10-30	4.2	8 160
DC-10-10	4.2	7 108
737	4.7	2 699

   a. How much fuel is used by each plane?
   b. Airplane fuel costs $0.437/L. Calculate the fuel cost for each flight.

8. Estimate your mass in kilograms. Use your estimate for the following.

   a. Human bones are about 0.181 of body mass. Find the mass of your bones.
   b. The brain is about 0.0299 of body mass. Find the mass of your brain.
   c. The amount of water in the human body is about 0.579 of the body mass. Find the mass of water in your body.

KEEPING SHARP

Evaluate.

a. $5 \times 3 - 2$
b. $8 + 10 - 4 \times 2$
c. $12 \div (6 - 4)$
d. $2 + 5 \times 4 \div 2$
e. $15 \div 3 + 2$
f. $\dfrac{20 - 8 + 2}{4 \times 2 - 1}$
g. $\dfrac{5 + 18 \div 6 - 4}{3 \times 2 - 2}$
h. $28 \div (3 + 4) + 8 \times 5 - 3$

Dividing by a Whole Number

The world's longest oil pipeline extends from Edmonton, Alberta to Fort Erie, Ontario, a distance of 2857.4 km. Along the length of the pipeline 13 pumping stations keep the oil flowing at a steady rate.

What is the average distance between stations?

Divide.
$$13\overline{)2857.4}$$

Place the decimal point in the quotient directly above the decimal point in the dividend.

Divide as with whole numbers.

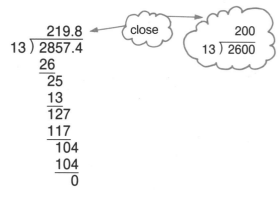

```
      219.8
13 ) 2857.4
     26
     ──
      25
      13
      ──
      127
      117
      ───
      104
      104
      ───
        0
```

close $13\overline{)2600}$ 200

The average distance between stations is 219.8 km.

WORKING TOGETHER

1. Divide.

  a. 114 ÷ 6   **b.** 145 ÷ 5

  c. 3564 ÷ 4   **d.** 442.4 ÷ 7

  e. 51.48 ÷ 9   **f.** 3.736 ÷ 8

2. Round the quotient to the nearest tenth.

  a. $9\overline{)7.54}$ **b.** $8\overline{)20.91}$

  c. $3\overline{)6.55}$ **d.** $12\overline{)85.49}$

  e. $11\overline{)0.652}$ **f.** $20\overline{)90.09}$

APPLICATIONS AND EXERCISES

1. Copy. Then place the decimal point in the quotient.
   a. $576.8 \div 7 = 824$
   b. $78.48 \div 12 = 654$
   c. $23.742 \div 9 = 2638$
   d. $175.5 \div 27 = 65$
   e. $200.2 \div 52 = 385$

2. Divide if the quotient is greater than 40.
   a. $6 \overline{)\ 151.2}$ b. $7 \overline{)\ 439.6}$ c. $9 \overline{)\ 468.9}$
   d. $18 \overline{)\ 55.98}$ e. $15 \overline{)\ 676.5}$ f. $25 \overline{)\ 802.5}$

3. Divide. Compare the quotients.
   a. $5 \overline{)\ 23.55}$ b. $8 \overline{)\ 1.752}$ c. $6 \overline{)\ 0.8034}$
   $\ \ 50 \overline{)\ 235.5}$ $\ \ 8 \overline{)\ 17.52}$ $\ \ 6 \overline{)\ 80.34}$

4. Calculate the unit cost to the nearest cent.
   a.
   $19.99
   b.
   $17.50
   c.
   $1.69
   d.
   $1.25
   e.
   $3.89
   f.
   $17.95

5. Which is the better offer?
   a. 3 granola bars for $0.79 or 12 granola bars for $3.19
   b. 2 bars of soap for $0.89 or 3 bars of soap for $1.29
   c. 4 kitchen chairs for $189.95 or 6 kitchen chairs for $275.59

6. The mass of 3 L of milk is 3.105 kg. Find the mass of 1 L of milk.

7. The snowfall at Jasper for one month was 100.8 cm. Find the average snowfall for each day it snowed, if it snowed for 18 d (days).

8. Felt-tipped pens sell for $0.79 each. Packages of 6 sell for $4.50. How much is saved on each pen by buying a package?

9. A store buys coffee mugs at $21.00 for 12. The mugs are sold at $2.59 each. Find the profit on each mug.

10. A piece of telephone cable 70.8 m long is cut into sections 8 m long.
    a. How many sections can be cut?
    b. How long is the remaining piece?

11. The record distance for human-powered flight is 35.616 km. It took 169 min.
    a. What distance was covered in 1 min?
    b. What distance was covered in 1 h?
    c. Estimate how long it took to fly 1 km.

A dozen cookies and a loaf of bread cost $2.80.
Half a dozen cookies and 2 loaves of bread cost $2.90.
How much does one loaf of bread cost?

Try This

Dividing by a Decimal

The cargo bay of a space shuttle has a volume of 77.55 m³. A new, compact, communications satellite has a volume of 5.5 m³. What is the greatest number of these satellites that could fit inside the cargo bay?

Multiply the divisor and dividend by a power of 10 to make the divisor a whole number.

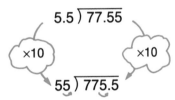

No more than 14 satellites could fit inside the cargo bay.

WORKING TOGETHER

1. What power of 10 should the divisor and dividend be multiplied by to make the divisor a whole number?

   a. $7.1\overline{)90.52}$　　**b.** $75.4\overline{)0.936}$

   c. $0.19\overline{)2.051}$　　**d.** $1.76\overline{)145.8}$

   e. $185.2 \div 0.04$　　**f.** $0.107 \div 22.2$

2. Rewrite the following with a whole number divisor.

   a. $1.7\overline{)19.75}$　　**b.** $0.76\overline{)1.413}$

   c. $207.1 \div 0.34$　　**d.** $0.185 \div 0.75$

3. Divide.

   a. $0.7\overline{)58.1}$　　**b.** $0.9\overline{)7.56}$

   c. $0.06\overline{)0.504}$　　**d.** $1.5\overline{)90.15}$

   e. $1.824 \div 1.2$　　**f.** $57.31 \div 0.11$

4. Find the quotient to the nearest tenth.

   a. $0.13\overline{)0.2705}$　　**b.** $1.4\overline{)0.305}$

   c. $2.5\overline{)53.127}$　　**d.** $0.11\overline{)0.3992}$

1. Choose the correct quotient for the expression.

   a. 1.4 ÷ 0.7   0.02, 0.2, 2

   b. 84 ÷ 2.1   0.4, 4, 40

   c. 0.042 ÷ 0.6   0.07, 0.7, 70

   d. 2.4 ÷ 0.3   0.08, 0.8, 8

   e. 0.63 ÷ 0.09   0.07, 0.7, 7

   f. 3.9 ÷ 1.3   0.3, 3, 30

   g. 244.8 ÷ 1.2   2.04, 20.4, 204

2. Divide mentally.

   a. $1.2\overline{)14.4}$ **b.** $0.11\overline{)7.70}$

   c. $1.5\overline{)0.015}$ **d.** $0.5\overline{)4.05}$

   e. 0.169 ÷ 1.3   **f.** 7.2 ÷ 0.08

   g. 0.48 ÷ 2.4   **h.** 9.6 ÷ 0.32

   i. $\dfrac{1.25}{0.25}$ **j.** $\dfrac{0.42}{2.1}$

3. Divide if the quotient is greater than 70.

   a. 279.89 ÷ 5.7   **b.** 192.7 ÷ 2.05

   c. 117.3 ÷ 0.23   **d.** 36.48 ÷ 5.7

   e. $\dfrac{2.125}{0.025}$ **f.** $\dfrac{32.55}{0.35}$

4. One kangaroo jump is about 2.5 m long. How many jumps would a kangaroo make in travelling each distance?

   a. 62.5 m **b.** 650 m **c.** 400 m **d.** 1 km

5. The record distance for leap frogging is 965 400 m. How many turns did it take for one player if each turn covered a length of 8.9 m?

6. Find the unit cost to the nearest cent.

   a. 1.5 m of cable for $2.75

   b. 0.36 kg of nuts for $3.09

   c. 2.5 L of oil for $4.90

   d. 0.75 m of ribbon for $0.95

   e. 1.75 kg of nails for $1.98

7. Ernst changes $42.60 Canadian into U.S. currency. He receives $30.25 U.S. What is the value of $1 Canadian in U.S. funds?

8. What is the greatest number of bagels that can be bought with $2.50?

38¢ each

9. The Canadarm has a mass of 407.3 kg and can lift a satellite with a mass of 2851.5 kg. How many times its own mass can the arm lift?

10. A 1280-page dictionary is 4.4 cm thick.

   a. How many leaves of paper are in the dictionary?

   b. Find the thickness of each leaf of paper.

   c. Find the thickness of 100 pages in the dictionary.

Describe how to divide the round of cheese into 8 equal pieces with 3 straight cuts.

Try This

Scientific Notation

The Voyager 2 spacecraft has travelled over 2 965 000 000 km to reach the planet Uranus.

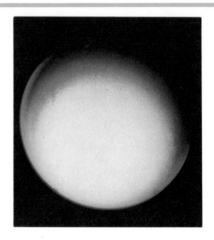

Large numbers can be written in a more compact form called **scientific notation**.

$2\ 965\ 000\ 000 = 2.965 \times 1\ 000\ 000\ 000$

A number between 1 and 10	A power of 10

$$= 2.965 \times 10^9$$

In scientific notation, 2 965 000 000 km is written 2.965×10^9 km.

The cost of the Voyager project is estimated to be $\$5.95 \times 10^8$.

This number is in scientific notation. It can be expressed in **standard form**.

$$5.95 \times 10^8 = 5.95 \times 100\ 000\ 000$$
$$= 595\ 000\ 000$$

In standard form, $\$5.95 \times 10^8$ is written $595\ 000\ 000$ or $595 million.

WORKING TOGETHER

1. Is the number expressed in scientific notation?

   a. 2.3×10^4 **b.** 0.8×10^6

   c. 912 **d.** 6.4×2^5

   e. 72.6×10^5 **f.** 1.5×10^7

2. Match the number with its correct expression in scientific notation.

   a. 5900 5.9×10^6

   b. 5 900 000 5.9×10^1

   c. 59 5.9×10^3

3. Copy and complete with the correct exponent.

   a. $714.8 = 7.148 \times 10^{\square}$

   b. $52\ 700 = 5.27 \times 10^{\square}$

   c. $8250 = 8.25 \times 10^{\square}$

   d. $12.4 = 1.24 \times 10^{\square}$

4. Copy and complete.

   a. $6\ 090\ 000 = \square \times 10^6$

   b. $700\ 000\ 000 = \square \times 10^8$

   c. $917\ 000\ 000\ 000 = \square \times 10^{11}$

1. Copy and complete to express the number in scientific notation.

   a. $48.6 = 4.86 \times 10^{\square}$

   b. $8000 = 8.0 \times 10^{\square}$

   c. $204\ 000 = 2.04 \times 10^{\square}$

   d. $1200 = \square \times 10^{\square}$

   e. $18.9 = \square \times 10^{\square}$

   f. $37\ 000\ 000 = \square \times 10^{\square}$

2. Express in scientific notation.

   a. 1200

   b. 5 050 000

   c. 42.8

   d. 23 000 000

   e. 872

   f. 591 700

   g. 89.17

   h. 7458.3

3. Express the number in scientific notation.

   a. The circumference of Earth is 39 928 800 m.

   b. The mass of Earth is 5 990 000 000 000 000 000 t (tonnes).

   c. The speed of light is 1 073 600 000 km/h.

   d. In an average winter 90 700 000 t of snow fall on Metropolitan Toronto.

4. Calculate the approximate number of seconds you have been living. Give the answer in scientific notation.

5. A telephone directory contains 1925 pages of phone numbers. On each page there are five columns with 91 seven-digit phone numbers in each column.

   a. Calculate how many telephone numbers are listed in the directory.

   b. Express the answer from part **a** in scientific notation.

   c. Calculate the number of digits in all the phone numbers.

   d. Express the answer from part **c** in scientific notation.

6. Express the number in standard form.

   a. Lake Superior is 3.9684×10^2 m deep.

   b. Labrador has rocks that are about 3.0×10^{15} years old.

   c. Light travelling from the Andromeda galaxy takes about 2.0×10^6 a to reach Earth.

   d. In a recent year Canada exported over $88 426 million worth of goods.

7. Express the result in standard form and then in scientific notation.

   a. $3 \times 10^2 \times 2 \times 10^5$

   b. $(2.6 \times 10^{18}) \div (1.3 \times 10^9)$

   c. $(7.5 \times 10^{12}) \div (2.5 \times 10^6)$

Murray used a computer with word processing software to print the poem *Alligator Pie*.

Heidi used the FIND AND REPLACE feature to change <u>pie</u> to <u>soup</u>, <u>die</u> to <u>droop</u>, <u>the green grass</u> to <u>my hockey stick</u>, and <u>the sky</u> to <u>my hoop</u>.

```
Alligator pie, alligator pie,
If I don't get some I think I'm gonna die.
Give away the green grass, give away the sky,
But don't give away my alligator pie.
```

1. a. Give Heidi's version of the poem.

   b. Create your own version.

2. Create versions of other rhymes or songs.

PRACTICE

1. Estimate the result.

    a. 748.5
    × 0.08

    b. 12.59
    × 0.009

    c. 78.17
    × 1.3

    d. 0.12) 8351.7

    e. 0.08) 14 925.64

2. Choose the best estimate.

1500	500	50
	2500	
100	9000	10

    a. 51.7
    × 11

    b. 787
    × 1.8

    c. 91.23
    × 95

    d. 4367 ÷ 110.5

    e. 1924.7 ÷ 18.6

3. Estimate the result.

    a. 386.1
    × 27.9

    b. 309
    × 5.82

    c. 683
    × 1.29

    d. 593.34 ÷ 6.2

    e. 38 421.4 ÷ 81.4

4. Multiply only if the product is greater than 100.

    a. 42 × 0.28

    b. 251.4 × 0.93

    c. 95.35 × 0.85

    d. 79.6 × 1.9

    e. $(10.4)^2$

    f. 109.8 × 0.75

5. You can jump six times as high on the moon as on Earth. Find how high a boy could jump on the moon if he can jump 1.21 m on Earth.

6. Copy showing the decimal point in the quotient.

    a. 593.34 ÷ 6.2 = 957

    b. 153 ÷ 0.25 = 6120

    c. 48.84 ÷ 81.4 = 6000

    d. 693.72 ÷ 1.23 = 56 400

7. Divide if the quotient is greater than 50.

    a. 131.04 ÷ 5

    b. 601.6 ÷ 8

    c. 934.5 ÷ 15

    d. 1311.42 ÷ 33

    e. 3569.16 ÷ 42

    f. 873.0392 ÷ 29

8. A piece of conveyor belt 39.15 m long is cut into sections 9 m long.

    a. How many sections can be cut?

    b. How long is the remaining piece?

9. Rewrite with a whole number divisor.

    a. 9.4) 106.2

    b. 1.04) 0.0926

    c. 1.413 ÷ 0.008

    d. 2191.6 ÷ 1.103

10. Divide.

    a. 576.28 ÷ 0.02

    b. 4.732 ÷ 1.4

    c. 235.50 ÷ 31.4

    d. 131.04 ÷ 5.6

11. Find the unit cost to the nearest cent.

    a. 1.5 m of binding for $2.39

    b. 35 g of wool for $2.95

    c. 1.5 L of oil for $4.90

    d. 5.2 kg of peat moss for $11.20

12. Express in scientific notation.

    a. 7 321 000

    b. 98 240

    c. 176 000 000

    d. 91 100 000 000

13. Every minute $1.6 × 10^8$ L of water flow over Niagara Falls. Find how much water flows over the falls each day. Express the answer in scientific notation.

14. Express in standard form.

    a. $2.5 × 10^6$

    b. $1.04 × 10^3$

    c. $9.008 × 10^2$

    d. $1.005 × 10^5$

Automatic Constants

Rhys earns $4.75 an hour.
He calculates his weekly earnings
by multiplying.

4.75 × hours worked

Week	Hours worked	Earnings ($)
1	18	4.75 × 18 = 85.50
2	12	4.75 × 12 = 57.00
3	17	4.75 × 17 = 80.75
4	20	4.75 × 20 = 95.00

He can also use his calculator's built-in multiplication constant.

		Display	
Entering	4.75 × 18 =	85.5	sets up 4.75 as an automatic
	12 =	57	constant for multiplication.
	17 =	80.75	

1. Mohammed works the same hours as Rhys but earns $4.95
   an hour. Calculate his earnings per week.

2. Calculate the first five multiples of the number.
   a. 19   **b.** 78   **c.** 326   **d.** 1988   **e.** 89 357

3. Enter   24 ÷ 2 =   Which number is set up as an automatic
                6 =   constant for division?
               12 =

4. Rhys' earnings for the next four
   weeks are shown in the table.
   How many hours does he work each week?

Week	Hours worked	Earnings ($)
5		90.25
6		76.00
7		61.75
8		66.50

5. Some calculators have built-in constants for addition and for subtraction.

   Enter   12 + 4 =   Enter   21 − 13 =
                 10 =   16 =
                 16 =   18 =

   Which number is set up as an automatic constant for addition? for subtraction?

6. Write the number that is 2.798 greater than the number.
   a. 8.695   **b.** 7.982   **c.** 13.202   **d.** 29.777   **e.** 153.068

7. Write the number that is 6.159 less than the numbers in exercise 6.

Word Processing

Depending on the type of software used, a computer can be used to
work with numbers   OR   **work with words**.

- to calculate a company payroll
- to make banking transactions
- to keep track of telephone bills

- to create business reports, letters, and magazine articles
- to publish newspapers and books

A computer with word processing (WP) software has many features
that make the job of producing letters or other documents easier.

These features allow you to
prepare a document or work with the information in it, and
format the document (decide how it will look when printed).

The students in Mr. Perot's class wanted to use their WP for
preparing reviews of the library books they were to read that term.
First they decided to work with five categories:
ADVENTURE (AD), GENERAL (GEN), HISTORY (HIS),
SCIENCE FICTION (SF), SPORT (SPO).
Then they agreed on what information would be listed for each review.

To set up the framework, Sonya loaded the
WP program and typed this information. ———————➤
She used the SAVE command to save the
document on a disk under the name SKELETON.
She made sure that her work had been
saved by typing CATALOG. Then she used
the CLEAR command to clear the memory.

Then Eugene typed a second document.

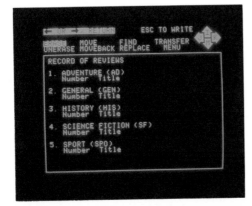

He saved this on the disk under the name
RECORD OF REVIEWS. Then he cleared the memory.

1. How could Eugene check that the
   categories had been saved before he
   cleared the memory?

2. What would have happened if Sonya had
   not cleared the memory before Eugene typed
   the RECORD OF REVIEWS document?

Marion was the first student to do a book review. She used the RETRIEVE command to get the file SKELETON on to the screen. Moving the cursor to the appropriate spot, she typed her review. ———————→
She saved this under the name SF1.

Marion used the CLEAR command, then retrieved the file called RECORD OF REVIEWS. In the science fiction section she typed the number SF1 and the title of the book. She saved the result under the same name RECORD OF REVIEWS.

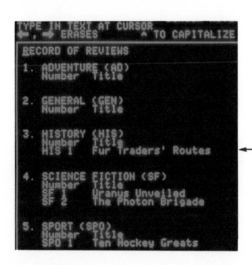

3. Why did Marion save her book review under a new name SF1, instead of SKELETON?

4. Why did she save the second document under its original name RECORD OF REVIEWS?

The RECORD OF REVIEWS is shown on the screen.

5. How many reviews have the students listed so far?

6. If you were a student in Mr. Perot's class and wanted to read one of the better science fiction stories listed, what steps would you follow in choosing a book?

7. Write a sequence of commands that would allow Mr. Perot to save all the reviews in one file called REVIEWS. Each review should be shown in the order shown in the RECORD OF REVIEWS.

8. Discuss any advantages or disadvantages in handwriting the reviews and keeping them in a binder.

Choose the Information

A DC-10 is flying from Winnipeg to Vancouver. Air traffic at Vancouver is heavy when the plane arrives and it must circle while waiting for permission to land. How long can the plane circle before it runs out of fuel?

Think. What is the distance from Winnipeg to Vancouver?
What quantity of fuel has been used?
How much fuel is left?
How much fuel is used per hour to circle?

Plan and do. Request flight data from the plane's computer.

> Number of passengers: 210
> Average mass of a passenger: 75 kg
> Average mass of a passenger's luggage: 20 kg
> Mass of cargo: 12 800 kg
> Mass of fuel at takeoff: 54 000 kg
> Distance from Winnipeg to Calgary: 1336 km
> Distance from Calgary to Vancouver: 1058 km
> Cruising speed: 725 km/h
> Cruising: DC-10 burns fuel at 7700 kg/h
> Climbing to cruise: DC-10 burns fuel at 6800 kg/h

- Add to calculate the distance flown: 1336 km + 1058 km = 2394 km
- Divide to find the time of flight: 2394 km ÷ 725 km/h ≐ 3.3 h
- Multiply to calculate the fuel used from Winnipeg to Vancouver: 7700 kg/h × 3.3 h = 25 410 kg
- Subtract to find the mass of the remaining fuel: 54 000 kg − 25 410 kg = 28 590 kg
- Divide to find how long the plane could circle at Vancouver: 28 590 kg ÷ 7700 kg/h ≐ 3.7 h

The plane can circle 3.7 h before it runs out of fuel.

Look back. Is this answer reasonable? Estimate to check.

WORKING TOGETHER

1. The fuel capacity of a DC-10 is 104 000 kg. How long can it stay in the air before it would need to land to refuel?

2. If the plane had to put down in Calgary because of fog in Vancouver, the airline would have to pay for accommodation for all the passengers. What would this cost if the hotel charges $42.50/person?

PROBLEMS

The Making of a Skyscraper

The world's tallest "tube" building is being assembled in Toronto. It will be a 68-storey office tower costing $430 million. A tube building has 80% of its structural strength in the outside frame rather than in the central elevator core. To achieve this requires the world's first use of 70 MPA concrete in a tall building. The average concrete mix has a strength of 320 kg/cm^2. The 70 MPA mix is rated at 775 kg/cm^2 and solidifies quickly. This allows the 76 concrete columns around the outside rim of the building to be poured continuously.

Two huge cranes will lift 7725 t of steel as the building rises. Each crane can lift 23.6 t and has a 200 m main cable.

28 000 pieces of granite,

quarried in northern Sweden and cut and polished in Massa, Italy, will be hung on the concrete and steel frame.

The building operation itself will rely on computers. One will run 44 double-decker elevator cabs operating in 22 shafts. In other buildings 35 elevator shafts are required to move the same volume of people. Each elevator will travel at about 37 km/h.

Another computer will control the 18 500 lighting fixtures.

A 2.95 million-litre water reservoir will be used to help heat and cool the building. There will be 5000 large windows, each 2.39 m by 1.9 m.

When completed the building will provide 139 000 m^2 of office space and 3158 m^2 of retail shopping space.

1. What is the approximate cost of the tower per floor?

2. How much stronger in kg/cm^2 is 70 MPA than the average concrete used? Why would they need to use 70 MPA?

3. About how many pieces of granite are needed for each floor in the building?

4. Using an atlas, calculate the total distance the granite must travel from its source to its final destination.

5. If each crane lifted its maximum load 8 times a day, how many tonnes would be lifted in a 2 week period (5 d = 1 week)?

6. What is the fraction of retail shopping space in the building? of leased office space?

7. a. How many square metres per floor are there?

   b. How many lighting fixtures per floor are there?

   c. How many square metres is one lighting fixture expected to light?

8. If one floor is about 4 m high, approximately how long would it take an employee to travel from the ground floor to the 68th floor non-stop?

9. If a window washer can wash one window in 5 min, how long will it take 2 window washers to wash all the windows in the building?

10. Make up 6 other problems.

Problem Solving Review

1. Draw a sketch to show how 7 trees can be planted in 6 rows of 3 each.

2. A Greek was born on the seventh day of 40 B.C. and died on the seventh day of 40 A.D. How many years did the Greek live?

3. How would you cash a cheque for $63.00 if it must be cashed in 6 bills—no one-dollar bills or coins?

4. It is easy to put each name in its own compartment by drawing 3 horizontal lines, but can you do it by drawing 2 straight lines?

```
F A T H E R
H E R M A N
L O U I S A
I S A B E L
```

5. To number the pages of a bulky volume, the printer used 2989 digits. How many pages has the volume?

6. Fresh beans cost $1.28/kg. Two 400 g cans of beans cost $1.00. What is the unit price of the canned beans?

7. a. What does the power company charge for each kilowatt hour used?

  b. What percent penalty is charged if the bill is late?

Previous bill	$85.59	Amount due : $151.98
Credits	$85.59	Amount due if paid after
Balance	$ 0.00	Oct 24 : $156.58

Present reading (kW.h)	Previous reading (kW.h)	kW.h used	Amount
6781	4993	1788	$151.98

8. The telephone company sends a bill to Ms. Jackson. It shows the following: base charge, $9.25; long distance calls within the country, $21.48; long distance calls to other countries, $57.95. There is a 7% tax on all calls within the country, including the base charge. There is a 10% tax on all calls to other countries. What is Ms. Jackson's total bill?

9. The Guedes family has to cut down on their electrical expense to afford a holiday. They are able to cut the bill exactly in half. How many kilowatt hours of electricity did they use in June?

May bill		
First 400 kwh @ 4¢	$16.00
Next 550 kwh @ 10¢	$55.00
	$71.00

10.

The blue whale is the largest mammal on Earth. It is bigger than 30 elephants, and it has a mass greater than 2000 people. Its heart is almost 2 m across, with a mass of 540 kg. Its tongue has a mass of 333 kg. The largest blood vessels are so large that a small child could crawl through them. These whales can speed up to 20 knots and can keep pace with ocean liners. Milk from a blue whale is four times as rich as a cow's. It can give 494 L of milk per day.

  a. Estimate the mass of a blue whale.

  b. Estimate the diameter of the whale's largest blood vessel.

  c. 20 knots is approximately equivalent to 37 km/h. How long would it take a blue whale to travel 500 km?

  d. How far can it travel in 3 h?

Chapter Checkup

1. Express in standard form.
   a. one hundred fifty-eight and sixty-seven hundredths
   b. $(8 \times 1000) + (7 \times 10) + (7 \times 1) + (4 \times \frac{1}{100})$
   c. $(5 \times 10^2) + (2 \times 1) + (6 \times \frac{1}{10}) + (9 \times \frac{1}{10^3})$

2. Express in expanded form using powers of 10.
   a. 25.705   b. 0.68   c. 52 100.5

3. To twenty decimal places π equals 3.141 592 653 589 793 238 46. Give the value of π rounded to the number of decimal places.
   a. 4   b. 5   c. 9   d. 10

4. Arrange in order from the least to the greatest.
   a. 9.6, 8.7, 10.1, 7.9
   b. 0.03, 0.31, 0.103, 0.031
   c. 1.58, 5.81, 8.15, 5.18, 1.85
   d. 0.96, 1.03, 0.9, 1.3, 1.69

5. A builder calculates the placement of windows to be centred in the walls of a house. Copy and complete the chart.

	Width of wall	Width of window	Width of wall on each side
a.	243.84 cm	121.92 cm	
b.	365.76 cm	91.44 cm	
c.	640 cm		251.42 cm
d.	670.56 cm		255.27 cm
e.	472.44 cm	106.68 cm	

6. Evaluate if the result is greater than 11.5.
   a. 11.5×0.001 b. $11.5 \times 10\ 000$
   c. $11.5 \div 0.01$ d. 11.5×100
   e. 11.5×0.1 f. $11.5 \div 0.0001$

7. Estimate.
   a. 6.5×9.8 b. 0.76×1.75
   c. $24.5 \div 3.5$ d. $568.4 \div 7$
   e. 162.2×9.6 f. $182.99 \div 29$
   g. $31.302 \div 0.07$ h. 0.83×0.25
   i. 14.1×0.48 j. $2.697 \div 0.058$

8. Find the cost of the purchase.
   a. 5 kg of onions at $0.49 kg
   b. 3 dozen eggs at $1.38 per dozen
   c. 2.75 kg of cashew nuts at $9.68/kg
   d. 0.72 kg of cheese at $3.97/kg

9. A butcher charges $16.07 for a roast of beef. If the beef sells for $8.49/kg, what is the mass of the roast to the nearest gram?

10. Express in scientific notation.
    a. 18 500   b. 2 300 000
    c. 126.1   d. 16.82
    e. 517 000 000   f. 1934.06

11. Express the number in standard form.
    a. The sun's mass is 2.0×10^{30} g.
    b. The mass of a blue whale is 1.755×10^8 g.

Cumulative Checkup

1. The table shows the number of residential telephones in use on private lines for a recent year.

Province	Number of phones
Alberta	682 206
British Columbia	866 240
Manitoba	328 037
New Brunswick	176 202
Newfoundland	134 529
Northwest Territories	9 913
Nova Scotia	234 162
Ontario	2 838 555
Prince Edward Island	26 301
Quebec	2 056 114
Saskatchewan	277 415
Yukon	5 460

   a. Estimate the total number of phones in the Atlantic provinces.

   b. Estimate the total number of phones in the Western provinces, Yukon, and Northwest Territories.

   c. Estimate the difference in the number of phones in part **a** and part **b**.

   d. About how many times greater is Ontario's phone count than Saskatchewan's?

   e. Make other size comparisons.

2. Find the result.

   a. 47 893
       619 008
    +   705

   b. 4819 + 73 + 11 012

   c. 7108 − 2099   **d.** 42 196 − 8889

   e. 509 × 86   **f.** 75 × 183

   g. $28\overline{)14896}$ **h.** 44 541 ÷ 21

   i. $\dfrac{33\,858}{18}$ **j.** $\dfrac{26\,576}{16}$

3. Is the number divisible by 2?

   a. 1024   **b.** 3600   **c.** 111 111

   d. 123 456   **e.** 58 473   **f.** 98 765

4. Which numbers in exercise 3 are divisible?

   a. by 3   **b.** by 6   **c.** by 5

5. Is the number divisible by 4?

   a. 3600   **b.** 154   **c.** 19 096

   d. 75 960   **e.** 23 692   **f.** 57 321

6. Which numbers in exercise 5 are divisible?

   a. by 8   **b.** by 9   **c.** by 10

7. Find all the factors of the number.

   a. 18   **b.** 30   **c.** 42   **d.** 64

   e. 100   **f.** 220   **g.** 196   **h.** 252

8. Express the number as the product of its prime factors.

   a. 36   **b.** 48   **c.** 72   **d.** 58

   e. 90   **f.** 256   **g.** 315   **h.** 441

9. Jitka is asked to arrange 28 desks in rows of equal length. How many desks can she put in each row?

10. Express as a power.

   a. 2 × 2 × 2   **b.** 4 × 4 × 4 × 4

   c. 3 × 3 × 3 × 3 × 3 × 3 × 3

   d. 10 × 10 × 10 × 10 × 10

11. Express as a product. Evaluate.

   a. 3^4 **b.** 4^3 **c.** 5^2 **d.** 2^5

   e. 10^5 **f.** 8^3 **g.** 9^4 **h.** 11^3

12. Express as a single power.

a. $2^5 \times 2^3$ b. $5^2 \times 5^4$

c. 10×10^6 d. $6^7 \times 6^8$

e. $4^3 \times 4^3$ f. $3^8 \times 3^5$

13. Express as a single power.

a. $4^7 \div 4^5$ b. $6^{12} \div 6^8$

c. $8^3 \div 8$ d. $9^9 \div 9^3$

e. $10^{12} \div 10^7$ f. $5^{10} \div 5^9$

14. Express as a single power. Evaluate.

a. $5^8 \div 5^5$ b. $3^9 \div 3^5$

c. $2^3 \times 2$ d. $3^2 \times 3^2$

e. $8^4 \div 8^2$ f. $10^7 \div 10^2$

15. Evaluate.

a. $\sqrt{81}$ b. $\sqrt{25}$ c. $\sqrt{100}$

d. $\sqrt{256}$ e. $\sqrt{196}$ f. $\sqrt{1024}$

g. $\sqrt{3600}$ h. $\sqrt{12\,100}$ i. $\sqrt{640\,000}$

16. Find a number for which the principal square root equals one-half of the number.

17. Find the length of a side of the square.

a.

16 cm²

b.

900 mm²

18. A parcel of land is divided into 35 square lots of equal size. The land covers an area of 14 000 m². What is the length of the side of each lot?

19. Find three more numbers in the sequence.

a. 1, 2, 4, 8   b. 1, 3, 6, 10

c. 3, 9, 27, 81   d. 2, 3, 5, 7

20.

$11 \times 11 = 121$

$111 \times 111 = \square$

$1111 \times 1111 = \square$

Study the pattern. Use a shortcut to find the product of 11 111 and 11 111.

21. Evaluate.

a. $6 \times 4 - 8$ b. $15 \div 3 + 2$

c. $1 + 24 \div 4 - 3$ d. $4^2 - 3 \times 5$

e. $27 + (2^3 \times 3 - 3^2) \div 5$

f. $48 \div (4^2 - 4 \times 2) \times 6 - 6$

g. $\dfrac{8 \times (12 - 7) - 3 \times 4 + 2}{3^2 - 28 \div 7}$

22. Copy and use parentheses to make the statement true.

a. $6 \times 5 - 3 = 12$

b. $8 \div 2 + 2 \times 3 = 10$

c. $3^3 - 9 \div 3 - 2 = 4$

d. $\dfrac{6 \times 3 + 8 \div 2}{18 \div 2 + 4} = 11$

23. Copy and insert $+$, $-$, $\times$, or $\div$ to make a true statement.

a. $3 \square 4 \square 5 = 2$

b. $4 \square 4 \square 3 \square 3 \square 2 = 19$

c. $(3 \square 6 \square 12) \square 2 \square 9 = 24$

d. $(8 \square 5) \square 14 \square (3 \square 2) = 7$

24. Evaluate. Look for a shortcut.

a. $5 \times 13 \times 20$ b. $28 + 193 + 72$

c. $42 \div 6 + 28 + 43$

d. $89 - 37 - 29$ e. 102×55

3/Perimeter and Area

A sailing race involves following the perimeter of a course outlined by the race officials. The area of sail used depends greatly on wind conditions.

Get Set

1. Match the item to be measured with the appropriate unit of measure.

   a. your height   **b.** length of a fly

   c. distance across Canada

   d. area of your classroom floor

   e. area of your province or territory

   | millimetre | centimetre | square kilometre |
   | kilometre | hectare | square metre |

2. Draw a sketch.

   a. $\overline{AB}$ **b.** $\overrightarrow{CD}$ **c.** $\overleftrightarrow{EF}$ **d.** $\overrightarrow{DC}$

3. Draw the figure and write the measures of all the sides.

   a. 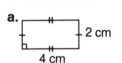 2 cm   4 cm

   b. 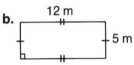 12 m   5 m

   c. 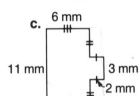 6 mm   11 mm   3 mm   2 mm

   d. 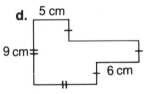 5 cm   9 cm   6 cm

4. Name the polygon.

   a. A B E C D

   b. 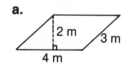 M R N Q O P

   c. 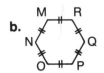 X Y Z

   d. P S Q R

   e. E H F G

   f. 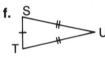 S U T

5. Round 421.784.

   a. nearest tenth   **b.** nearest hundred

   c. nearest one   **d.** nearest hundredth

6. Name the parts of the circle.

   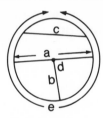 c a d b e

7. Measure to the nearest millimetre.

   a. the radius   **b.** the diameter

8. Find the approximate area of the shape. ☐ represents 1 cm².

   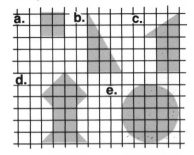 a. b. c. d. e.

9. Write the base and the height.

   a. 2 m 3 m 4 m

   b. 10 cm 9 cm 8 cm 2 cm

10. Identify the shapes that can be used to make the figure.

    a.

    b.

    c.

    d.

11. Calculate mentally.

    a. 4.2×1000 **b.** $0.09 \times 10\,000$

    c. $31.7 \div 100$ **d.** $421 \div 100\,000$

    e. $1570 \times 10\,000$ **f.** $1570 \div 10\,000$

69

Linear Measurement

The **millimetre**, **centimetre**, **metre**, and **kilometre** are the most commonly used units of length.

The diameter of a bicycle wheel is measured in centimetres (cm).

The width of a bicycle spoke is measured in millimetres (mm).

The width of each lane is measured in metres (m).

The length of the race is measured in kilometres (km).

| 1 cm = 10 mm |
| 1 m = 100 cm |
| 1 km = 1000 m |

The race is 8.2 km.
How many metres is this?

The unit is smaller so there will be more. **Multiply**.

8.2 km = (8.2 × 1000) m

larger unit   smaller unit

= 8200 m

The race is 8200 m.

The diameter of the wheel is 66.6 cm.
How many metres is this?

The unit is larger so there will be fewer. **Divide**.

66.6 cm = (66.6 ÷ 100) m

smaller unit   larger unit

= 0.666 m

The diameter of the wheel is 0.666 m.

WORKING TOGETHER

1. Would you use kilometres, metres, centimetres, or millimetres to measure?

   a. height of a tree   **b.** length of a river

   c. height of a swing set

   d. thickness of a piece of string

2. A   B   C D   E   F

   Estimate the length of the line segment in centimetres. Then measure the segment to the nearest tenth of a centimetre.

   a. $\overline{AC}$ **b.** $\overline{BE}$ **c.** $\overline{CD}$ **d.** $\overline{AF}$

3. Copy and complete.

	Millimetres	Centimetres	Metres
a.		14	
b.			47
c.	32		
d.			5.1
e.		730	
f.			0.95
g.	590		
h.		2.3	

APPLICATIONS AND EXERCISES

1. Would you use kilometres, metres, centimetres, or millimetres to measure?

   a. height of a bicycle seat

   b. thickness of a licence plate

   c. length of a bicycle

   d. distance to the next town

   e. length of your school

2. Estimate, then measure.

   a. width of your hand

   b. length of your shoe

   c. length of your thumbnail

   d. width of your classroom

3. Choose the best estimate.

   a. length of a pencil

       18 cm   18 mm   18 m

   b. height of a basketball player

       2 km   2 m   2 cm

   c. width of a ruler

       5 cm   2 cm   5 mm

   d. width of a two-lane highway

       70 m   70 cm   7 m

4. Measure the path of the cycling race to the nearest tenth of a centimetre. If 1 cm represents 2.5 km, what is the total distance for the race?

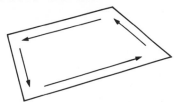

5. Copy and complete.

	Millimetres	Centimetres	Metres
a.		2.6	
b.			7.9
c.	180		
d.	5.8		
e.			0.96

6. Copy and complete.

	Centimetres	Metres	Kilometres
a.	350		
b.		500	
c.		38.1	
d.	28		
e.			0.92

Try This

Changing from one linear unit to another in the metric system is simple because it involves only multiplying or dividing by 10, 100, 1000, . . .

50 km = ☐ m

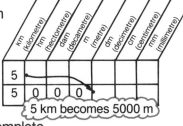

5 km becomes 5000 m

1300 cm = ☐ m

1300 cm becomes 13 m

Copy and complete.

a. 24 hm = ☐ m

b. 4 km = ☐ dm

c. 250 cm = ☐ dam

d. 21 hm = ☐ dm

e. 29 cm = ☐ hm

f. 412 mm = ☐ dam

g. 316 m = ☐ dm

h. 14 mm = ☐ dm

Perimeter

The sailing instructor sketched a course for the weekend's race. What is the total length of the course?

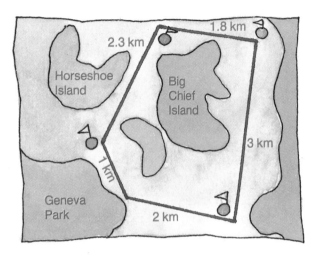

The length of the course is 2 km + 3 km + 1.8 km + 2.3 km + 1 km, or 10.1 km.

The distance around a closed figure is its **perimeter**.

WORKING TOGETHER

1. Find the perimeter.

a.
4 m
7 m

b.
5.2 cm
40 mm
26 mm

c.
2.5 cm
2.2 cm
4.2 cm

d.
3.6 m
250 cm
6 m

2. Estimate the perimeter in centimetres. Then measure each side to the nearest tenth of a centimetre and find the perimeter.

a.

b.
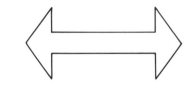

APPLICATIONS AND EXERCISES

1. Find the perimeter.

a.
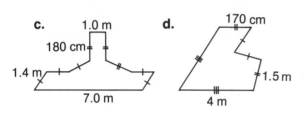
26 mm
4.6 cm
39 mm

b. 10 mm
2.6 cm
1.5 cm

c. 1.0 m
180 cm
1.4 m
7.0 m

d. 170 cm
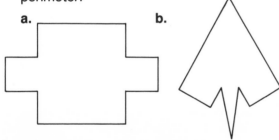
1.5 m
4 m

2. Estimate the perimeter in centimetres. Then measure each side to the nearest tenth of a centimetre and find the perimeter.

a.
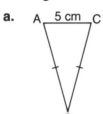

b.

3. Estimate, then measure the perimeter.

   a. a page of your notebook

   b. your desk top

   c. the front cover of this book

   d. the back of your chair

4. Maria is putting binding around the edges of a triangular scarf. The sides of the scarf measure 40 cm, 70 cm, and 40 cm. How much binding does she need?

5. A doorway is 2.2 m high and 90 cm wide. What length of lumber is needed to frame the doorway?

6. The sides of a sail measure 2 m, 3.5 m, and 335 cm. Almost 1.15 cm of thread are needed to hem 1 cm of sail. To the nearest centimetre, how much thread is needed to hem all sides of the sail?

7. The perimeter of the figure is 24 cm. Find the length of $\overline{AB}$.

a.
A   5 cm   C
B
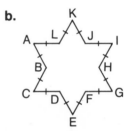

b.
K
L   J
A   I
B   H
C   G
D   F
E

8. Find the perimeter. The length of each side of a small square is 5 mm.

a.

b.

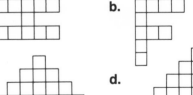

c.
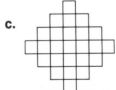

d.
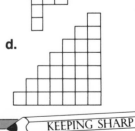

Perimeters of Special Polygons

Students are building two stone patios and planting shrubs to landscape part of the schoolyard. Each patio has a frame made of preserved lumber. How much lumber did they use for each frame?

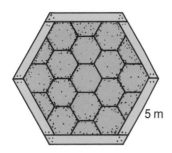

This patio has equal angles and equal sides. The shape is a **regular hexagon**.

To find the perimeter, add the sides.
5 m + 5 m + 5 m + 5 m + 5 m + 5 m = 30 m

OR

Multiply the length of one side by the number of equal sides.
5 m × 6 = 30 m

They used 30 m of lumber for the hexagonal patio.

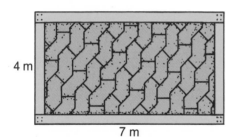

This patio has square corners and opposite sides that are equal. The shape is a **rectangle**.

To find the perimeter, add the sides.
4 m + 7 m + 4 m + 7 m = 22 m

OR

Double the sum of the base and the height.
2 × (7 m + 4 m) = 2 × 11 m or 22 m

They used 22 m of lumber for the rectangular patio.

WORKING TOGETHER

1. Copy and complete.

	Regular polygon	Number of sides	Length of one side	Perimeter
a.	triangle		3 cm	
b.	square		5 m	
c.	pentagon		4 mm	
d.	hexagon			30 cm
e.	octagon			48 m

2. a. Which sides need to be measured to find the perimeter of rectangle ABCD?

b. Estimate, then find the perimeter.

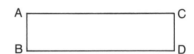

3. a. Use straws and pipecleaners to make a 5-sided polygon with equal sides that is not a regular pentagon.

b. How would you find its perimeter?

APPLICATIONS AND EXERCISES

1. Find the perimeter.
   a. square with sides 8.5 cm
   b. regular octagon with sides 15.2 mm
   c. equilateral triangle with sides 2.7 m
   d. regular hexagon with sides 0.9 cm

2. The Pentagon building in Washington is so named because of its shape. Each of the outer walls is 302 m long.
   a. If you walked around the outside of the Pentagon, what is the minimum distance you would walk?
   b. Express the distance in kilometres.

3. The perimeter of the polygon is 56 cm. Find the length of one side.

   a.
   b.

   c.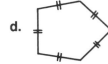
   d.

4. Copy and complete.

Regular polygon	Length of one side	Number of sides	Perimeter
a. triangle	6 cm		
b. pentagon			26 m
c. octagon	8.3 cm		
d. square			36 mm
e. decagon			108 cm

5. Estimate, then find, the perimeter.

   a.   b.

   c.    d.

6. Find the perimeter of the rectangle.
   a. with base 2.8 cm and height 1.9 cm
   b. with sides 8.4 m and 5.1 m
   c. with dimensions of 45 mm and 63 mm

7. A window measures 122 cm by 96 cm.
   a. Find the length of weather stripping needed to go around the window.
   b. The weather stripping is sold only by the metre. It sells at 35¢/m. Find the cost of the weather stripping.

Try This

Measure the circumference and the diameter of four circular objects to the nearest tenth of a centimetre. Then copy and complete the chart.

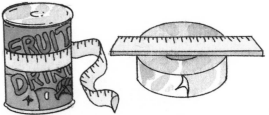

	Circumference C (cm)	Diameter d (cm)	$\frac{C}{d}$ (estimate)	$\frac{C}{d}$
1.				
2.				
3.				
4.				

Copy and complete this statement.
"The circumference of a circle is about ☐ times its diameter."

Circumference

The circumference (C) is the distance around the circle.

Object	Circumference (C)	Diameter (d)	$\frac{C}{d}$
Bicycle wheel	207.5 cm	66 cm	$\frac{207.5}{66} \doteq 3.14$
Stereo record	95.8 cm	30.5 cm	$\frac{95.8}{30.5} \doteq 3.14$

The quotient $\frac{C}{d}$ is the same for all circles.

This quotient is represented by the Greek letter π (pi). π is about 3.14.

$$\frac{C}{d} = \pi \text{ or } C = \pi \times d$$

Finding the Circumference

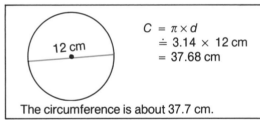

12 cm

$C = \pi \times d$
$\doteq 3.14 \times 12 \text{ cm}$
$= 37.68 \text{ cm}$

The circumference is about 37.7 cm.

5 cm

$C = \pi \times d$
$\doteq 3.14 \times 10 \text{ cm}$
$= 31.4 \text{ cm}$

Diameter is twice the radius.

The circumference is about 31.4 cm.

WORKING TOGETHER

1. Sketch a circle and label the measurement.

   a. diameter 5 cm   **b.** radius 32 mm

   c. radius 6 m   **d.** diameter 10 km

   e. radius 2 cm   **f.** diameter 1.4 m

2. Estimate, then calculate the circumference of each circle in exercise 1 to the nearest tenth. Use the rule $C = \pi \times d$ and $\pi \doteq 3.14$.

3. Copy and complete to the nearest tenth.

	C(m)	π	d(m)	r(m)
a.		3.14	2	
b.		3.14	6	
c.		3.14		5
d.		3.14		4.2

1. Estimate, then find the circumference of the circle to the nearest tenth.

   a.

   10 cm

   b.

   59.7 cm

   c.

   45.0 cm

   d.

   12 mm

   e. diameter 20 mm   **f.** diameter 36 m

   g. radius 6 mm   **h.** radius 5.8 m

2. Copy and complete to the nearest tenth of a metre.

	C(m)	π	d(m)	r(m)
a.		3.14	8	
b.		3.14	5	
c.		3.14		8
d.		3.14		7.2

3. The greatest distance across a circular swimming pool is 10.5 m. Find the circumference of the pool to the nearest tenth of a metre.

4. A "45" record has a diameter of 17.4 cm. A "33" record has a diameter of 30.2 cm. How much greater is the circumference of the "33" record?

5. The diameter of a basketball is 24.5 cm. The diameter of a basketball hoop is 45 cm. How much smaller is the circumference of the ball than the hoop?

6. Find the perimeter to the nearest tenth.

   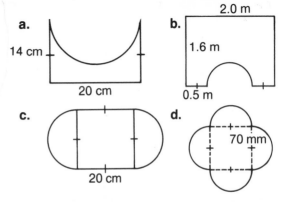

   a. 14 cm, 20 cm

   b. 2.0 m, 1.6 m, 0.5 m

   c. 20 cm

   d. 70 mm

7. A bicycle wheel has a diameter of 0.6 m.

   a. If the wheel makes 346 revolutions as the bicycle travels around the block, how far is it around the block, to the nearest tenth of a metre?

   b. How many revolutions to the nearest tenth does the wheel make as the bicycle travels a distance of 1 km?

Figure ABCDEFGHIJKL is a regular dodecagon.

a. How many sides does a dodecagon have?

b. Find and name three squares and four equilateral triangles within the figure.

c. Find the perimeter of the dodecagon.

d. Find the circumference of the circle to the nearest tenth. What do you notice?

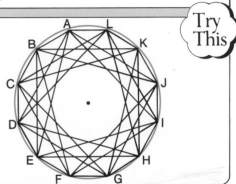

Area of a Rectangle

During an underwater treasure hunt, regions are partitioned with a metre grid system.

Remnants of a sunken ship were found in the designated squares. What seems to be the area covered by the sunken ship?

◻ represents 1 m².

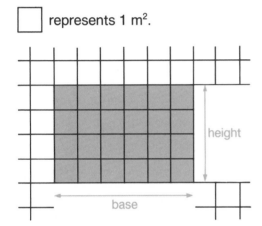

Area measures the amount of surface covered by a shape.

The ship seems to cover 6 m by 4 m
$$= 6 \text{ m} \times 4 \text{ m}$$
$$= 24 \text{ m}^2$$
The area of the sunken ship is about 24 m².

> **Area of a rectangle = base × height**
> or **b × h**

WORKING TOGETHER

1. Find the area in square centimetres.

◻ represents 1 cm².

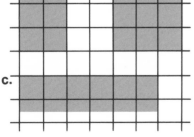

a.
b.
c.

2. Copy . Complete the chart for rectangles.

	Base	Height	Area
a.	15 cm	20 cm	
b.	2.5 m	6 m	
c.	7.1 km	3.2 km	

3. Find the area of the rectangle.

a.
3.0 cm
5.2 cm

b.
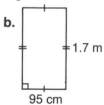
1.7 m
95 cm

78

APPLICATIONS AND EXERCISES

1. Measure the base and height of the rectangle to the nearest tenth of a centimetre. Calculate the area.

   a. 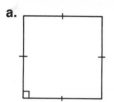   b.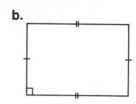

2. A credit card measures 8.5 cm by 5.5 cm. Find the area of the card.

3. Copy. Complete the chart for rectangles.

	Base	Height	Area
a.	6.5 cm	8 cm	
b.	3.5 km	1.9 km	
c.	32.5 m	20.1 m	

4. Copy. Complete the chart for rectangles.

	Base	Height	Area in smaller units	Area in larger units
a.	8 m	700 cm		
b.	120 cm	1.5 m		
c.	23 cm	105 mm		
d.	12.5 km	930 m		

5. An average rectangular NHL rink is approximately 61 m long and 26 m wide. A rectangular Olympic rink measures 61.0 m by 30.5 m. About how much more playing surface do Olympic players have than NHL players?

6. Ms. Turner is carpeting her living room and dining room. The cost of carpeting is $21.35/m² (dollars per square metre).

   a. Find the amount of carpeting needed.

   b. Estimate the cost of the carpeting.

   c. Calculate the cost of the carpeting.

   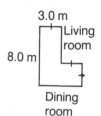
   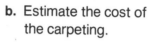

7. The cost of an underwater metre grid system is $32/m². Find the cost of the grid system for a deep-sea treasure hunt that covers 0.5 km by 280 m.

8. Copy. Complete the chart for rectangles.

	Base	Height	Area
a.		5 m	100 m²
b.	2.1 cm		8.4 cm²
c.	32.5 cm		520 cm²

The map shows the land use on a farm.
The area of each small square on the grid is about 2500 m².

Try This

1. Find the approximate area used.

   a. corn   b. mixed woodland   c. farm yard and garden

2. Express each area from exercise 1 in hectares (ha).

   10 000 m² = 1 ha (hectare)

3. Find the approximate total area of the farm in hectares.

Map key:
Mixed woodland
Corn
Farm yard and garden

Area of a Parallelogram

On a rectangular sheet of paper draw a slanted line. Cut along the line.

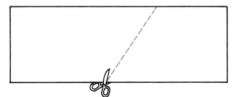

Slide the right part of the rectangle to the left of the other part.

The shape formed is a **parallelogram**.

Since the parallelogram and the rectangle are made with the same sheet of paper, they have the same area.

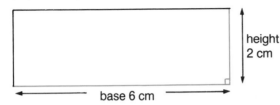

Area of a rectangle = base × height
$$= b \times h$$
$$= 6 \text{ cm} \times 2 \text{ cm}$$
$$= 12 \text{ cm}^2$$

Area of a parallelogram = base × height
$$= b \times h$$
$$= 6 \text{ cm} \times 2 \text{ cm}$$
$$= 12 \text{ cm}^2$$

WORKING TOGETHER

1. Find the area of the rectangle and of the parallelogram by counting square centimetres.

   ▢ represents 1 cm².

   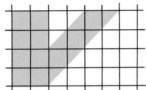

2. What are the base and the height of the rectangle in exercise 1?

3. What are the base and the height of the parallelogram in exercise 1?

4. What is the base of the parallelogram?
   a. 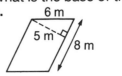   b.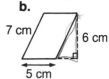

5. What is each height in exercise 4?

6. Find the area of the parallelogram.
   a. 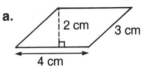   b.

   c. 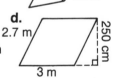   d.

80

APPLICATIONS AND EXERCISES

1. Find the area of the parallelogram.

a.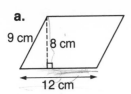
9 cm 8 cm 12 cm

b.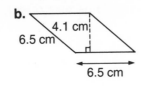
4.1 cm 6.5 cm 6.5 cm

c.
4.6 m 5.3 m 2.0 m

d.
6.0 mm 7.1 mm 1.1 cm

e. base 15 m and height 8 m

f. base 9.6 cm and height 11.3 cm

g. height 12.3 m, base 750 cm

h. height 7.1 cm and base 35 mm

2. Copy and complete the chart for parallelograms.

	Base	Height	Area
a.	18 m	4 m	
b.	10 cm	15 cm	
c.	4.4 mm	6.8 mm	
d.	2.8 cm	12 mm	

3. The zero digit in a calculator display has the shape of a parallelogram. Find the area enclosed by the zero digit.

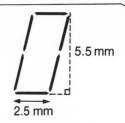
5.5 mm 2.5 mm

4. A section of highway 20 m wide and 90 m long is built across a rectangular field measuring 100 m by 75 m. Find the area of the remaining field.

20 m 90 m

5. The leaded window measures 30 cm by 40 cm. Find the area of each small parallelogram in it.

6. Copy and complete the chart for parallelograms.

	Base	Height	Area
a.	25 cm		250 cm²
b.		6.8 m	27.2 m²
c.		3.5 cm	43.4 cm²
d.	16.3 m		146.7 m²

Use the automatic constants that are built into your calculator.

1. Multiply and record the products of each of 92.048, 3.75, 4703.5, 78 000, 0.025.

  a. by 10   **b.** by 0.1   **c.** by 1000   **d.** by 0.001

2. How is the position of the decimal point in relation to the digits of the original number changed when multiplying by 10, 100, 1000, 0.1, 0.01, 0.001?

3. Divide and record the quotients of each of 92.048, 3.75, 4703.5, 78 000, 0.025.

  a. by 100   **b.** by 0.1   **c.** by 0.0001   **d.** by 10 000

4. Repeat exercise 2 for dividing by 10, 100, 1000, 0.1, 0.01, 0.001.

1. Choose the best estimate.

   a. length of a pen
      14 cm   140 cm   14 m

   b. width of a lake
      0.5 cm   0.5 m   0.5 km

   c. thickness of a hair
      0.4 mm   0.4 cm   4 cm

2. a. Estimate the length of each line segment.

   b. Measure each length.

3. a. Find the total length of the line segments in exercise 2.

   b. Express the total length in metres.

4. Find the perimeter of the polygon.

   a.
   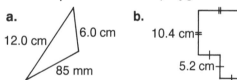

   b.

5. Copy and complete.

	Regular polygon	Length of one side	Number of sides	Perimeter
a.	triangle	8.7 cm		
b.		0.75 m	5	
c.	square			82 cm
d.	hexagon	3.2 cm		
e.	octagon			99.2 m
f.	decagon	15.3 cm		

6. A pool table measures 1.5 m by 3.4 m. What is the perimeter of the pool table?

7. The rubber gasket around the edge of a refrigerator door has to be replaced. The height of the door is 152.4 cm and its width is 76.2 cm.

   a. Find the length of gasket needed.

   b. Find the cost of the gasket at $2.33/m.

8. The diameter of a circular cake tin is 24 cm. Calculate the circumference of the cake tin to the nearest tenth.

9. Find the perimeter of the figure to the nearest tenth.

   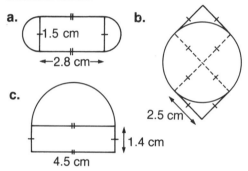

   a.

   b.

   c.

10. Find the area of the rectangle.

    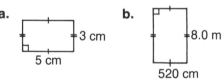

    a.

    b.

    c. with base 6 m and height 3 m

    d. with base 16 cm and height 120 mm

11. Find the area of the parallelogram.

    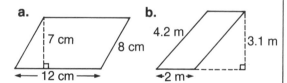

    a.

    b.

    c. with base 8.1 m and height 250 cm

    d. with base 410 mm and height 50 cm

Number Patterns

A calculator can be used to help discover patterns.

There is a pattern in the
multiplication statements.
Is there a pattern
in the products?

37×3
37×33
37×333
37×3333
$37 \times 33\,333$

Calculate the products.

$37 \times 3\ \ = 111$
$37 \times 33\ = 1221$
$37 \times 333 = 12321$

What is the pattern?
Continue the pattern for

$37 \times 3333\ \ = $ ☐
$37 \times 33\,333 = $ ☐

---

1. Use a calculator to discover a pattern for the products. Continue the
   pattern for the next 3 products without calculating.

   a. 9×6
   9×66
   9×666
   9×6666

   b. 91×4
   91×44
   91×444
   91×4444

   c. 101×3
   101×33
   101×333
   101×3333

   d. $1 \times 9 + 2$
   $12 \times 9 + 2$
   $123 \times 9 + 2$
   $1234 \times 9 + 2$

2. The product may be too large for your calculator. If so,
   set up a pattern of lesser products similar to exercise 1.
   Use the pattern to predict the product.

   a. $53 \times 1\,111\,111\,111$

   b. $7 \times 908\,070\,605\,040\,302$

   c. $9 \times 987\,654\,321$

   d. $36 \times 900\,000\,001$

   e. $39\,999\,999 \times 50\,000\,01$

   f. $5\,555\,556^2 - 4\,444\,445^2$

3. Investigate $143 \times$ ☐ $\times 7$.

   a. Find a pattern for the products.
   $143 \times 1 \times 7, 143 \times 2 \times 7, 143 \times 3 \times 7, \ldots$

   b. Predict the result for $143 \times 9 \times 7$. Check your result.

   c. Predict the pattern for
   $143 \times 10 \times 7, 143 \times 11 \times 7, 143 \times 12 \times 7, \ldots$

   d. Predict the result for $143 \times 99 \times 7$. Check your result.

   e. Predict the pattern for
   $143 \times 100 \times 7, 143 \times 101 \times 7, 143 \times 102 \times 7, \ldots$
   Check using $143 \times 698 \times 7$.

Area of a Triangle

Draw a triangle inside a parallelogram.
Cut out triangle A.

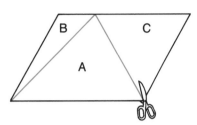

Try to fit triangles B and C onto
triangle A.

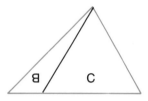

The smaller triangles fit onto the larger triangle.
The area of the triangle is one-half the area of the parallelogram.

Area of a triangle $= \dfrac{\text{base} \times \text{height}}{2}$

or $\dfrac{b \times h}{2}$

base times height
divided by 2

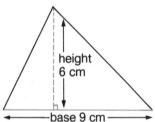

height
6 cm

base 9 cm

$$\text{Area of triangle} = \dfrac{b \times h}{2}$$
$$= \dfrac{9 \text{ cm} \times 6 \text{ cm}}{2}$$
$$= \dfrac{54}{2} \text{ cm}^2$$
$$= 27 \text{ cm}^2$$

WORKING TOGETHER

1. Find the area of the parallelogram and of the triangle by counting square centimetres.

2. What are the base and the height of the parallelogram in exercise 1?

3. What are the base and the height of the triangle in exercise 1?

4. What are the base and height?

a. 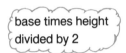   b.

c.

4.2 cm

3.0 cm

d.

80 mm

9 cm

11 cm

5. Find the area of each triangle in exercise 4.

84

1. What are the base and the height?
   ☐ represents 1 cm².

   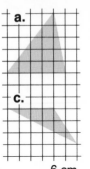
   a.

   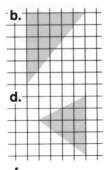
   b.

   c.

   d.

   e.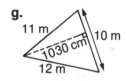
   6 cm
   5 cm
   7 cm   8 cm

   f.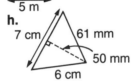
   12 m
   6 m
   5 m

   g.
   11 m
   10 m
   1030 cm
   12 m

   h.
   7 cm   61 mm
   50 mm
   6 cm

2. Calculate the area of each triangle in exercise 1.

3. Measure the base and the height of the triangle to the nearest tenth of a centimetre. Calculate the area of the triangle.

   a.

   b.

4. Copy and complete the chart for triangles.

	Base	Height	Area
a.	14 m	6 m	
b.	4.6 cm	3.2 cm	
c.	8 mm	15 mm	
d.	2.1 m	120 cm	
e.	52 mm	3.1 cm	
f.	1.8 km	850 m	

5. Find the area of the shaded part of the regular hexagon.

   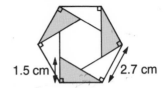
   1.5 cm   2.7 cm

6. How much felt is needed to make 20 carnival flags?

   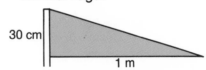
   30 cm
   1 m

7. The triangles on the backgammon board are made of white leather. How much white leather was needed to make all the triangles?

   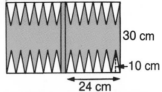
   30 cm
   10 cm
   24 cm

Try This

Investigate the statement. Show examples to verify or disprove the statement.

a. All rectangles with equal areas have equal perimeters.

b. All triangles with equal areas have equal perimeters.

c. All squares with equal areas have equal perimeters.

d. All parallelograms with equal areas have equal perimeters.

Areas of Other Polygons

What is the area of each of these signs?

Each shape can be divided into rectangles and/or triangles.

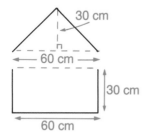

Area of $\triangle = \dfrac{b \times h}{2}$

$= \dfrac{60 \text{ cm} \times 30 \text{ cm}}{2}$

$= \dfrac{1800 \text{ cm}^2}{2}$

$= 900 \text{ cm}^2$

Area of $\square = b \times h$

$= 60 \text{ cm} \times 30 \text{ cm}$

$= 1800 \text{ cm}^2$

Total area of the school sign is 2700 cm².

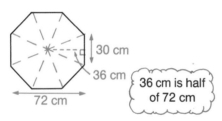

36 cm is half of 72 cm

Area of $\bigcirc = 8 \times$ Area of $\triangleleft$

$= 8 \times \dfrac{b \times h}{2}$

$= 8 \times \dfrac{30 \text{ cm} \times 36 \text{ cm}}{2}$

$= 8 \times \dfrac{1080 \text{ cm}^2}{2}$

$= 8 \times 540 \text{ cm}^2$

$= 4320 \text{ cm}^2$

Total area of the stop sign is 4320 cm².

WORKING TOGETHER

1. Copy the figure.

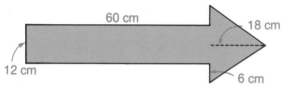

   a. Divide the figure into regions for which areas can be calculated.

   b. Calculate the area of each region.

   c. Find the total area of the figure.

2. Find the area of the figure.

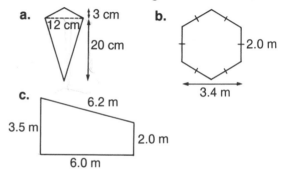

86

APPLICATIONS AND EXERCISES

1. Find the area of the figure.

a.

b.

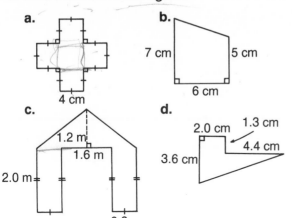

7 cm   5 cm

6 cm

c.

1.2 m
1.6 m
2.0 m
0.8 m

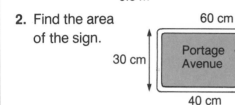

d.

2.0 cm   1.3 cm

4.4 cm

3.6 cm

2. Find the area of the sign.

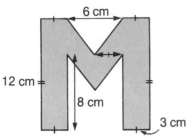

60 cm

30 cm   Portage Avenue

40 cm

3. Maggie cut her initial out of a 12 cm by 12 cm piece of felt. How many square centimetres were used? How much felt was not used?

6 cm

12 cm

8 cm

3 cm

4. Find the area. ☐ represents 1 cm².

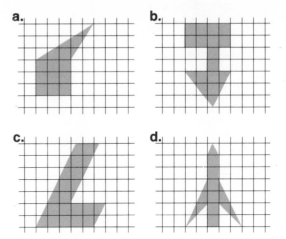

a.   **b.**

c.   **d.**

5. Find the area of the shaded region.

a.

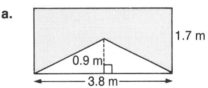

1.7 m

0.9 m

3.8 m

b.

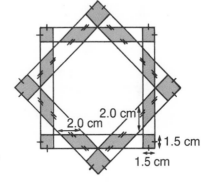

2.0 cm
2.0 cm
1.5 cm
1.5 cm

Try This

1. Arrange the five squares so that the resulting figure has this perimeter.

a. 16 cm   **b.** 10 cm   **c.** 12 cm   **d.** 11 cm

2. What is the smallest perimeter that can be obtained by arranging the five squares?

Area of a Circle

The parachutist is aiming for
the target circle. How big is it?

Finding the Area of a Circle

1. Draw a large circle and cut it out.
   Fold the circle in half three times.
   Unfold the circle and color half of it.
   Cut the circle along the fold lines.

   fold lines

2. Fit the eight pieces together to
   resemble a parallelogram.

   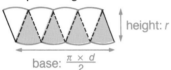
   height: r

   base: $\frac{\pi \times d}{2}$

   The base is one-half the circumference
   of the circle. The height is the radius
   of the circle.

   Area of the parallelogram
   $$= b \times h$$
   $$= \frac{\pi \times d}{2} \times r$$
   $$= \frac{\pi \times 2r}{2} \times r$$
   $$= \pi \times r \times r$$
   $$= \pi \times r^2$$

   Area of the circle $= \pi \times r^2$

   $\pi \doteq 3.14$

The target circle has radius 10 m.
$$\text{Area} = \pi \times r^2$$
$$\doteq 3.14 \times 10\,\text{m} \times 10\,\text{m}$$
$$= 314\,\text{m}^2$$
The parachutist is aiming for a target
circle with area 314 m².

WORKING TOGETHER

1. Approximate the area of the circle by
   counting squares.

   a.   b.

   c.

2. Calculate the area to the nearest tenth.

   a.   3 cm   b.   7 m

   c.   12 km   d.    8 m

3. Calculate the area of each circle in
   exercise 1 to the nearest tenth.

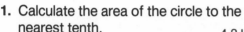
1. Calculate the area of the circle to the nearest tenth.

a.
9 m

b.
4.2 km

c.
16 cm

d.
21 cm

e.
63 cm

f.
30.2 cm

g. radius 12 cm   **h.** radius 1.5 m

i. diameter 1.8 km   **j.** diameter 2.5 m

2. Measure the radius of the circle in centimetres. Calculate the area to the nearest tenth.

a.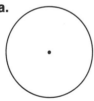

b.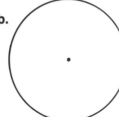

3. A circular table has a diameter of 1.4 m. Calculate the area of the table to the nearest tenth.

4. A face-off circle has a radius of 4.6 m. Calculate the area of the face-off circle to the nearest tenth.

5. A rotating sprinkler sprays water to a distance of 3.2 m. Find the area of grass that will be watered by the sprinkler to the nearest tenth.

6. How much greater is the area of a quarter than the area of a dime?

7. Find the area of the skating rink to the nearest tenth.

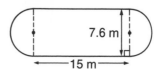
7.6 m
15 m

8. Calculate the area of the shaded region to the nearest tenth.

a.
12 cm

b.
5 m

c.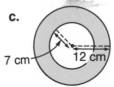
7 cm   12 cm

d.
16.0 m
13.0 m
1.5 m

e.
2 cm

f.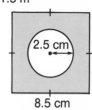
2.5 cm
8.5 cm

1. Express in scientific notation.

　a. 1400　　**b.** 6 721 000　　**c.** 14.7　　　**d.** 312.6　　　**e.** 3 912 000 000

　f. The mass of Earth is 5 990 000 000 000 000 000 t.

2. Express in standard form.

　a. 4.27×10^3　**b.** 3.71×10^6　　**c.** 2.98×10^1　　**d.** 4.1×10^5　　**e.** 7.0×10^2

Units of Area

Square centimetres (cm²) are used to measure smaller areas such as the strike zone of a batter.

Square metres (m²) are used to measure larger areas such as the infield of a baseball diamond.

The **hectare (ha)** is used to measure large areas such as the entire baseball field or the park.

Square kilometres (km²) are used to measure very large areas such as the the land within a city's limits.

1 cm² represents an area 10 mm × 10 mm.	1 cm² = 100 mm²
1 m² represents an area 100 cm × 100 cm.	1 m² = 10 000 cm²
1 ha represents an area 100 m × 100 m.	1 ha = 10 000 m²
1 km² represents an area 1000 m × 1000 m.	1 km² = 1 000 000 m²
Since 1 km² = 1 000 000 m² and 1 ha = 10 000 m², 1 km² = (1 000 000 ÷ 10 000) ha or 100 ha.	1 km² = 100 ha

The area of the strike zone for a batter who is 190 cm tall could be 4730 cm². Express this in square millimetres and in square metres.

4730 cm² = ☐ mm²

4730 cm² = (4730 × 100) mm²
    = 473 000 mm²

4730 cm² = ☐ m²

4730 cm² = (4730 ÷ 10 000) m²
    = 0.473 m²

The area of this strike zone is 437 000 mm² or 0.473 m².

WORKING TOGETHER

1. Copy and complete.
   a. 260 mm² = (260 ÷ ☐) cm²
   b. 9500 cm² = (9500 ÷ ☐) m²
   c. 0.5 km² = (0.5 × ☐) ha
   d. 92.1 m² = (92.1 × ☐) cm²

2. The area of another strike zone could be 0.39 m². Express the area in square centimetres.

3. The area of the ball park is 5.1 ha. Express the area in square metres.

1. Copy and complete.

a. $50 \text{ mm}^2 = \square \text{ cm}^2$ **b.** $6000 \text{ cm}^2 = \square \text{ m}^2$

c. $95 \text{ ha} = \square \text{ km}^2$ **d.** $250 \text{ m}^2 = \square \text{ ha}$

e. $300 \text{ m}^2 = \square \text{ km}^2$ **f.** $4000 \text{ m}^2 = \square \text{ ha}$

g. $0.8 \text{ km}^2 = \square \text{ ha}$ **h.** $32 \text{ cm}^2 = \square \text{ mm}^2$

i. $0.12 \text{ km}^2 = \square \text{ m}^2$ **j.** $35 \text{ m}^2 = \square \text{ cm}^2$

k. $140 \text{ cm}^2 = \square \text{ mm}^2$ **l.** $140 \text{ ha} = \square \text{ m}^2$

2. Find the area of the baseball infield. Express the area in hectares.

27 m

3. A rectangular field measures 100 m by 120 m. Find the area of the field. Express the area in hectares.

4. Copy and complete with >, <, or = to make true statements.

a. $650 \text{ ha} \bigcirc 3.5 \text{ km}^2$

b. $0.95 \text{ m}^2 \bigcirc 9500 \text{ cm}^2$

c. $52 \text{ mm}^2 \bigcirc 5.2 \text{ cm}^2$

d. $33\,000 \text{ m}^2 \bigcirc 0.33 \text{ km}^2$

5. The diameter of each hole in a telephone dial is 11 mm. Find the area of one hole.

6. A standard playing card measures 6.2 cm by 8.7 cm. A pack of cards is laid out side by side in four rows of thirteen cards each.

a. Find the area of the rectangle formed.

b. Express the area in square metres to the nearest tenth of a square metre.

7. Mr. Gretsky plans to sod part of his yard. Each piece of sod measures 40 cm by 150 cm and costs $1.55.

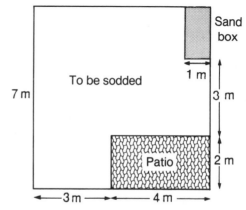

Sand box

To be sodded

1 m

7 m

3 m

Patio

2 m

←—3 m—→←——4 m——→

a. Find the area to be sodded.

b. Find the area of each piece of sod.

c. How many pieces of sod are needed?

d. Find the cost of the sod.

In **Logo**, there are different ways to have the turtle (▲) draw a square on the computer screen. You can use **commands** like

FD 25 RT 90 FD 25 RT 90 FD 25 RT 90 FD 25 RT 90,

or a **REPEAT statement** like REPEAT 4 [FD 25 RT 90],

or a **procedure** like

```
TO SQUARE
REPEAT 4 [FD 25 RT 90]
END
```

1. Write a procedure to have the turtle draw.

a. a larger square

b.

c.

d.

e. a circle

1. Calculate the area of the triangle.

a.
9 cm
7 cm
10 cm

b.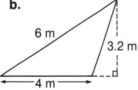
6 m
3.2 m
4 m

c. with base 6.1 cm and height 42 mm

d. with base 300 cm and height 2.1 m

2. Find the area of the figure.

a.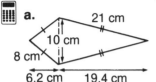
21 cm
10 cm
8 cm
6.2 cm   19.4 cm

b.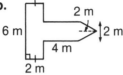
2 m
6 m
2 m
4 m
2 m

3. Find the area. ☐ represents 1 cm².

a.

b.

c.

d.

4. a. Which has the greater area, a square with a side of 5 cm or a circle with a diameter of 5 cm?

b. How much larger is the figure with the greater area?

5. The signal from a radio station transmitter can be picked up at places up to 80 km away. What is the maximum area that the radio station serves?

6. Calculate the area of the shaded region.

a.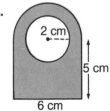
3.3 cm
6.6 cm

b.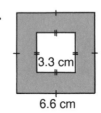
2 cm
5 cm
6 cm

c.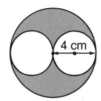
4 cm

d.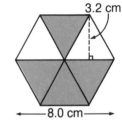
3.2 cm
8.0 cm

7. Copy and complete.

a. $0.08 \text{ m}^2 = \square \text{ cm}^2$ **b.** $39 \text{ ha} = \square \text{ km}^2$

c. $0.5 \text{ ha} = \square \text{ m}^2$ **d.** $8700 \text{ mm}^2 = \square \text{ m}^2$

8. Find the area of the playing field. Express the area in hectares.

a.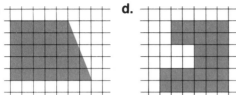
54.9 m
field hockey
91.4 m

b.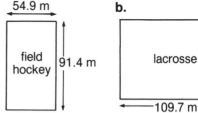
lacrosse
75 m
109.7 m

c.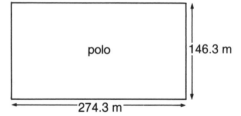
polo
146.3 m
274.3 m

Special Areas and Volumes

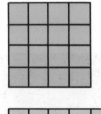

This figure has an **area** of 16 square units and a perimeter of 16 units.

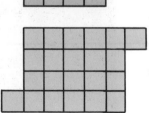

This figure has an area of 22 square units and a perimeter of 22 units.

1. Find three other figures such that the area and the perimeter have the same numerical value.

2. Find three other figures such that the area is half the perimeter.

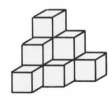

This solid shape has a **volume** of 10 cubic units and a surface area of 36 square units.

This solid shape has a volume of 10 cubic units and a surface area of 34 square units.

3. How small can you make the surface area by rearranging the 10 cubes?

4. Copy and complete the table. Use cubes to help you find the numbers.

Volume	Maximum surface area	Minimum surface area
10		
11		
12		
13		
⋮		

Logo

In Logo, the **RANDOM** function generates random positive integers.
RANDOM 30 outputs a positive integer less than 30.

Compare the commands **A.**
for diagrams A and B.

In diagram A, the lines
have different lengths.
In diagram B, the turns
have different sizes.

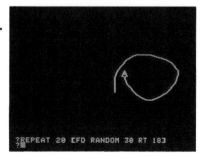

B.

REPEAT 20 [FD 30 RT RANDOM 360]

1. Write the range of outputs for the command.

    a. RANDOM 360   **b.** RANDOM 100   **c.** 50 – RANDOM 100

Logo language also includes commands to control the turtle's movements using
X and Y coordinates. The origin of the coordinates is the HOME position at the centre.
X values lie horizontally between –140 and 140. Y values lie vertically between –120 and 120.

Starting with the turtle in the HOME position, follow this sequence of commands.

SETX 40	The turtle moves to **A** (X coordinate changes).
SETY 60	The turtle moves to **B** (Y coordinate changes).
SETX –70	The turtle moves to **C** (X coordinate changes).
SETXY –100 (–60)	The turtle moves to **D** (both coordinates change).

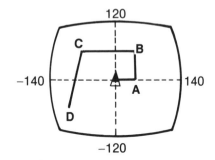

2. Write the command required to move the turtle.

    a. from **D** to **A**   **b.** from **A** to **C**   **c.** from **C** to **B**   **d.** from **B** to the origin

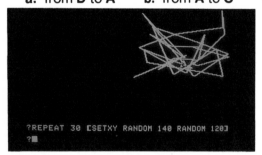

The SETXY command used with the RANDOM
function will move the turtle randomly.

3. Why are all the lines in the top right
corner of the screen?

4. Write a command that will cover the
whole screen with lines.

94

The commands **XCOR** and **YCOR** output the turtle's current X and Y coordinates. If you move the turtle to **B** and type XCOR, the computer gives the output 40.

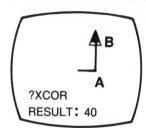

?XCOR
RESULT: 40

5. What output does the command YCOR give?

Here are two other useful commands.

HEADING outputs the turtle's current heading. The heading is given in degrees from 0 (pointing to the top of the screen) to 360, counting in a clockwise direction.

SETHEADING or **SETH** tells the turtle what direction to face. SETH 45 turns the turtle 45 degrees to the right from facing straight up.

6. If the turtle's HOME position is at the centre of a compass, pointing north, give the SETHEADING required to point the turtle.

    a. south   **b.** northwest   **c.** southeast   **d.** west

7. a. Give commands using SETH values and PENUP (PU) and PENDOWN (PD) to have the turtle mark the 8 points of the compass as shown. →

    b. Improve your compass drawing by adding an arrow and a letter N to indicate north.

8. Predict the output of these procedures, then try them on the computer.

    a. TO WHAT
        SETX XCOR + 20
        SETY YCOR + 20
        SETX XCOR – 20
        SETY YCOR – 20
        END

    b. TO NOW.WHAT
        WHAT
        SETX XCOR + 20
        IF XCOR < 100 THEN NOW.WHAT
        END

9. a. Write a procedure, using coordinates, to draw a small rectangle.
    b. Write a procedure to draw a sequence of rectangles diagonally across the screen.

10. Modify the procedure in exercise 9b so that each rectangle is erased before the next is drawn. (Hint: Explore the differences between the HOME and CLEARSCREEN commands.)

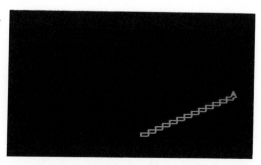

Draw a Diagram

A rectangular piece of felt measures 81 cm by 36 cm.
Jeff wants to cut the felt to make a square for a bulletin board.
What is the length of a side of the largest square that can be made?

Think. A square 36 cm by 36 cm is possible.
Is there any way to use all the felt?

Plan and do. Draw a diagram.
Using grid paper is helpful.

You can make a model
by cutting out the
pieces and rearranging
them.

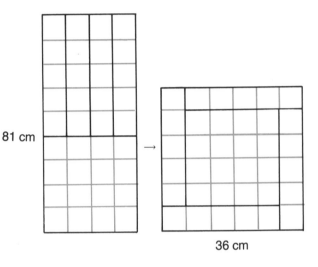

81 cm

36 cm

Look back. The largest square is
54 cm along each side.

Jeff solved the problem another way.
He used a calculator with a √ key.

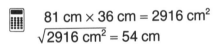 81 cm × 36 cm = 2916 cm²
√2916 cm² = 54 cm

WORKING TOGETHER

1. How many squares are there altogether?

   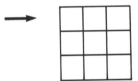

   a. Draw a diagram of each size of square
   and find the number of each size.

   b. Give a concluding statement.

2. How many rectangles are in the diagram above?

3. Each set of Lee's grandparents
   had 2 children, who also had
   2 children each. How many first
   cousins does Lee have?

   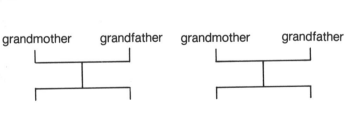

   a. Complete the diagram.

   b. Give a concluding statement.

PROBLEMS

Draw diagrams to help you solve the problems.

1. A bikeathon started at the school. The participants rode 3 blocks west, 2 blocks north, 6 blocks west, and 8 blocks south. How many blocks away from the school were they?

2. Frames need to be built for the set of a school production. Two door frames with outside dimensions, 2 m by 1.5 m; one sign frame, 1.75 m by 0.67 m; and two window frames, 0.67 m by 0.67 m are needed. If lumber comes in 2.67 m lengths, what is the minimum number of lengths required?

3. In the model, 32 marbles are placed in the slot at the top. When the marbles hit the vertex of a hexagon, half go left and half go right. How many marbles will be in each slot at the bottom?

4. On a checkerboard, there is a 2 cm wide border around the checkered area. The whole board has an area of 784 cm². What is the length of a side of each small square?

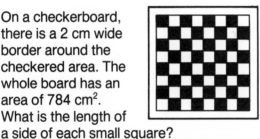

5. A bug is sitting at the tip of the minute hand, 10 cm from the centre of a clock. The bug starts to crawl along the minute hand toward the centre at the rate of 1 cm every 2.5 min. Draw the path on the clock that the bug takes to reach the centre.

6. A pizza with a diameter of 20 cm serves 2 people. How many people would 2 pizzas serve if each pizza has a diameter of 30 cm?

7. Two bicycle riders, 50 km apart, begin travelling toward each other, one at 30 km/h and the other at 20 km/h. A butterfly, which was sitting on the front tire of one of the bicycles, begins flying back and forth between the bicycles at the speed of 35 km/h. If the butterfly is able to reverse directions without losing any time, how far does it fly before the bicycles meet?

8. A bicycle wheel has a diameter of 63.5 cm. The wheel made 346 revolutions in one trip around the block. How far is it around the block?

9. A farmer rakes hay using a 4 m wide hay rake. If the field is raked in the manner shown, how many rounds must the farmer make to rake half the hay?

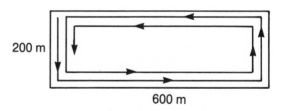

Problem Solving Review

Tell how you would solve the problem. Use **Think**, **Plan and do**, and then **Look back**.

1. Suppose you had $1 billion and gave away $1 every second. How long would it take to give away all of the money?

2. How would you estimate?

   a. the depth of a river

   b. the number of blades of grass in a football field

   c. the amount of water that leaks from a dripping tap in a day

Solve.

3. A plant 12 cm tall grows at the rate of 2 cm/week. Planted beside it is a plant 3 cm tall that grows 5 cm/week.

   a. How long will it be before both plants are the same height?

   b. How long will it be before the smaller plant is twice the height of the other?

4. How many loaves of bread are needed to serve 180 pieces of toast? Loaves are 34 cm in length, and sliced into slices 2 cm thick. The slice from either end is not used for toast, and 1 out of every 5 pieces is burned and discarded.

5. The minute hand on a clock is 9.5 cm long. How far does the tip of the minute hand travel in 24 h?

6. A square is made with 16 toothpicks. How can you divide the square into 4 regions of 4 small squares each, using an odd number of toothpicks?

7. Remove squares so that the perimeter remains the same but gives this area.

   a. 7 cm²   **b.** 6 cm²   **c.** 5 cm²

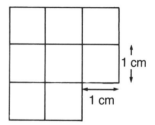

8. Choose the necessary information from the list below. Write a recipe for making maple syrup.

   • Drill three holes spaced apart, in 75 large maple trees.
   • Boil the sap until it is syrupy and most of the water has evaporated.
   • Sterilize 150 spouts, also called spiles, and 150 pails.
   • Collect 40 L of sap to make 1 L of syrup.
   • Hammer a spile into each hole, then hang a pail under it.
   • It takes 30 s to drill a hole in a tree with a hand-operated drill.
   • Filter and cool the maple syrup.
   • Bottle the syrup.
   • About 2 L of syrup per season can be made from one tree.

Chapter Checkup

1. Copy and complete.

	Millimetres	Centimetres	Metres
a.		1400	
b.	2100		
c.			3
d.			4.9
e.		325	
f.		14.5	

2. Find the perimeter of the figure.

a.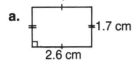
1.7 cm
2.6 cm

b.
1.0 m 0.8 m
0.6 m

c.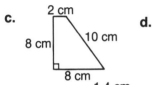
2 cm
8 cm 10 cm
8 cm

d.
1.4 cm
1.5 km

e.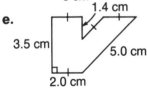
1.4 cm
3.5 cm 5.0 cm
2.0 cm

3. Find the perimeter.

a. square whose sides are each 4.2 cm

b. hexagon whose sides are each 8.5 m

c. octagon whose sides are each 21 cm

d. pentagon whose sides are each 15.6 m

4. Find the area.

a. triangle with base 10 cm, height 8 cm

b. square with side 13 m

c. rectangle measuring 1.5 km by 0.8 km

d. parallelogram, base 5.6 cm, height 3.7 cm

e. triangle with base 7 cm, height 3 cm

f. rectangle measuring 13.5 m by 8.4 m

5. The diameter of a plastic covered button is 5 cm.

a. Find the circumference of the button.

b. Find the area of the button to the nearest tenth.

6. Find the area. $\square$ represents $1\ cm^2$.

a. 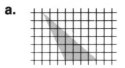   **b.**

c. 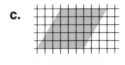   **d.**

e.

7. Derek is covering his kitchen floor with tiles. Each side of a square tile measures 20 cm. Each tile costs $0.89.

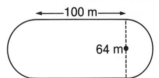

a. Find the area of the kitchen floor.

2.2 m 1.0 m
2.6 m Kitchen 2.0 m

b. How many tiles are needed?

c. Find the cost of tiling the floor.

8. a. Find the distance around the Olympic-sized track.

b. Find the area of the field inside the track to the nearest tenth.

c. Express the area in hectares, rounded to the nearest whole number.

←100 m→

64 m

Cumulative Checkup

1. Choose the best estimate.

10 000	12 000	30 000
60 000	90 000	45 000

   a. 82 195   **b.** 77 281   **c.** 4976
      + 11 838   − 18 055   × 9

   d. $\frac{61\,572}{5}$ **e.** $3\overline{)92\,173}$ **f.** 68 804 ÷ 7

2. Multiply if the product is greater than 15 000.

   a. 857   **b.** 926   **c.** 286
      × 11   × 19   × 78

3. Is 35 520 divisible by the number?

   a. 2   **b.** 3   **c.** 4   **d.** 5
   e. 6   **f.** 8   **g.** 9   **h.** 10

4. A strip of sheet metal 275 cm long is to be cut into 9 cm long pieces. Will there by any waste?

5. Express the number as the product of its prime factors.

   a. 15   **b.** 28   **c.** 30   **d.** 45
   e. 56   **f.** 80   **g.** 96   **h.** 128

6. Express as a single power. Evaluate.

   a. $2^2 \times 2^3$ **b.** $5^4 \div 5^3$ **c.** $3^2 \times 3$
   d. $8^6 \div 8^4$ **e.** $10^5 \times 10^2$ **f.** $4^{10} \div 4^5$

7. Evaluate.

   a. $\sqrt{900}$ **b.** $\sqrt{3600}$ **c.** $\sqrt{12\,100}$
   d. $\sqrt{490\,000}$ **e.** $\sqrt{40\,000}$ **f.** $\sqrt{640\,000}$

8. A square carpet has an area of 16 m². Find the length of each side.

9. The first nine numbers in the Fibonacci sequence are 1, 1, 2, 3, 5, 8, 13, 21, 34.

   a. Give the next three numbers in the Fibonacci sequence.

   b. Copy and complete.
$$1 + 1 = \square$$
$$1 + 1 + 2 = \square$$
$$1 + 1 + 2 + 3 = \square$$
$$1 + 1 + 2 + 3 + 5 = \square$$
$$1 + 1 + 2 + 3 + 5 + 8 = \square$$
$$1 + 1 + 2 + 3 + 5 + 8 + 13 = \square$$

   c. Study part **b**. What shortcut can be used to find each sum?

10. Evaluate.

   a. $48 \div 3 + 9 \times 2^3$

   b. $20 - 5 \times 2 + 1$

   c. $36 - (3^2 \times 2 + 20) \div 2$

11. Express in standard form.

   a. thirty-two and seventeen thousandths

   b. five and twelve hundredths

   c. $(3 \times 1) + (7 \times \frac{1}{10}) + (2 \times \frac{1}{100})$

   d. $(9 \times 10) + (9 \times \frac{1}{10}) + (9 \times \frac{1}{1000})$

   e. $(3 \times 1) + (5 \times \frac{1}{10^2})$

12. Express in expanded form using powers of ten.

   a. 350.67   **b.** 40 001.06   **c.** 0.0102
   d. 2700   **e.** 9090.09   **f.** 134.91

13. Copy and complete the number line.

   a.

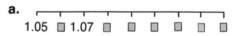

      1.05 ▨ 1.07 ▨ ▨ ▨ ▨ ▨ ▨

   b.

      ▨ ▨ 2.11 ▨ 2.13 ▨ ▨

14. Arrange in order from greatest to least.

   a. 0.123, 0.321, 0.231

   b. 27.372, 30.2, 27.4

   c. 9.7, 90.07, 0.97

   d. 7.2, 7.24, 7.42, 4.72

15. Copy and complete.

		Rounded to the nearest	
		one	tenth	hundredth
a.	35.174			
b.	9.746			
c.	0.975			
d.	49.91			
e.	12.155			

16. Round to the nearest metre.

   a. 8.4 m   **b.** 13.09 m   **c.** 0.85 m

   d. 1.52 m   **e.** 0.2 m   **f.** 4.49 m

17. Copy and complete the Magic Square.

35.7		
	21.9	
	40.3	8.1

18. Evaluate.

   a. $1.059 \times 10\ 000$ **b.** $486.5 \div 100$

   c. 52.7×0.001 **d.** 0.93×0.1

   e. $168 \div 0.0001$ **f.** $0.008 \div 0.01$

19. Estimate.

   a. 12.4×0.087 **b.** $420.3 \div 0.9$

   c. 0.81×0.009 **d.** $29.4 \div 0.079$

   e. $13.57 \div 2.3$ **f.** $53.732 \div 10.01$

   g. 827.9×7.65 **h.** $448.4 \div 8.6$

20. Estimate the cost of the purchase.

   a. 3 records at $8.99 each

   b. 12 hamburgers at $1.89 each

   c. 2.5 m of fabric at $6.89/m

   d. 0.48 kg of peanuts at $7.85/kg

21. Employees are paid 2.5 times their regular rate for working statutory holidays. Copy and complete the chart.

	a.	**b.**	**c.**	**d.**
Regular rate ($/h)	$5.00	$4.50	$3.75	$6.40
Holiday rate ($/h)				

22. How much is saved by buying in bulk?

   a. Cans of corn are $0.56 each or $6.48 for a dozen.

   b. Ears of corn are $0.25 each or $1.89 for a dozen.

   c. Lemons are $0.35 each or 3/$0.99.

   d. Orange juice is $0.60 each or $12.85 for a case of 24 boxes.

23. Divide if the quotient is less than 40.

   a. $143.325 \div 2.1$ **b.** $123.424 \div 3.2$

   c. $\dfrac{4.4356}{0.13}$ **d.** $\dfrac{4.9176}{0.072}$

24. Express in scientific notation.

   a. 354.1   **b.** 500 800   **c.** 79.62

25. Express the number in standard form.

   a. In a recent year Canadians made over 27.55 billion local phone calls.

   b. Canada Post delivers mail to over 8 million homes and businesses in Canada.

4/Surface Area and Volume

Pets require a certain amount of space. In a pet store, cages must be built to specific measurements, food and medicine must be given in suitable quantities, and the number of pets in a certain area is strictly defined.

Get Set

1. Copy and complete the chart.

	Solid shape	Number of faces	Number of vertices	Number of edges
a.				
b.				
c.				
d.				

2. a. What is the shape of the bottom face and the top face?

   b. What is the shape of each side face?

   c. How many side faces are there?

3. a. What is the shape of the base?

   b. What is the shape of each side face?

   c. How many side faces are there?

4. Match the solid with its name.

   a.   b.

   c.   d.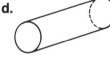

   e.   f.

cylinder   square prism   cone
triangular pyramid   triangular prism
rectangular pyramid

5. Use tracing paper to find congruent figures.

   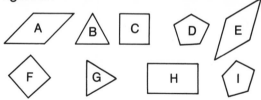

6. Find the area.

   a. 6 m, 6 m   b. 7 cm, 13 cm

   c. 3 m, 5 m, 4 m   d. 11 cm

7. Find the volume in cubic centimetres.
   ▱ represents 1 cm³.

   a.   b.

   c. 2 cm, 5 cm, 3 cm   d. 5 cm, 9 cm, 4 cm

   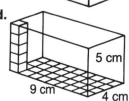

8. Choose the best unit to measure.

   a. capacity of a milk jug

   b. volume of a train's boxcar

   c. mass of a truck   d. mass of a baby

   e. capacity of an eyedropper

   f. volume of a toy block

gram   cubic centimetre   tonne
cubic metre   kilogram   millilitre   litre

103

Polyhedrons

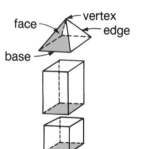

A **polyhedron** is a 3-dimensional object with all flat surfaces.

This **square pyramid** is a polyhedron that has 4 triangular faces and a square face.

This **square prism** is a polyhedron that has 4 rectangular faces and 2 square faces.

This square prism or **cube** has 6 **congruent** squares as its faces.

A polyhedron whose faces are all congruent regular polygons is a **regular polyhedron**.

There are only five regular polyhedrons.

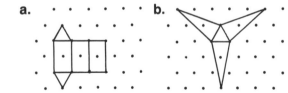

Regular tetrahedron — tetra 4

Regular hexahedron — hexa 6

Regular octahedron — octa 8

Regular dodecahedron — dodeca 12

Regular icosahedron — icosa 20

WORKING TOGETHER

1. Is the shape a polyhedron?

a.   b.   c.

d.   e.   f.

2. Copy the **net** on dot paper and make the polyhedron. Then name it.

a.   b.

3. Which regular polyhedron can be made from the net?

a. 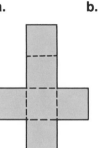   b. 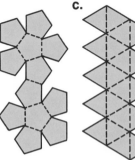   c.

4. Name the regular polygon that is used to make a face of each regular polyhedron in exercise 3.

1. Copy the net on dot paper and make the polyhedron. Then name it.

a.

b.

c.

2. Match the polyhedron with its net. Name the polyhedron.

a.

b.

c.

i.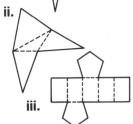

ii.

iii.

3. Can the net be used to make a triangular prism?

a.

b.

c.

4. Match the regular polyhedron with its net. Name the regular polyhedron.

a.

b.

c.

i.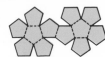

ii.

iii.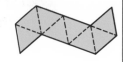

5. Copy and complete the chart for regular polyhedrons.

	Name	Number of faces	Number of vertices	Number of edges
a.	tetrahedron			
b.	hexahedron			
c.	octahedron			
d.	dodecahedron			
e.	icosahedron			

6. Study the completed chart from exercise 5. Find a pattern that relates the number of faces, the number of vertices, and the number of edges.

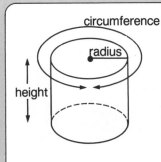

circumference

radius

height

Try This

1. Can the pattern be used to make a cylinder with a height of 8 cm and a circumference of 31.4 cm?

a.
8 cm
31.4 cm

b.
8 cm
31.4 cm

c.
31.4 cm
8 cm

Sketching Three-Dimensional Objects

Objects change in appearance as they are viewed from different directions.
Designers use directional views to help them portray three-dimensional objects.

front view

side view

top view

WORKING TOGETHER

1. Name the view.

a.    **b.**    **c.**

2. Identify the object from the views shown.

a.

front view   bottom view   back view

b.

top view   side view   bottom view

106

APPLICATIONS AND EXERCISES

1. Name the view.

a.

c.

b.

d.

e.

f.

2. Identify the household object from the view shown.

a.

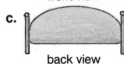

front view

b.

side view

c.

back view

d.

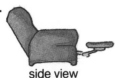

top view

3. Sketch a front view, a side view, and a top view of the object.

   a. table   **b.** door   **c.** hammer

4. Draw an accurate front view, side view, and top view.

a.

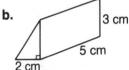

3 cm, 3 cm, 6 cm

b.

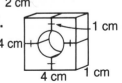

3 cm, 2 cm, 5 cm

c.

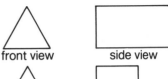

1 cm, 2 cm, 3 cm, 6 cm

d.

1 cm, 4 cm, 4 cm, 1 cm

5. Identify the polyhedron from these views.

a.

front view   side view

b.

side view   bottom view

6. a. Name the polyhedron.

5 cm 3 cm side view

5 cm 4 cm front view

3 cm 4 cm top view

b. Draw an accurate net.

c. Make a model.

For some calculations, the calculator memory is useful.

[M+] adds to memory.   [M−] subtracts from memory.   [MR] recalls the number from memory to the display.   [MC] clears memory.

1. Calculate using calculator memory.

   a. $4 \times 3 + 6 \times 4 + 3 \times 6$ **b.** $2 \times (7 \times 8 + 4 \times 7 + 8 \times 4)$ **c.** $3^5 - 4 \times \left(\dfrac{6 \times 8}{2} \right)$

   d. $500 \times (1 - 0.125)^6 + 400 \times (1 - 0.115)^6$ **e.** $\dfrac{12 \times 9 + 2^4}{10^2 - 19 \times 2}$

Surface Area of Prisms and Pyramids

Tyler wants to buy screen for a new rabbit hutch. About how much does he need?

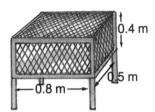

0.4 m

0.5 m

0.8 m

Tyler needs to know the area of each surface.

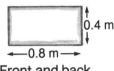

0.4 m

←0.8 m→

Front and back

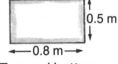

0.5 m

←0.8 m→

Top and bottom

0.4 m

◄0.5 m►

Sides

Each surface is a rectangle.
Area = base × height

Front:
    0.8 m × 0.4 m = 0.32 m²
Top:
    0.8 m × 0.5 m = 0.40 m²
Side:
    0.5 m × 0.4 m = 0.20 m²

Front and back:
            2 × 0.32 m² = 0.64 m²
Top and bottom:
            2 × 0.40 m² = 0.80 m²
Two sides:
            2 × 0.20 m² = 0.40 m²
Total surface area   1.84 m²

Tyler needs about 1.9 m² of screen.

WORKING TOGETHER

1. Tyler sketched the different faces of this square pyramid.

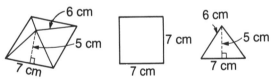

6 cm

5 cm

7 cm

6 cm

7 cm

5 cm

7 cm

a. How many square faces are there?

b. Find the area of the square face.

c. How many triangular faces are there?

d. Find the area of the triangular face.

e. Find the total area of the triangular faces.

f. What is the total surface area of the square pyramid?

2. Use the sketches of the different faces to find the surface area of this square prism.

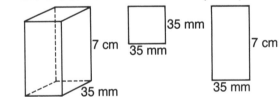

35 mm

7 cm   35 mm

7 cm

35 mm

35 mm

35 mm

3. a. Sketch the different faces of this triangular prism.

b. Find the surface area.

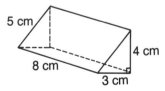

5 cm

4 cm

8 cm

3 cm

1. Use the sketches of the different faces to find the surface area.

   a.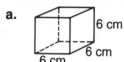
   6 cm
   6 cm
   6 cm

   6 cm
   6 cm

   b.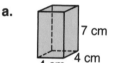
   6 cm
   5.2 cm
   6 cm   8 cm

   5.2 cm
   6 cm

   6 cm
   8 cm

2. Sketch the different faces. Then find the surface area.

   a.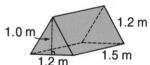
   7 cm
   4 cm
   4 cm

   b.
   13 cm
   10 cm
   12 cm   5 cm

3. This tent has an attached ground sheet. If 0.4 m² are added for the seams, what is the area of material used to make the tent?

   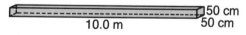
   1.0 m
   1.2 m
   1.2 m
   1.5 m

4. Find the surface area of the duct for a furnace. The duct is open at both ends.

   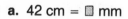
   10.0 m
   50 cm
   50 cm

5. Sketch the different faces of the square pyramid. Then find the surface area.

   a.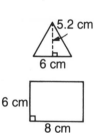
   9 cm
   8 cm
   8 cm

   b.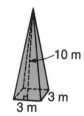
   7.0 cm
   4.6 cm
   4.6 cm

6. A church spire is built in the shape of a square pyramid. Find the area of copper sheeting needed to cover the spire.

   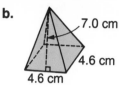
   10 m
   3 m
   3 m

7. Sketch the different faces of the regular tetrahedron. Then find the surface area.

   a.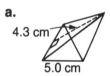
   4.3 cm
   5.0 cm

   b.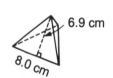
   6.9 cm
   8.0 cm

8. The display platforms are to be completely covered with carpeting. Find the amount of carpeting needed.

   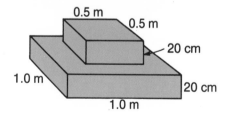
   0.5 m
   0.5 m
   20 cm
   1.0 m
   20 cm
   1.0 m

---

1. Copy and complete.

   a. 42 cm = ▢ mm
   b. 421 cm = ▢ m
   c. 13 m = ▢ cm
   d. 751 m = ▢ km

   e. 1.4 km = ▢ m
   f. 27.9 km = ▢ m
   g. 3 mm = ▢ cm
   h. 4 ha = ▢ m²

   i. 5 km² = ▢ m²
   j. 6.1 m² = ▢ cm²
   k. 3 cm² = ▢ mm²
   l. 2.1 km² = ▢ ha

Surface Area of Cylinders

Cans can be recycled.
About how much metal
can be recycled from this can?

The amount of metal is related to
the total surface area of the can.
The can is a **cylinder**. Its two ends
are circles. Its curved surface can
be cut to form a rectangle.

The length of the base of the rectangle
equals the circumference
of the circle.

8 cm

13 cm

8 cm

$\pi \times d$

13 cm

 Area of one end:
$\pi \times r^2 \doteq 3.14 \times 4 \text{ cm} \times 4 \text{ cm}$
$= 50.24 \text{ cm}^2$

Area of two ends:
$2 \times 50.24 \text{ cm}^2$ or 100.48 cm^2

Area of rectangle forming
the curved surface:
$$b \times h = \pi \times d \times h$$
$$\doteq 3.14 \times 8 \text{ cm} \times 13 \text{ cm} \quad \text{or} \quad \underline{326.56 \text{ cm}^2}$$
$$\text{Total surface area} \quad 427.04 \text{ cm}^2$$

This can recycles about 427 cm² of metal.

🖩 WORKING TOGETHER

1. Use the sketches of the surfaces.

8 cm

5 cm

10 cm

8 cm

$\pi \times d$

a. Find the area of the two ends.

b. Find the length of the base of the
rectangle forming the curved surface.

c. Find the area of the rectangle forming
the curved surface.

d. Find the surface area of the cylinder to
the nearest tenth.

2. Sketch the surfaces of the cylinder. Then
find the surface area to the nearest tenth.

a.

7 cm

9 cm

b.

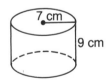

20 cm

12 cm

c.

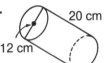

20.5 cm

77 mm

110

1. Use the sketches of the surfaces to find the surface area of the cylinder to the nearest tenth.

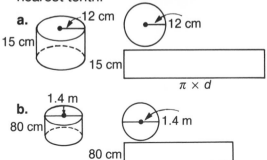

a.
12 cm
15 cm
12 cm
15 cm
π × d

b.
1.4 m
80 cm
1.4 m
80 cm
π × d

2. Sketch the surfaces of this can. Then find the surface area to the nearest tenth.

10 cm
4.5 cm

3. Sketch the surfaces of the cylinder. Then find the surface area to the nearest tenth.

   a. radius 18 cm, height 25 cm

   b. diameter 6 cm, height 4 cm

   c. radius 1 m, height 50 cm

4. Find the area of sheet metal used to make this garbage can and its lid to the nearest tenth. Allow 70 cm² for overlap.

30 cm
0.5 m

5. Find the area covered in one rotation of the paint roller to the nearest tenth.

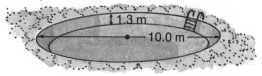

6 cm
24 cm

6. The inside of a circular swimming pool is to be painted.

1.3 m
10.0 m

   a. Find the area to be painted to the nearest tenth.

   b. How many litres of paint should be bought if 1 L covers 2 m²?

   c. Find the cost of the paint at $5.89/L.

7. A pet store displays birds in large cylindrical cages that are covered with screening wire.

0.8 m
1.2 m

   a. What is the area of wire needed for one cage to the nearest tenth?

   b. Find the cost of the wire at $7.95/m².

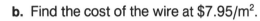
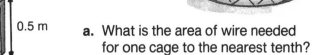

Try This

Angelo's Bakery is making a three-tier wedding cake. The bottom layer has a diameter of 30 cm. Each smaller layer has a diameter one-third less than the diameter of the previous layer. Each layer is 9 cm thick. Find the surface area of cake to be iced.

111

1. Name the polyhedron that can be made from the net.

   a.

   b.

   c.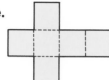

   d.

   e.

   f.

2. Which polyhedrons from exercise 1 are regular polyhedrons? Name them.

3. Identify the polyhedron from the views shown.

   a.

   bottom view   side view

   b.

   top view   side view

   c.

   front view   side view

4. **a.** Sketch the faces of this triangular prism.

   b. Find the surface area.

   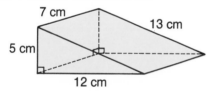

5. Sketch the faces of the rectangular prism. Then find the surface area.

   a.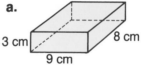

   3 cm   8 cm   9 cm

   b.

   10 m   4 m   4 m

6. Sketch the faces of the square pyramid. Then find the surface area.

   a.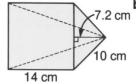

   7.2 cm   10 cm   14 cm

   b.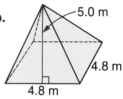

   5.0 m   4.8 m   4.8 m

7. Sketch the faces of the regular tetrahedron. Then find the surface area.

   a.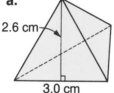

   2.6 cm   3.0 cm

   b.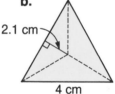

   2.1 cm   4 cm

8. Sketch the surfaces of the cylinder. Then find the surface area to the nearest tenth.

   a.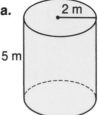

   2 m   5 m

   b.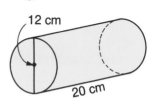

   12 cm   20 cm

9. A penny has a diameter of 19 mm and a height of 1 mm.

   a. Find the surface area of a roll of 50 pennies to the nearest tenth.

   b. Express the surface area in square centimetres.

Calculator Accuracy

Jordan measures the length, width, and height
of the cookie container.
He uses his calculator to find the volume.

Volume $\boxed{10.2}\boxed{\times}\boxed{12.3}\boxed{\times}\boxed{14.}\boxed{=}$ $\boxed{1756.44}$

The volume of the container is 1756.44 cm³.

The calculator product contains six significant digits.
However, the least accurate measure, 14, contains
two significant digits.
If we write the product with six significant digits, this
means that the volume is more accurate than the height.

Since accuracy depends on the quality of the measuring
instrument and cannot be improved by calculation, the
volume cannot be more accurate than the height.
To make the volume as accurate as the height, round to two
significant digits.
            1756.44 rounds to 1800.
The volume of the container is about 1800 cm³.

---

1. The factors represent measurements. Calculate the product
   with the correct number of significant digits.
   - **a.** 0.2641×7.449
   - **b.** 11.79×0.925
   - **c.** $346 \times 7.8 \times 15.88$
   - **d.** $0.2077 \times 5.00 \times 8.0$
   - **e.** 10.1^2
   - **f.** 6.2^3

2. The same principle for accuracy with multiplication applies to division.
   Calculate the quotient with the correct number of significant digits.
   - **a.** $\dfrac{0.784}{2.49}$
   - **b.** $\dfrac{64.9}{7.6}$
   - **c.** $\dfrac{420.80}{13.4}$
   - **d.** $\dfrac{6.2}{9.00}$

3. Calculate with the correct accuracy.
   - **a.** $\dfrac{4.70}{86.3 \times 6.2}$
   - **b.** $\dfrac{17.8 + 21.6}{14.9}$
   - **c.** $\dfrac{253.96 \times 9.014}{72.38 \times 0.407}$

4. Evaluate $\dfrac{6.28 \times a \times b}{4.32 \times c}$ to the correct accuracy for these values of a, b, and c.
   - **a.** $a = 1.71, b = 5.24, c = 1.03$
   - **b.** $a = 1.9, b = 11.3, c = 10.0$
   - **c.** $a = 0.014, b = 0.103, c = 0.05$
   - **d.** $a = 12.02, b = 9.07, c = 8.10$

Volume of Rectangular Prisms

A pet store must ship four puppies. If each puppy must have
120 000 cm³ of space, which cage should be used to ship the puppies?

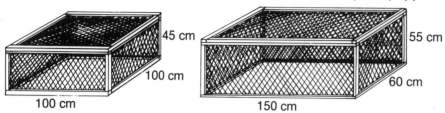

The amount of space that an object occupies is the **volume** of the object.
Volume is measured in cubic units.

To find the volume of this rectangular prism, →
count how many cubes would fit inside.

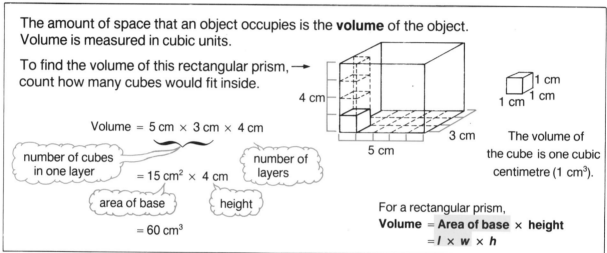

Volume = 5 cm × 3 cm × 4 cm

number of cubes in one layer

= 15 cm² × 4 cm   number of layers

area of base   height

= 60 cm³

The volume of
the cube is one cubic
centimetre (1 cm³).

For a rectangular prism,
Volume = Area of base × height
$= l × w × h$

Volume of first cage
= Area of base × h
= 100 cm × 100 cm × 45 cm
= 10 000 cm² × 45 cm
= 450 000 cm³

Volume of second cage
= Area of base × h
= 150 cm × 60 cm × 55 cm
= 9000 cm² × 55 cm
= 495 000 cm³

Since four puppies need 480 000 cm³ of space, the second cage should be used.

WORKING TOGETHER

1. Find the volume.

a.

TRANS CANADA SHIPPING   2 m
2 m

b.

CAGES   0.6 m
32 cm
0.5 m

2. Which measure is more reasonable?

a. a refrigerator with a volume of
1.5 m³ or 1.5 cm³

b. a garage with a volume of
40 m³ or 40 mm³

c. a crayon box with a volume of
108 mm³ or 108 cm³

1. a. Estimate the length, width, and thickness of this book.

b. Estimate its volume.

c. Measure the length, width, and thickness of this book to the nearest tenth of a centimetre.

d. Calculate its volume to the nearest cubic centimetre.

2. Estimate the volume.

a.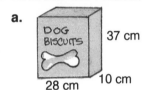

37 cm
28 cm 10 cm

b.
32 cm
18 cm
32 cm

3. Calculate each volume in exercise 2.

4. Find the volume of the rectangular prism.

a. length 5 cm, width 6 cm, height 3 cm

b. dimensions 20 m by 18 m by 50 m

c. base 15 mm by 8 mm, height 1.1 cm

5. a. Estimate the length, width, and height of your classroom.

b. Estimate the volume.

c. Measure the length, width, and height of your classroom.

d. Calculate the volume in cubic metres.

6. What is the maximum number of people for your classroom if there should be 12 m³ of space for each person?

7. a. Find the amount of space occupied by the freezer.

b. Find the volume of the inside of the freezer if each side is 5 cm thick.

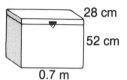

28 cm
52 cm
0.7 m

8. Find the volume.

a.
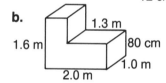
2 cm
2 cm
4 cm 4 cm
12 cm
12 cm

b.
1.3 m
1.6 m
80 cm
1.0 m
2.0 m

9. Copy and complete the chart for rectangular prisms.

	Length	Width	Height	Volume
a.	10 cm	9 cm		720 cm³
b.		2 m	3 m	30 m³
c.	5.8 cm	4.0 cm		116 cm³
d.	8 cm		20 cm	960 cm³

This Logo procedure makes the turtle draw a regular hexagon.

```
TO HEXAGON
REPEAT 6 [FD 15 RT 60]
END
```

A **variable** can be used to draw hexagons of different sizes.

```
TO HEXAGON :L
REPEAT 6 [FD :L RT 60]
END
```

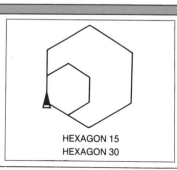

HEXAGON 15
HEXAGON 30

1. Write a procedure to draw a shape in different sizes.

Volume of Prisms and Cylinders

Formula air racing uses pylons to designate where aircraft must turn. What volume of concrete would be needed to make each style of marker? Which style of pylon is probably the more popular?

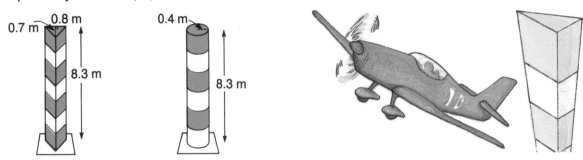

For prisms and cylinders, **Volume = Area of base × height**

 Volume of triangular prism
= **Area of base** × height
$$= \frac{base \times height}{2} \times h$$
$$= \frac{0.8\ m \times 0.7\ m}{2} \times 8.3\ m$$
= 2.3 m³ (nearest tenth)

Volume of cylinder
= **Area of base** × height
$= \pi \times r^2 \times h$
$\doteq 3.14 \times 0.4\ m \times 0.4\ m \times 8.3\ m$
= 4.2 m³ (nearest tenth)

The volume of concrete needed for the triangular prism is 2.3 m³.
For the cylinder, 4.2 m³ are needed.

The triangular prism needs less concrete and is probably more popular.

WORKING TOGETHER

1. Find the area of the base.

a. 6 cm   8 cm   7 cm

b. 3.4 cm   8.0 cm   40 mm

3. Find the area of the base to the nearest tenth.

a. 4 m   10 m

b. 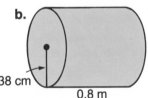 38 cm   0.8 m

2. Find the volume of each triangular prism in exercise 1.

4. Find the volume of each cylinder in exercise 3.

116

■ APPLICATIONS AND EXERCISES

1. Find the volume of the prism.

a.
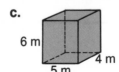
10 cm
12 cm
20 cm

b.
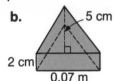
5 cm
2 cm
0.07 m

c.
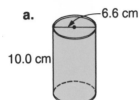
6 m
4 m
5 m

d.
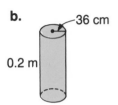
3 cm
4 cm
6 cm

2. Find the volume of the cylinder to the nearest tenth.

a.
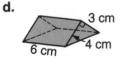
6.6 cm
10.0 cm

b.
36 cm
0.2 m

3. A piece of cheese is in the shape of a triangular prism. What is the volume of the piece?
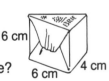
6 cm
6 cm
4 cm

4. A gasoline storage tank has a diameter of 10 m and a height of 8 m. What is the volume of the tank to the nearest tenth?

5. A silo has a diameter of 4 m, a height of 10 m, and it is filled to a height of 8 m.

  a. Find the volume of the silo to the nearest tenth.

  b. Find the volume of the empty section of the silo to the nearest tenth.

6. The floor of an elevator measures 2 m by 3 m. The elevator is 2.2 m high.

  a. Find the volume of the elevator.

  b. The elevator serves a building that is 30 m high. What is the volume of the elevator shaft?

7. A drill-bit 8 mm in diameter is used to drill a hole through a rectangular block of wood. What is the volume of the remaining wood to the nearest tenth?

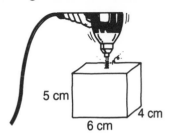
5 cm
6 cm
4 cm

8. The copper pipe has an outside diameter of 3 cm and an inside diameter of 2.4 cm. Find the volume of copper in a 4 m length of the pipe to the nearest tenth.

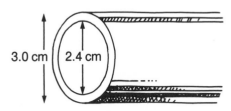
3.0 cm   2.4 cm

9. There are 10 m³ of gravel in a rectangular storage bin. The area of the base is 2.5 m². What is the depth of the gravel in the storage bin?

KEEPING SHARP

1. Evaluate.

  a. $15 - 7 + 1$

  b. $24 - 3 \times 5$

  c. $30 - 3 \times 3 + 6$

  d. $4 + 3 \times 5 - 4 \div 4$

  e. $\dfrac{8 + 4 \times 3}{3^2 + 1}$

  f. $\dfrac{30 \div 6 + 9}{8 - 1}$

  g. $60 - 10 \times 2 + 2^3$

  h. $\dfrac{1 + 24 \div 8}{3 \times 2 - 4}$

Volume and Capacity

The **capacity** of a container is the amount it can hold.

The teapot has a capacity of 1 L.
The teacup has a capacity of 200 mL.
The teaspoon has a capacity of 5 mL.

| 1 L = 1000 mL |
| 1 mL = 0.001 L |

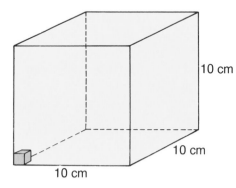

10 cm

10 cm

10 cm

Volume	Capacity
1 cm³	1 mL
1000 cm³	1000 mL or 1 L
1 000 000 cm³ or 1 m³	1 000 000 mL or 1000 L or 1 kL

(kilolitre)

1 cm
1 cm 1 cm

1 mL fills 1 cm³.   1000 mL or 1 L fills 1000 cm³.

For this coffee mug, Volume of cylinder
$$= \text{Area of base} \times \text{height}$$
$$= \quad \pi \times r^2 \quad \times \quad h$$
$$\doteq 3.14 \times 3\ \text{cm} \times 3\ \text{cm} \times 8\ \text{cm}$$
$$= 226.08\ \text{cm}^3$$

6 cm

8 cm

The volume of the coffee mug is 226 cm³.
The capacity of the coffee mug is 226 mL.

WORKING TOGETHER

1. Which measure is more reasonable?

   a. an egg cup holding 20 L or 20 mL

   b. a garbage truck holding 25 L or 25 kL

2. Copy and complete.

	a.	**b.**	**c.**	**d.**	**e.**
Volume	20 cm³	3 m³	☐m³	☐cm³	☐m³
Capacity	☐mL	☐L	5 kL	2 L	500 L

3. Find the volume. Then write the capacity in litres or kilolitres.

   a.

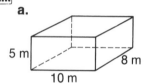

   5 m   8 m
   10 m

   b.

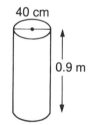

   40 cm

   0.9 m

118

APPLICATIONS AND EXERCISES

1. Which measure is more reasonable?

   a. coffee can
   1 L   1 mL

   b. swimming pool
   100 kL   100 L

   c. can of juice
   250 L   250 mL

   d. tube of toothpaste
   100 mL   100 L

2. Write the capacity in millilitres, then litres.

   a. a glass with volume 300 cm³

   b. an aquarium with volume 50 000 cm³

   c. a thermos with volume 750 cm³

3. Find the capacity in litres.

   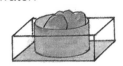 **a.** 35 mm, 4 cm, 35 mm, 16.5 cm (Candy)

   b. 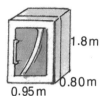 JUICE 30 cm, 20 cm, 15 cm

   c. 20 cm, 15 cm

   d. LEMONADE 4 cm, 12 cm

4. A rectangular swimming pool is 15 m long and 5 m wide. How many litres of water are needed to fill the pool to a depth of 1 m?

5. A refrigerated truck carries ice cream to a chain of milk stores. How many litres of ice cream can the truck hold?

   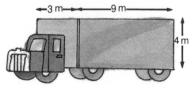
   ←3 m→ ←9 m→ 4 m

6. A milk store has a freezer for ice cream. How many litres of ice cream can the freezer hold?
   1.8 m, 0.95 m, 0.80 m

7. A coffee urn has a diameter of 30 cm and a height of 40 cm. How many litres of coffee, to the nearest tenth, can it hold?

To find the volume of an irregular object, such as a rock, measure the amount of water displaced by the object.

Try This

Fill a container with water. Place a rock in the water.

Measure the water that overflows.

1.
   a. What is the measure of the overflow water?

   b. What is the volume of the rock?

2. Use three-dimensional solid models to find the **displacement volume** of these shapes.

   a.

   b. same base same height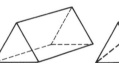

   c.

3. What relationships do you notice in exercise 2?

Mass

What is the approximate mass of the water in the aquarium when it is full?

The commonly used units for mass are gram, kilogram, and tonne.

gram (g) for the mass of a guppy

kilogram (kg) for the mass of an air pump

tonne (t) for the mass of a Great White Shark

To find the mass of the water in the aquarium, find the volume of the aquarium.

Volume = Area of base × height
$$= 95 \text{ cm} \times 40 \text{ cm} \times 20 \text{ cm}$$
$$= 76\,000 \text{ cm}^3$$

76 000 cm³ = 76 000 mL or 76 L
with mass
76 000 g or 76 kg

Volume	Capacity	Mass
1 cm³	1 mL	1 g
1000 cm³	1000 mL or 1 L	1000 g or 1 kg
1 m³	1000 L or 1 kL	1000 kg or 1 t

The chart shows how volume, capacity, and mass are related for water at 4°C.

The mass of the water in the aquarium is about 76 kg.

WORKING TOGETHER

1. What measure is more reasonable?

   a. mouse
   50 g   50 kg

   b. man
   70 g   70 kg

   c. elephant
   2 kg   2 t

   d. horse
   650 kg   650 t

2. Copy and complete for water.

	a.	**b.**	**c.**	**d.**	**e.**
Volume	2000 cm³	☐ cm³	3 m³	☐ cm³	☐ cm³
Capacity	☐ L	450 mL	☐ L	☐ mL	☐ L
Mass	☐ kg	☐ g	☐ t	61 kg	15 kg

3. **a.** Find the volume and capacity of the aquarium.

   b. Find the mass of the water that fills the aquarium.

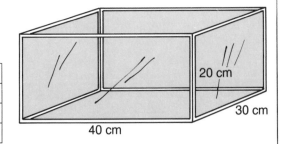

APPLICATIONS AND EXERCISES

1. Which measure is more reasonable?

   a. bowling ball
      7 g 7 kg

   b. ping pong ball
      1 g 1 kg

   c. load of bricks
      2 kg 2 t

   d. pencil
      6 g 6 kg

   e. potato
      50 g 50 kg

   f. sack of potatoes
      5 kg 5 t

2. Copy and complete.

   a. sack of potatoes with mass 3 ☐

   b. apple with mass 275 ☐

   c. adult human with mass 75 ☐

   d. egg with mass 50 ☐

   e. school bus with mass 5 ☐

   f. can of soup with mass 305 ☐

3. Copy and complete.

   a. 5 kg = ☐ g

   b. 2000 g = ☐ kg

   c. 3.1 kg = ☐ g

   d. 1400 g = ☐ kg

   e. 1650 g = ☐ kg

   f. 0.4 kg = ☐ g

   g. 750 g = ☐ kg

   h. 0.06 kg = ☐ g

   i. 5000 kg = ☐ t

   j. 21 t = ☐ kg

   k. 760 kg = ☐ t

   l. 1.3 t = ☐ kg

   m. 82 kg = ☐ g

   n. 67 kg = ☐ t

   o. 0.5 t = ☐ kg

   p. 0.08 t = ☐ kg

4. Copy and complete for water.

	a.	**b.**	**c.**	**d.**
Volume	6 m³	300 cm³	☐ cm³	☐ cm³
Capacity	☐ kL	☐ mL	☐ mL	☐ mL
Mass	☐ t	☐ g	15 g	750 g

5. Write the approximate mass of water in grams, kilograms, or tonnes.

   a. 8000 cm³ **b.** 400 cm³ **c.** 112 m³

   d. 19 000 cm³ **e.** 0.8 m³ **f.** 25 cm³

6. Write the approximate volume of water in cubic centimetres or cubic metres.

   a. 5 kg   **b.** 250 g   **c.** 3.5 kg

   d. 427 t   **e.** 0.79 kg **f.** 56.5 g

7. Find the volume and capacity of the aquarium. Then find the mass of the water that fills the aquarium.

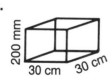

a. 30 cm, 0.5 m, 35 cm

b. 200 mm, 30 cm, 30 cm

8. When a rock is placed in a container full of water, it displaces 250 mL of the water. The mass of the rock is 5.63 times as much as the mass of the water. What is the volume (cm³) and mass (g) of the rock?

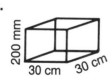

Try This

A pure gold nugget with a volume of 5 cm³ has a mass of about 96 g. It is pounded into a thin layer, called gold leaf, which is 0.0001 cm thick. Approximately how much area does the gold leaf cover? Express the answer in square metres.

1. Which measure is more reasonable?

   a. book with a volume of
      1440 m³ or 1440 cm³

   b. button with a volume of
      157 cm³ or 157 mm³

   c. shipping container with a volume of
      30 cm³ or 30 m³

2. Find the volume.

   a.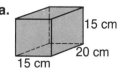
   15 cm
   20 cm
   15 cm

   b.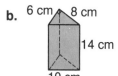
   6 cm 8 cm
   14 cm
   10 cm

   c.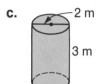
   —2 m
   3 m

   d.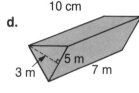
   5 m
   3 m   7 m

3. At a building site, earth is being
   excavated to a depth of 8 m from an
   area 70 m by 50 m. The earth is being
   removed in dump trucks that can carry
   40 m³ of earth.

   a. Find the volume of earth that has to
      be excavated.

   b. How many truck loads of earth have
      to be removed?

4. A section of road 4 m wide and 100 m
   long is to be paved. If 12 m³ of asphalt
   are to be spread evenly over the section,
   what is the depth of the new asphalt?

5. A rectangular block of candle wax
   measures 15.7 cm by 20 cm by 5 cm. It
   is melted down and used to make four
   matching cylindrical candles. What is the
   volume of each cylindrical candle?

6. Copy and complete.

   a. 14 cm³ = ☐ mL   b. 3 L = ☐ cm³

   c. 5 m³ = ☐ L   d. 7 m³ = ☐ kL

   e. 120 mL = ☐ cm³   f. 3100 L = ☐ m³

7. Find the capacity in millilitres, then litres
   of each shape in exercise 2.

8. Which measure is more reasonable?

   a. teaspoon with a capacity of
      5 mm or 5 L

   b. teacup with a capacity of
      150 mL or 150 L

   c. gasoline truck with a capacity of
      77 L or 77 kL

   d. fish pond with a capacity of
      75 L or 75 kL

9. A truck has a cylindrical tank 9 m long
   for transporting gasoline. The diameter
   of the tank is 3 m. How many litres of
   gasoline can the tank hold?

10. A bottle of nail polish is
    4 cm high and has a
    diameter of 2.5 cm.
    How many millilitres of
    nail polish can the
    bottle hold?

11. Find the volume and capacity of the
    swimming pool. Then find the mass of
    the water that fills the swimming pool.

    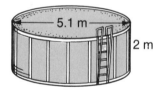
    5.1 m
    2 m

Planes of Symmetry

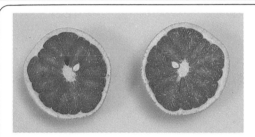

The grapefruit has symmetry because both halves are identical or are congruent.

If a sheet of clear acetate is placed as shown, the clear acetate is the **plane of symmetry**.

1. State the number of planes of symmetry.

a.

b.

c.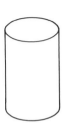

d.

e.

f.

g.

h.

2. The object has been cut through a plane of symmetry and half is shown. Sketch the complete object.

a.

b.

c.

d.

3. List five objects in your classroom that have more than one plane of symmetry.

Computers in Our Lives

Computers play a large part in many areas of our lives.

A. Government

All levels of government use large mainframe computers to keep different kinds of records. Statistics Canada analyses data about all citizens. The Ministry of Revenue calculates taxes. Social agencies use computers to print pension and welfare cheques.

1. a. What records about your family might the government want to keep?

b. What are some of the numbers that the government assigns to citizens to assist with record keeping?

c. Why do you think the government needs to keep records?

2. Tell whether or not you think a computer would help to get the task done better.

a. processing paycheques for all the people who work for a city

b. listing all the people who are eligible to vote

c. choosing the next prime minister

B. The Workplace

Designers are using computer graphics to test out ideas for new products. With the development of robots, many industries are using automation to increase productivity and reduce personal injury.

In business offices, accounting and billing are maintained by computer. The word processor makes a secretary's job much easier and more efficient.

In supermarkets, the optical scanner and the Universal Product Code make the cashier's job almost mechanical but make inventory management a much more accurate and scientific process.

Pumping gas at a gas station used to be a common part-time job. This is now being replaced in many areas by self-serve gas bars with computerized cash registers.

3. a. List some careers that require knowledge of computers. Use a newspaper to help you.

  b. List other careers that use computers but do not require specific knowledge of them.

4. Discuss.
  "The use of computers can eliminate routine manual tasks, and allow workers to be more creative and have more leisure time."

C. School

As government and business rely more and more on the computer to carry out their office routines, so also do schools. Computers are used for preparing and storing letters, budgets, and student records; for scheduling individual student time-tables; and for keeping catalogues and records in the library.

In some classrooms, computers are used for Computer Assisted Instruction, or CAI. For example, a student types an answer in a math drill or game and is told instantly whether the answer is right or wrong. With computers, students can work individually at their own pace without worrying about making mistakes. A computer presents information as many times as required. It never gets tired or bored, and it cannot make judgments about human intelligence.

5. How does your school office use computers?

6. How might you use a computer in your math class?

7. Do you think computers in the classroom will replace teachers? Discuss.

Guess and Test

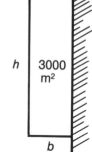

Ruth's plan for a rectangular pasture has an area of 3000 m². To reduce costs, she decides to use her neighbor's fence for one of the sides. What dimensions should she use for the pasture so that fencing costs are as low as possible?

Think. Draw diagrams.
The neighbor's fence should be along one of the longest sides.

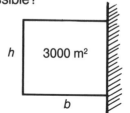

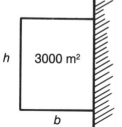

Area of a rectangle is base times height.
Distance around rectangle = $2(b + h)$
Distance to be fenced = $2b + h$

Plan and do. Guess and test the dimensions. Make an organized list.

Given Area	Guess. Base (m)	Calculate. Height (m)	Calculate $2b + h$. Amount of new fence (m)
3000	20	$3000 \div 20 = 150$	$2(20) + 150 = 190$
3000	30	$3000 \div 30 = 100$	$2(30) + 100 = 160$

Look back. Ruth found that a rectangle with dimensions 40 m by 75 m gave the minimum amount of new fence.
What if decimal amounts are used?

WORKING TOGETHER

1. What is the largest rectangular yard that can be enclosed with 24 m of fencing?

   a. Draw a diagram of one possibility.

   b. Make a table and guess and test.

Perimeter	Length	Width	Area

   c. Give a concluding statement.

   d. What if you had 34 m of fencing?

2. **a.** What is the least amount of fencing needed to enclose a garden of 48 m²? The length of each side must be a whole number of metres.

   b. What if the length of each side need not be a whole number?

3. Suppose Ruth could use two neighbors' fences for two adjacent sides of the pasture in the example. How would this alter the problem?

PROBLEMS

**Use a calculator to guess and test.
Solve the problems.**

1. Where would you open a book so that the product of the two facing pages is 25 122?

2. Find three consecutive even numbers whose sum is 294.

3. A golfer said, "If I had used 20 more strokes, my score would have been a perfect square. If I had used 20 fewer strokes, my score would still have been a perfect square." What was the golfer's score for 18 holes?

4. Find three consecutive odd numbers such that the sum of their squares is a four-digit number with all digits the same.

**Use an organized list to guess and test.
Solve the problems.**

5. Rip Van Winkle II lived for 52 a. He spent a total of 20 more years asleep than he spent awake. How many years in total was he awake?

6. Pat needs 17 kg of fertilizer to grow this year's crop of tomatoes. How can Pat buy at least that amount for the lowest cost?

Solve.

7. What digit must D represent if the number D434D0 is divisible by 36?

8. Beth collected $14 more than Holly. Holly collected $10 more than Garry. Altogether they collected $88. How much did Garry collect?

9. A cheque for $63.00 is cashed. Six bills, none of which is a $1 bill, are received. What are the bills and how many of each denomination are received?

10. Twenty blue counters and sixteen yellow counters are used to make this design.

Two similar designs can be made with equal numbers of blue and yellow counters. Draw them.

11. Arrange these eight dominoes to form a four by four square so that each row, column, and diagonal has the same total (a Magic Domino Square).

Problem Solving Review

Tell how you would solve the problem. Use **Think, Plan and do,** and then **Look back**.

1. How many sheets of wrapping paper are needed to wrap a rectangular gift measuring 52 cm by 14 cm by 14 cm? A sheet of wrapping paper measures 70 cm by 40 cm.

2. The light bulbs around the edge of a sign are 20 cm apart. The sign measures 3 m by 2 m. How many light bulbs are needed around the sign?

Use the clues to identify the mystery number.

3. The product of the digits of the number is a multiple of 6.

   The number is between $\sqrt{900}$ and 6^3.
   It is one less than a square number.
   Its tens digit is less than its ones digit.

Solve.

4. Janet and Fran live beside each other. The product of their apartment numbers is 1023. What are their apartment numbers?

5. A 40 m cable is divided into two sections. One section is 4 m more than twice the length of the other section. How long is each section?

6. Travis attempts to climb a 10 m pole. At every attempt he climbs up 1 m but slips back 0.5 m. After how many attempts will he reach the top?

7. The area of the front of an LP album cover is 1156 cm². What is the area of one side of the record album?

8. Pigs and chickens are kept in the red barn. They have a total of 35 heads and 100 legs. How many pigs are there?

9. Art and Eddie are playing a game. At the end of each game the loser gives the winner a penny. After 10 min Art has won three games and Eddie has three more pennies than he did before he started. How many games did they play?

10. A rectangular piece of paper is folded in half, then cut along the fold line. One piece is rolled to form a short tube, and the edges are taped. The other piece is rolled to form a long tube, and the edges are taped.

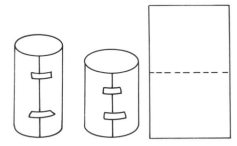

Do both tubes hold the same amount?

11. A wooden cube that measures 10 cm along each edge is painted red. The painted cube is then cut into 2 cm cubes. How many of the 2 cm cubes do not have red paint on any face?

Chapter Checkup

1. Name the polyhedron that can be made from the net.

   a.

   b.

   c.

   d.

2. Which polyhedron from exercise 1 is a regular polyhedron?

3. Copy and complete the chart for regular polyhedrons.

	Name	Number of faces	Shape of each face
a.	tetrahedron		equilateral triangle
b.	icosahedron	20	
c.		6	square
d.		8	equilateral triangle
e.	dodecahedron		regular pentagon

4. Identify the polyhedron from the views shown.

   a.
   top view   side view

   b.
   top view   side view

   c.
   bottom view   side view

5. Draw an accurate front view, side view, and top view of the triangular prism.

   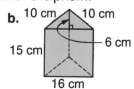
   3 cm, 4 cm, 6 cm

6. Find the surface area of the prism.

   a.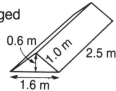
   9 cm, 7 cm, 10 cm

   b. 10 cm, 10 cm, 15 cm, 6 cm, 16 cm

7. Find the volume of each prism in exercise 6.

8. A sheet of plastic is rigged up to form a shelter for storing logs. Find the volume of space under the plastic.

   0.6 m, 1.0 m, 2.5 m, 1.6 m

9. a. Calculate the surface area of the cylinder to the nearest tenth.
   b. Calculate its volume to the nearest tenth.

   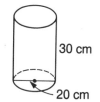
   30 cm, 20 cm

10. The diameter of a well is 1 m. How many litres of water are in the well if the water is 7 m deep?

11. a. What is the possible capacity of this can?
    b. Why is it sold with only 3 L in it?

    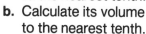
    20 cm, 16 cm, 10 cm

12. Copy and complete the chart for water.

Volume	5 m³	▨ cm³	▨ m³
Capacity	▨ kL	500 mL	▨ L
Mass	▨ t	▨ g	6100 kg

129

Cumulative Checkup

1. Multiply if the product is less than 10 000.

  a. 128   **b.** 293   **c.** 313
    $\times\,88$ $\times\,44$ $\times\,29$

  d. 482×18 **e.** 514×17

2. Is the remainder 0?

  a. $8692 \div 2$ **b.** $27\,424 \div 3$

  c. $9561 \div 5$ **d.** $12\,748 \div 4$

  e. $13\,962 \div 6$ **f.** $41\,834 \div 8$

  g. $6183 \div 9$ **h.** $5722 \div 3$

3. Express each even number between 2 and 11 as the sum of two prime numbers.

4. Express the number as the product of its prime factors.

  a. 12   **b.** 42   **c.** 90   **d.** 315

5. Express as a product. Evaluate.

  a. 2^7 **b.** 5^4 **c.** 10^6 **d.** 3^5

6. Evaluate.

  a. $\sqrt{25}$ **b.** $\sqrt{49}$ **c.** $\sqrt{144}$

  d. $\sqrt{100}$ **e.** $\sqrt{900}$ **f.** $\sqrt{360\,000}$

  g. $\sqrt{2 \times 2 \times 13 \times 13}$

  h. $\sqrt{2 \times 2 \times 2 \times 2 \times 5 \times 5}$

7. Describe the pattern. Then list the next three numbers in the sequence.

  a. 1, 3, 5, 7   **b.** 1, 2, 4, 8   **c.** 1, 8, 16, 25

8. Express in expanded form using powers of ten.

  a. 3.14   **b.** 4040.5

  c. 521.02   **d.** 100 000.9

9. Express in standard form.

  a. twenty-seven and thirty-four hundredths

  b. one hundred seven thousandths

  c. $(3 \times 1000) + (2 \times 10) + (5 \times 1) + (6 \times \frac{1}{10})$

  d. $(4 \times 100) + (7 \times 1) + (3 \times \frac{1}{100})$

  e. $(7 \times 10^4) + (6 \times 10^3) + (2 \times 10^1) + (2 \times \frac{1}{10^1})$

10. Copy and use > or < to make a true statement.

  a. 5.07 ◯ 5.7   **b.** 0.08 ◯ 0.07

  c. 7.92 ◯ 8.13   **d.** 5.462 ◯ 5.452

  e. 10.9 ◯ 10.08   **f.** 3.2 ◯ 3.199

11. Insert a decimal point between two of the digits of 74865 to give the number.

  a. between 10 and 100

  b. between 1 and 10

  c. between 1000 and 10 000

12. The value of $\sqrt{3}$ rounded to seven decimal places is 1.732 050 8. Give the value of $\sqrt{3}$ rounded to this number of decimal places.

  a. 3   **b.** 1   **c.** 4   **d.** 6

13. Evaluate.

  a. 312.87   **b.** 77   **c.** 0.917
    $-\,178.09$ 7.17   0.86
            $+\,0.083$ $+\,9.3$

  d. $835.2 - 407.08$ **e.** $4.173 + 89.04$

14. Is the result greater than 16.4?

    a. 16.4×100 **b.** $16.4 \div 0.01$

    c. 16.4×0.1 **d.** $16.4 \div 1000$

    e. $16.4 \div 0.0001$ **f.** $16.4 \times 10\,000$

15. a. Calculate the cost of buying one pair of jeans and two T-shirts.

    b. How much change would be received if the items in part **a** were paid for with two $20 bills?

$25.99 $6.98

16. Which is the better buy?

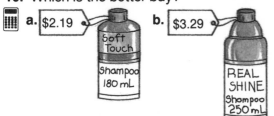

  a. $2.19   **b.** $3.29

17. Copy and complete.

	Millimetres	Centimetres	Metres	Kilometres
a.	720			
b.		150		
c.			2	
d.			4.1	
e.		2100		
f.				7

18. Find the perimeter of the figure.

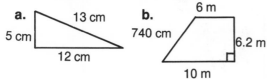

  a. 13 cm, 5 cm, 12 cm

  b. 6 m, 740 cm, 6.2 m, 10 m

19. Find the perimeter of the regular polygon.

    a. a pentagon with side 21.2 m

    b. a square with side 3.25 cm

    c. an octagon with side 2.5 cm

    d. a triangle with side 1.3 m

    e. a decagon with side 3.8 cm

20. a. Estimate the measure of the diameter and the circumference.

    b. Measure the diameter to the nearest millimetre. Calculate the circumference.

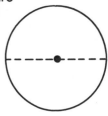

21. The circumference of a bicycle wheel is 2.1 m. How many times does a wheel go round in a distance of 300 m?

22. Find the area of each figure in exercise 18.

23. Find the area of the figure.

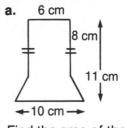

  a. 6 cm, 8 cm, 11 cm, 10 cm

  b. 1 m, 2 m, 3 m

24. Find the area of the circle in exercise 20.

25. Find the area of the shaded region to the nearest tenth.

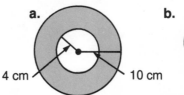

  a. 4 cm, 10 cm

  b. 5 cm, 3 cm, 4 cm

5/Fractions

Athletes use fractions to compare individual performances and team performances. A soccer team's goal average may determine its standing in the league.

Get Set

1. Copy and complete the missing factors.

    a. $15 = 1 \times \square$
          b. $10 = 1 \times \square$
        $15 = 3 \times \square$
              $10 = 2 \times \square$

    c. $18 = 1 \times \square$
          d. $12 = 1 \times \square$
        $18 = 2 \times \square$
              $12 = 2 \times \square$
        $18 = 3 \times \square$
              $12 = 3 \times \square$

    e. $30 = 1 \times \square$
          f. $24 = 1 \times \square$
        $30 = 2 \times \square$
              $24 = 2 \times \square$
        $30 = 3 \times \square$
              $24 = 3 \times \square$
        $30 = 5 \times \square$
              $24 = 4 \times \square$

2. List the next three multiples.

    a. 3, 6, 9, . . .
          b. 8, 16, 24, . . .

    c. 10, 20, 30, . . .
        d. 25, 50, 75, . . .

    e. 6, 12, 18, . . .
         f. 12, 24, 36, . . .

3. What is the least number the pair will divide into exactly?

    a. 2, 3 **b.** 4, 5 **c.** 3, 7   **d.** 4, 6

    e. 5, 8 **f.** 3, 4 **g.** 12, 16 **h.** 6, 8

4. What fraction of the figure is shaded?

    a.   **b.**   **c.**

    d.   **e.**   **f.**

5. What fraction of the group is shaded?

    a.

    b.

    c.

6. Which does not belong?

    a.

    b.

    c.

7. Arrange from greatest to least.

    a. 9, 7, 12, 3, 8, 6, 10

    b. 4, 15, 2, 5, 11, 12, 7

8. Is the illustration true or false?

    a.  and   →

    b. take away   →

    c. and   →

    d. take away   →

9. Write the quotient with a remainder.

    a. $19 \div 4$ **b.** $17 \div 2$ **c.** $\frac{22}{5}$

10. What happens if you multiply any number by 1?

11. Copy and complete.

    a. $0.1 = \frac{\square}{10}$
        b. $0.29 = \frac{\square}{100}$

    c. $0.375 = \frac{\square}{1000}$
    d. $1.07 = 1\frac{\square}{100}$

12. Write the decimal.

    a. 7 tenths   **b.** 7 hundredths

    c. 7 thousandths **d.** 25 hundredths

Fraction Tools—GCF and LCM

Larry bought several containers of oil for $12.
Clare also bought some of the oil for $18.
What prices are possible for
one container of the oil?
What would the greatest price possible be?

List the factors of 12 and 18.

Factors of 12: 1, 2, 3, 4, 6, 12
Factors of 18: 1, 2, 3, 6, 9, 18

1, 2, 3, and 6 are the **common factors** of 12 and 18.
The possible prices for one container are $1, $2, $3, and $6.

6 is the **greatest common factor**, **GCF**, of 12 and 18.

The greatest price possible is $6.

Clare changes oil every 3 weeks and spark plugs every 5 weeks.
How often are both jobs done in the same week?

List the multiples of 3 and 5.

Multiples of 3: 3, 6, 9, 12, 15, 18, 21, 24, 27, 30, 33, 36, 39, 42, 45,...
Multiples of 5: 5, 10, 15, 20, 25, 30, 35, 40, 45,...

15, 30, 45,... are the **common multiples** of 3 and 5.

15 is the **lowest common multiple**, **LCM**, of 3 and 5.

Both jobs are done in the same week every 15 weeks.

WORKING TOGETHER

1. a. List the factors of 8 and 20.
   b. Which factors are common?
   c. Which is the greatest common factor?

2. Find the greatest common factor.
   a. 6, 10   **b.** 15, 45   **c.** 42, 56

3. a. List the first ten multiples of 4 and 6.
   b. Which multiples are common?
   c. Which is the lowest common multiple?

4. Find the lowest common multiple.
   a. 6, 8   **b.** 3, 14   **c.** 9, 15

APPLICATIONS AND EXERCISES

1. Find the GCF of the pair.

    a. 10, 12   **b.** 6, 13   **c.** 30, 42

    d. 18, 25   **e.** 24, 40   **f.** 39, 65

    g. 36, 60   **h.** 18, 72   **i.** 42, 98

2. Find the LCM of the pair.

    a. 10, 15   **b.** 6, 9   **c.** 5, 6

    d. 7, 12   **e.** 16, 18   **f.** 18, 24

    g. 9, 15   **h.** 12, 15   **i.** 11, 13

3. Find the GCF of the group.

    a. 6, 8, 12   **b.** 8, 12, 20

    c. 9, 15, 27   **d.** 12, 18, 36

    e. 48, 64, 80   **f.** 28, 70, 98

4. Find the LCM of the group.

    a. 5, 6, 8   **b.** 3, 4, 6

    c. 10, 15, 20   **d.** 3, 8, 10

    e. 14, 21, 49   **f.** 16, 18, 24

5. Marc bought a number of pencils for 78¢. Sumi bought some of the same pencils for $1.17. What is the most each pencil could have cost?

6. Bus #182 leaves the depot once every 18 min. Bus #205 leaves once every 30 min. How often do both buses leave the depot together?

7. A hobby store sells packages of foreign stamps. Each package contains the same number of stamps. Carlos bought 30 stamps and Andrea bought 75 stamps. What is the greatest number of stamps possible in a package?

8. A sheet of corkboard is 90 cm by 120 cm. Patricia wants to divide it evenly into identical squares. What are the dimensions of the largest squares possible?

9. Camilla and Barb left the starting line at the same time. It takes Camilla 3 min and Barb 5 min to run one lap of the course. In how many minutes, at those rates, will they be at the starting line together?

10. Erik changes the oil in his van every 5000 km. He rotates the tires on his van every 7500 km. After how many kilometres will he change the oil and rotate the tires at the same time?

11. During the past two years, Laura wore out a pair of runners every 12 months, a pair of socks every 6 months, and a T-shirt every 9 months. How often, at those rates, will she have to replace all three items at the same time?

Try This

1. a. Find the GCF of 16 and 20.

    b. Find the LCM of 16 and 20.

    c. Find the product of 16×20.

    d. Find the product of the GCF and the LCM. What do you notice?

2. Repeat exercise 1 for 18 and 42.

3. How is the product of two numbers related to the product of their GCF and LCM?

4. How can you find the LCM of two numbers if you know the numbers and their GCF?

Equivalent Fractions

A class made small pizzas and then cut them in different ways.

Matthew divided 1 pizza into 6 pieces. Each piece is $\frac{1}{6}$ of the pizza. $\frac{1}{6}$ means the same as $1 \div 6$.

Michelle ate $\frac{1}{2}$ of her pizza. Chafik ate $\frac{2}{4}$ of his. Matthew ate $\frac{3}{6}$ of his pizza. Rachel ate $\frac{4}{8}$ of hers.
Each fraction represents the same amount of pizza.

$\frac{1}{2}, \frac{2}{4}, \frac{3}{6},$ and $\frac{4}{8}$ are **equivalent fractions**. $\qquad \frac{1}{2} = \frac{2}{4} = \frac{3}{6} = \frac{4}{8} \leftarrow$ numerator
$\qquad\qquad\qquad\qquad\qquad\qquad\qquad\qquad\qquad\qquad\quad \leftarrow$ denominator

Equivalent fractions are formed by multiplying or dividing the numerator and the denominator by the same number.

$$\overset{\times 5}{\frac{3}{6}} = \underset{\times 5}{\frac{15}{30}} \qquad\qquad \overset{\div 3}{\frac{3}{6}} = \underset{\div 3}{\frac{1}{2}}$$

When the GCF of the numerator and denominator is 1,
a fraction is in **lowest terms**. $\frac{1}{2}$ is in lowest terms.

A fraction is expressed in lowest terms by dividing the numerator and the denominator by the GCF.
For $\frac{9}{12}$, the GCF of 9 and 12 is 3.

$$\overset{\div 3}{\frac{9}{12}} = \underset{\div 3}{\frac{3}{4}}$$

$\frac{3}{4}$ is an equivalent fraction in lowest terms.

WORKING TOGETHER

1. Copy and complete.

a. $\overset{\div \bigcirc}{\underset{\div \bigcirc}{\frac{5}{15}}} = \frac{1}{\square}$ **b.** $\overset{\times \bigcirc}{\underset{\times \bigcirc}{\frac{2}{3}}} = \frac{\square}{12}$

c. $\frac{30}{100} = \frac{3}{\square}$ **d.** $\frac{5}{4} = \frac{\square}{12}$

2. Express in lowest terms.

a. $\frac{5}{10}$ **b.** $\frac{3}{9}$ **c.** $\frac{9}{15}$ **d.** $\frac{10}{8}$

3. Give the fractional name for 1.

a.  **b.** **c.**

d. **e.** **f.**

4. What fraction of the pizzas have $\textcircled{P}$ pepperoni?

136

APPLICATIONS AND EXERCISES

1. What fraction of the figure is shaded?

a.   **b.**   **c.**

2. What fraction of the checkers are red?

3. Copy and complete.

a. $\frac{2}{3} = \frac{\square}{9}$ **b.** $\frac{3}{4} = \frac{12}{\square}$ **c.** $\frac{12}{10} = \frac{\square}{5}$

d. $\frac{30}{40} = \frac{15}{\square}$ **e.** $\frac{5}{5} = \frac{15}{\square}$ **f.** $\frac{15}{10} = \frac{3}{\square}$

4. List three equivalent fractions.

a. $\frac{1}{2}$ **b.** $\frac{3}{4}$ **c.** $\frac{7}{5}$ **d.** $\frac{1}{3}$

e. $\frac{3}{10}$ **f.** $\frac{4}{1}$ **g.** $\frac{2}{5}$ **h.** $\frac{4}{3}$

5. Express in lowest terms.

a. $\frac{3}{12}$ **b.** $\frac{8}{20}$ **c.** $\frac{6}{16}$ **d.** $\frac{12}{64}$

e. $\frac{24}{80}$ **f.** $\frac{15}{48}$ **g.** $\frac{10}{5}$ **h.** $\frac{75}{100}$

6. There are 32 students in a class. Of these, 12 do not like pizza. What fraction of the class likes pizza?

7. Express in lowest terms.

a. 4 eggs as a fraction of a dozen

b. 15 min as a fraction of 1 h

c. 25¢ as a fraction of $1

8. Find a hidden message.

1	2	3	4	5	6	7	8	9	10	11	12	13
F	H	Y	I	V	!	P	.	A	U	J	'	M

15	17	18	20	21	25	28	30	36	39	48	50	80
E	K	B	G	T	C	Q	D	R	Z	O	N	S

a. $\frac{5}{8} = \frac{\square}{32}$ **b.** $\frac{9}{16} = \frac{\square}{64}$ **c.** $\frac{1}{2} = \frac{\square}{30}$

d. $\frac{3}{4} = \frac{\square}{12}$ **e.** $\frac{7}{9} = \frac{\square}{27}$ **f.** $\frac{20}{24} = \frac{5}{\square}$

g. $\frac{\square}{9} = \frac{12}{36}$ **h.** $\frac{7}{8} = \frac{42}{\square}$ **i.** $\frac{2}{3} = \frac{\square}{15}$

j. $\frac{6}{8} = \frac{\square}{16}$ **k.** $\frac{\square}{100} = \frac{1}{20}$ **l.** $\frac{45}{300} = \frac{\square}{100}$

m. $\frac{2}{\square} = \frac{32}{16}$ **n.** $\frac{8}{\square} = \frac{4}{2}$ **o.** $\frac{5}{6} = \frac{\square}{24}$

p. $\frac{1}{2} = \frac{\square}{20}$ **q.** $\frac{6}{6} = \frac{\square}{36}$ **r.** $\frac{3}{40} = \frac{\square}{200}$

s. $\frac{3}{8} = \frac{\square}{80}$ **t.** $\frac{\square}{16} = \frac{2}{8}$ **u.** $\frac{7}{1} = \frac{\square}{3}$

v. $\frac{8}{14} = \frac{\square}{84}$ **w.** $\frac{5}{50} = \frac{\square}{100}$ **x.** $\frac{2}{\square} = \frac{6}{63}$

9. Use the diagram of the normal adult mouth.

a. How many teeth are there in all?

b. What fraction of the teeth are incisors?

c. If 2 molars are extracted, what fraction of the remaining teeth are molars?

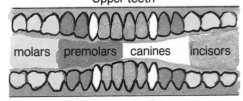

Upper teeth

molars premolars canines incisors

Lower teeth

KEEPING SHARP

1. Multiply only if the product is less than 100.

a. 5.8×2.1 **b.** 18.7×3.9 **c.** 0.85×32.14 **d.** 15.9×7.2

e. 34.3×0.01 **f.** 265.4×5.8 **g.** 0.07×0.93 **h.** 4.75×18.92

Comparing and Ordering

Lisette and Kim are the same height.
Lisette can jump $\frac{2}{3}$ of her height and

Kim, $\frac{3}{4}$ of her height. Who can jump higher?

Number lines can be used to compare
$\frac{2}{3}$ and $\frac{3}{4}$.

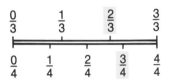

$\frac{3}{4}$ is to the right of $\frac{2}{3}$. $\frac{3}{4} > \frac{2}{3}$

Fractions can also be compared if they have the same denominator.

For $\frac{3}{4}$ and $\frac{2}{3}$, the LCM of the denominators is 12.

The LCM is used to write equivalent fractions.

$$\overset{\times 3}{\frac{3}{4}} = \underset{\times 3}{\frac{9}{12}} \qquad \overset{\times 4}{\frac{2}{3}} = \underset{\times 4}{\frac{8}{12}}$$

$\frac{9}{12} > \frac{8}{12}$, therefore $\frac{3}{4} > \frac{2}{3}$.

Kim can jump higher?

WORKING TOGETHER

1. Which is greater, $\frac{4}{5}$ or $\frac{5}{7}$?

| $\frac{0}{5}$ | $\frac{1}{5}$ | $\frac{2}{5}$ | $\frac{3}{5}$ | $\frac{4}{5}$ | $\frac{5}{5}$ |

| $\frac{0}{7}$ | $\frac{1}{7}$ | $\frac{2}{7}$ | $\frac{3}{7}$ | $\frac{4}{7}$ | $\frac{5}{7}$ | $\frac{6}{7}$ | $\frac{7}{7}$ |

2. Find the LCM of the denominators
(the lowest common denominator).

  a. $\frac{2}{3}, \frac{1}{7}$ **b.** $\frac{2}{5}, \frac{1}{2}$

  c. $\frac{1}{9}, \frac{1}{6}$ **d.** $\frac{3}{4}, \frac{5}{6}$

3. Copy and use > or < to make a true
statement.

  a. $\frac{3}{5} \bigcirc \frac{2}{5}$ **b.** $\frac{7}{10} \bigcirc \frac{9}{10}$ **c.** $\frac{1}{5} \bigcirc \frac{3}{10}$

  d. $\frac{5}{8} \bigcirc \frac{3}{4}$ **e.** $\frac{1}{4} \bigcirc \frac{1}{3}$ **f.** $\frac{3}{4} \bigcirc \frac{7}{10}$

4. Arrange from least to greatest.

  a. $\frac{3}{10}, \frac{1}{10}, \frac{9}{10}, \frac{7}{10}$ **b.** $\frac{7}{9}, \frac{18}{18}, \frac{4}{9}, \frac{11}{18}, \frac{1}{18}$

  c. $\frac{1}{4}, \frac{2}{3}, \frac{1}{12}$ **d.** $\frac{2}{3}, \frac{3}{4}, \frac{1}{2}, \frac{5}{6}$

  e. $\frac{11}{10}, \frac{6}{5}, \frac{9}{8}$

APPLICATIONS AND EXERCISES

1. What fractions do A and B represent?

a.

b.

2. Which is the lesser fraction in each part of exercise 1?

3. Which is the greater fraction?

a. $\frac{4}{12}, \frac{5}{12}$ **b.** $\frac{3}{4}, \frac{5}{8}$ **c.** $\frac{12}{5}, \frac{9}{4}$

d. $\frac{7}{8}, \frac{3}{4}$ **e.** $\frac{15}{10}, \frac{15}{8}$ **f.** $\frac{2}{3}, \frac{7}{10}$

4. Which figure has the greater fraction of its area shaded?

a.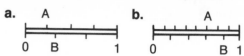

b.

5. Renata and Bonnie have the same mass. Renata can lift $\frac{4}{5}$ of her mass. Bonnie can lift $\frac{3}{4}$ of her mass. Who can lift the greater mass?

6. Find the LCM of the denominators.

a. $\frac{1}{2}, \frac{4}{5}, \frac{9}{10}$ **b.** $\frac{7}{8}, \frac{1}{3}, \frac{5}{4}$ **c.** $\frac{7}{6}, \frac{3}{8}, \frac{5}{3}$

7. Which is the least fraction?

a. $\frac{2}{3}, \frac{5}{6}, \frac{3}{4}$ **b.** $\frac{7}{8}, \frac{4}{5}, \frac{9}{10}$ **c.** $\frac{7}{4}, \frac{11}{7}, \frac{3}{2}$

8. Arrange from least to greatest.

a. $\frac{3}{4}, \frac{8}{4}, \frac{5}{4}$ **b.** $\frac{1}{3}, \frac{2}{5}, \frac{1}{10}$

c. $\frac{8}{5}, \frac{9}{5}, \frac{5}{5}$ **d.** $\frac{9}{4}, \frac{7}{2}, 2$

9. Of the 30 students in Mrs. Paolucci's class, 3 were absent. On the same day, 2 students were absent from Mr. Clark's class of 25. Which class had the greater fraction of students present?

10. A construction company is building Phase II of a housing development. Of the 30 homes in Phase I, 11 have three bedrooms. In Phase II, 17 of the 45 homes have three bedrooms. Which phase has the greater fraction of three-bedroom homes?

11. While playing golf, Neil lost 3 of his 10 golf balls. Gabrielle lost 6 of her 15 golf balls. Which player lost the lesser fraction of golf balls?

12. The Yost family spent $72 of their $264 weekly income on food. The Seymours spent $93 of their $330 weekly income on food.

a. How much did each family spend on food in a year?

b. Which family spent the greater fraction of their income on food?

Recent developments in science and technology can be used to help handicapped people become more independent and lead a fuller life. For example, a person who loses an arm through injury or disease can be fitted with a bionic arm. It can do many of the things a normal arm can.

1. Discuss how computer technology might be used now or in the future to help a blind person or a person who is paralyzed.

Adding and Subtracting

At lunch $\frac{3}{8}$ of the pie was eaten.

At dinner $\frac{5}{8}$ of the pie was eaten.

lunch   dinner

What fraction of the pie was eaten altogether?

Add. $\frac{3}{8} + \frac{5}{8} = \frac{3 + 5}{8}$

$= \frac{8}{8}$

$= 1$

Altogether $\frac{8}{8}$ or the entire pie was eaten.

How much more was eaten at dinner than at lunch?

Subtract. $\frac{5}{8} - \frac{3}{8} = \frac{5 - 3}{8}$

$= \frac{2}{8}$

$= \frac{1}{4}$

At dinner $\frac{1}{4}$ more pie was eaten than at lunch.

To add or subtract fractions with the same denominator, add or subtract the numerators and keep the denominator.

To add or subtract fractions with different denominators, express each as an equivalent fraction with the same **LCD** (lowest common denominator). Then add or subtract.

Add. $\frac{3}{4} + \frac{1}{3}$

$= \frac{9}{12} + \frac{4}{12}$

$= \frac{9 + 4}{12}$

$= \frac{13}{12}$

Subtract. $\frac{3}{5} - \frac{1}{2}$

$= \frac{6}{10} - \frac{5}{10}$

$= \frac{6 - 5}{10}$

$= \frac{1}{10}$

WORKING TOGETHER

1. a. Find the LCD in the expression $\frac{1}{4} + \frac{2}{5}$.

   b. Write the expression using equivalent fractions.

   c. Find the sum.

2. Find the sum.

   a. $\frac{3}{8} + \frac{1}{8}$ **b.** $\frac{4}{5} + \frac{3}{10}$ **c.** $\frac{1}{3} + \frac{3}{5}$

3. Find the difference.

   a. $\frac{7}{10} - \frac{3}{10}$ **b.** $\frac{3}{4} - \frac{1}{2}$ **c.** $\frac{9}{10} - \frac{2}{3}$

1. Add.

  a. $\frac{3}{12} + \frac{7}{12}$ **b.** $\frac{7}{11} + \frac{2}{11}$ **c.** $\frac{3}{7} + \frac{5}{7}$

  d. $\frac{1}{2} + \frac{1}{3}$ **e.** $\frac{3}{5} + \frac{1}{4}$ **f.** $\frac{1}{4} + \frac{2}{3}$

  g. $\frac{3}{10} + \frac{4}{5}$ **h.** $\frac{7}{12} + \frac{3}{4}$ **i.** $\frac{9}{10} + \frac{1}{3}$

2. Subtract.

  a. $\frac{8}{9} - \frac{4}{9}$ **b.** $\frac{7}{11} - \frac{2}{11}$ **c.** $\frac{11}{12} - \frac{5}{12}$

  d. $\frac{3}{4} - \frac{2}{3}$ **e.** $\frac{11}{15} - \frac{3}{5}$ **f.** $\frac{5}{5} - \frac{3}{4}$

  g. $\frac{7}{10} - \frac{5}{12}$ **h.** $\frac{3}{5} - \frac{1}{2}$ **i.** $\frac{7}{25} - \frac{1}{4}$

3. Lorne spent $\frac{2}{3}$ of his allowance on movies and $\frac{1}{4}$ on snack foods. What fraction of his allowance did he spend on these items altogether?

4. The gasoline tank on Karen's moped was $\frac{3}{4}$ full when she left home. When she returned, it was $\frac{1}{3}$ full. What fraction of a tank did she use?

5. Find the sum.

  a. $\frac{3}{4} + \frac{5}{12} + \frac{1}{2}$ **b.** $\frac{1}{2} + \frac{2}{3} + \frac{3}{5}$

6. Petra took $\frac{1}{2}$ h to wash and $\frac{1}{3}$ h to dry her laundry. Folding and sorting altogether took $\frac{1}{4}$ h. How long did it take her to do the laundry?

7. A spinach quiche and a shrimp quiche were made the same size. Monday $\frac{1}{2}$ of the spinach quiche and $\frac{3}{8}$ of the shrimp quiche were eaten. On Tuesday $\frac{1}{6}$ of the spinach quiche and $\frac{5}{8}$ of the shrimp quiche were eaten.

  a. How much more quiche was eaten on Monday than on Tuesday?

  b. How much more shrimp quiche than spinach quiche was eaten?

8. Copy and complete.

  a. $\frac{1}{3} + \frac{2}{5} = \frac{2}{5} + \square$ **b.** $\frac{3}{7} + \square = \frac{7}{8} + \frac{3}{7}$

9. a. State a rule that is illustrated in exercise 8.

  b. Does this rule work for subtraction? Give an example.

The sequence $\frac{1}{4}, \frac{1}{3}, \frac{1}{2}, \frac{2}{3}, \frac{3}{4}$ is called the **Farey sequence** of order 4.

It lists in increasing order all the fractions less than 1 whose denominators are 4 or less.

1. How can $\frac{1}{3}$ be obtained from $\frac{1}{4}$ and $\frac{1}{2}$?

2. Does this method work for any three consecutive fractions in the sequence?

3. a. Find the missing fractions in this Farey sequence.

  $\frac{1}{5}, \square, \frac{1}{3}, \square, \square, \frac{3}{5}, \square, \frac{3}{4}, \frac{4}{5}$

  b. What is the order number?

Fractions and Mixed Numbers

A period in hockey is $\frac{1}{3}$ of a game.

Steve played $4\frac{1}{3}$ games without allowing a goal. How many periods was that?

$4\frac{1}{3}$ games means 4 games and $\frac{1}{3}$ of a game.

 $+$ $+$ $+$ $+ \frac{1}{3} = \dfrac{3 + 3 + 3 + 3 + 1}{3}$

$\qquad\qquad\qquad\qquad\quad = \dfrac{13}{3}$

Steve played 13 periods without allowing a goal.

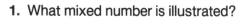

$\qquad\qquad 4\frac{1}{3} \ = \ \frac{13}{3}$

a **mixed number**   a fraction greater than 1

OR $\qquad 4\frac{1}{3} \ = \ \dfrac{4 \times 3 + 1}{3}$

$\qquad\qquad\quad = \dfrac{12 + 1}{3}$

$\qquad\qquad\quad = \dfrac{13}{3}$

Fractions greater than 1 can be expressed as mixed numbers.

Express $\frac{15}{4}$ as a mixed number.

$\frac{15}{4} = $ $+$ $+$ ... $+ \frac{3}{4}$

$\qquad = 3 + \frac{3}{4}$

$\qquad = 3\frac{3}{4}$

OR $\qquad \frac{15}{4}$ means $15 \div 4$.

$\qquad\qquad\quad$ 3 R3 $\quad$ 3 wholes,

$\qquad\quad 4\,\overline{)\,15} \qquad \frac{3}{4}$ remaining

$\qquad\quad \frac{15}{4} = 3\frac{3}{4}$

WORKING TOGETHER

1. What mixed number is illustrated?

a.

  ...

b.

2. Express the mixed numbers in exercise 1 as fractions.

3. Express as a fraction.

a. $3\frac{3}{5}$ b. $2\frac{7}{8}$ c. $1\frac{9}{10}$ d. $4\frac{6}{7}$

4. Express as a mixed number.

a. $\frac{19}{4}$ b. $\frac{17}{2}$ c. $\frac{22}{5}$ d. $\frac{27}{6}$

5. Which is greater?

a. $\frac{7}{5}, 1\frac{1}{5}$ b. $\frac{13}{4}, 3\frac{3}{4}$ c. $\frac{13}{5}, 2\frac{2}{5}$

1. Express as a mixed number.

   a. $\frac{11}{4}$ **b.** $\frac{27}{10}$ **c.** $\frac{38}{3}$ **d.** $\frac{25}{6}$

   e. $\frac{22}{5}$ **f.** $\frac{37}{8}$ **g.** $\frac{19}{2}$ **h.** $\frac{30}{11}$

2. Express as a fraction.

   a. $7\frac{1}{2}$ **b.** $8\frac{3}{4}$ **c.** $9\frac{2}{5}$ **d.** $6\frac{4}{7}$

   e. $2\frac{2}{9}$ **f.** $10\frac{7}{10}$ **g.** $9\frac{3}{11}$ **h.** $3\frac{7}{8}$

3. Express as a mixed number with the fraction in lowest terms.

   a. $\frac{14}{8}$ **b.** $\frac{24}{14}$ **c.** $\frac{60}{18}$ **d.** $\frac{50}{15}$

   e. $\frac{130}{25}$ **f.** $\frac{90}{25}$ **g.** $\frac{44}{6}$ **h.** $\frac{33}{9}$

4. Copy and use >, <, or = to make a true statement.

   a. $\frac{7}{5}$ ○ $1\frac{1}{4}$ **b.** $\frac{6}{4}$ ○ $\frac{12}{8}$ **c.** $3\frac{3}{8}$ ○ $3\frac{1}{2}$

   d. $2\frac{3}{4}$ ○ $\frac{22}{8}$ **e.** $4\frac{7}{10}$ ○ $4\frac{2}{3}$ **f.** $\frac{22}{7}$ ○ $3\frac{1}{5}$

5. Ms. Thomas fertilizes her lawn 3 times in a year. She uses 11 bags of fertilizer in all. How many bags does she use each time?

6. Kent played 35 periods of hockey before he was injured. How many games is that equivalent to?

7. A football quarterback played 17 quarters before throwing an interception. How many games is that equivalent to?

8. A 60 min cassette tape has 14 songs on it. What is the average length of each song?

9. Simone ran 1500 m at the track and field competition. How many times around the track did she run?

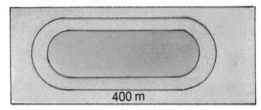

400 m

10. To complete one orbit around Earth, a satellite travels about 40 000 km. How many orbits does a satellite make for the distance travelled?

    a. 25 000 km   **b.** 100 000 km

    c. 180 000 km   **d.** 750 000 km

11. In $5\frac{3}{4}$ games of basketball, Jesse scored 92 points.

    a. How many quarters is that equivalent to?

    b. What is the average number of points scored per quarter?

Try This

1. Find the sum. Express it as a mixed number.

   a. $1 + \frac{1}{2} + \frac{1}{4} + \frac{1}{8}$ **b.** $1 + \frac{1}{10} + \frac{1}{100} + \frac{1}{1000}$

2. Extend the patterns in exercise 1 by adding more fractions. Predict what happens to each sum.

1. Find the GCF of the group.

   a. 10, 5, 15   **b.** 16, 24, 40

   c. 24, 60, 84   **d.** 27, 63, 81

2. Find the LCM of the pair.

   a. 5, 6   **b.** 8, 10   **c.** 6, 8

   d. 14, 12   **e.** 9, 15   **f.** 9, 13

3. Alberta bought a number of buttons for 84¢. Carrie bought some of the same buttons for $1.40. What is the most each button could have cost?

4. The doctor instructs a nurse to take a patient's temperature every 4 h, to measure his blood pressure every 6 h, and to change his dressing every 10 h. At what time intervals will all three duties be carried out at the same time?

5. What fraction of the figure is shaded? Express the fraction in lowest terms.

   a. 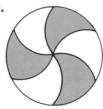   **b.**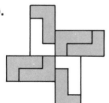

6. Copy and complete.

   a. $\frac{3}{4} = \frac{\square}{8}$ **b.** $\frac{10}{15} = \frac{2}{\square}$ **c.** $\frac{20}{10} = \frac{\square}{5}$

7. Express in lowest terms.

   a. $\frac{6}{10}$ **b.** $\frac{18}{9}$ **c.** $\frac{12}{36}$ **d.** $\frac{25}{15}$

8. List three equivalent fractions.

   a. $\frac{1}{4}$ **b.** $\frac{6}{10}$ **c.** $\frac{8}{4}$ **d.** $\frac{5}{3}$

9. Copy and use >, <, or = to make a true statement.

   a. $\frac{3}{4} \bigcirc \frac{1}{4}$ **b.** $\frac{5}{8} \bigcirc \frac{1}{2}$ **c.** $\frac{6}{6} \bigcirc \frac{4}{4}$

   d. $6\frac{1}{3} \bigcirc 5\frac{1}{2}$ **e.** $\frac{14}{3} \bigcirc 4\frac{5}{8}$ **f.** $2\frac{2}{3} \bigcirc \frac{24}{9}$

10. Francesca got 17 out of 20 on her History test, 19 out of 25 on her Math test, and 7 out of 10 on her English essay. In which subject did she receive her highest mark?

11. Find the result.

   a. $\frac{1}{8} + \frac{3}{8}$ **b.** $\frac{7}{16} - \frac{5}{16}$ **c.** $\frac{2}{3} + \frac{1}{2}$

   d. $\frac{3}{4} - \frac{2}{5}$ **e.** $\frac{5}{8} + \frac{1}{3}$ **f.** $\frac{5}{6} - \frac{3}{10}$

   g. $\frac{1}{2} + \frac{3}{4} + \frac{5}{8}$ **h.** $\frac{7}{10} + \frac{1}{2} + \frac{2}{5}$

12. The Pacific Ocean, the Atlantic Ocean, and the Indian Ocean cover about $\frac{7}{10}$ of the surface of Earth. The Pacific Ocean covers about $\frac{1}{3}$. The Atlantic Ocean covers about $\frac{1}{5}$.

   a. What fraction do the Pacific Ocean and Atlantic Ocean cover together?

   b. What fraction does the Indian Ocean cover?

13. Express as a fraction.

   a. $1\frac{2}{3}$ **b.** $3\frac{1}{2}$ **c.** $6\frac{3}{4}$ **d.** $4\frac{5}{6}$

14. Express as a mixed number with the fraction in lowest terms.

   a. $\frac{12}{5}$ **b.** $\frac{26}{8}$ **c.** $\frac{32}{10}$ **d.** $\frac{28}{6}$

Fraction Skills

Fractions and mixed numbers can be expressed as decimals with the use of a calculator.

For $\frac{29}{8}$, press $\boxed{29}\boxed{÷}\boxed{8}\boxed{=}$.

$\boxed{3.625}$

For $3\frac{5}{8}$, press $\boxed{5}\boxed{÷}\boxed{8}\boxed{+}\boxed{3}\boxed{=}$.

$\boxed{3.625}$

$\frac{29}{8}$ or $3\frac{5}{8} = 3.625$

For $\frac{10}{11}$, press $\boxed{10}\boxed{÷}\boxed{11}\boxed{=}$.

$\boxed{0.9090909}$

This can be written with a bar to show the digits that repeat.

$\frac{10}{11} = 0.\overline{90}$

1. Express as a decimal.

   a. $\frac{7}{8}$ **b.** $\frac{13}{16}$ **c.** $6\frac{1}{16}$ **d.** $4\frac{19}{20}$

2. Express as a decimal using bar notation.

   a. $\frac{5}{6}$ **b.** $\frac{7}{11}$ **c.** $4\frac{1}{9}$ **d.** $4\frac{19}{27}$

Fractions can be added or subtracted by expressing each fraction as a decimal.

Then add or subtract. For example, $\frac{3}{5} + \frac{1}{4} = 0.6 + 0.25$.

These operations can be performed directly by using a calculator with memory.

Add. $\frac{3}{5} + \frac{1}{4}$

Press $\boxed{3}\boxed{÷}\boxed{5}\boxed{M+}\boxed{1}\boxed{÷}\boxed{4}\boxed{M+}\boxed{MR}$.

$\boxed{0.85}$

Subtract. $\frac{3}{5} - \frac{1}{4}$

Press $\boxed{3}\boxed{÷}\boxed{5}\boxed{M+}\boxed{1}\boxed{÷}\boxed{4}\boxed{M-}\boxed{MR}$.

$\boxed{0.35}$

3. Use a calculator to find the result. Check by using paper and pencil.

   a. $\frac{3}{4} + \frac{2}{5}$ **b.** $\frac{3}{10} + \frac{5}{8}$ **c.** $\frac{3}{4} + \frac{3}{8} + \frac{1}{2}$ **d.** $\frac{2}{3} + \frac{4}{9}$

   e. $\frac{5}{8} - \frac{1}{4}$ **f.** $\frac{7}{10} - \frac{3}{8}$ **g.** $\frac{9}{10} - \frac{2}{5} - \frac{1}{8}$ **h.** $\frac{5}{6} - \frac{2}{9} + \frac{1}{3}$

A calculator can be used to multiply and divide fractions directly.

Multiply. $\frac{3}{8} \times \frac{5}{6}$

Press $\boxed{3}\boxed{÷}\boxed{8}\boxed{×}\boxed{5}\boxed{÷}\boxed{6}\boxed{=}$.

$\boxed{0.3125}$

Divide. $\frac{3}{8} ÷ \frac{5}{6}$

Press $\boxed{5}\boxed{÷}\boxed{6}\boxed{M+}\boxed{3}\boxed{÷}\boxed{8}\boxed{÷}\boxed{MR}\boxed{=}$.

$\boxed{0.45}$

4. Use a calculator to find the result. Check by using pencil and paper.

   a. $\frac{7}{8} \times \frac{2}{5}$ **b.** $\frac{9}{10} \times \frac{5}{9}$ **c.** $\frac{7}{10} \times \frac{11}{14}$ **d.** $\frac{2}{3} \times \frac{3}{8} \times \frac{10}{9}$

   e. $\frac{3}{5} ÷ \frac{4}{9}$ **f.** $\frac{7}{10} ÷ \frac{4}{5}$ **g.** $\frac{2}{3} ÷ \frac{12}{11}$ **h.** $\frac{5}{6} ÷ \frac{10}{3} \times \frac{4}{11}$

Adding and Subtracting Mixed Numbers

Rosa used $4\frac{1}{2}$ loaves of bread and Yves used $2\frac{3}{4}$ loaves for sandwiches.
How many loaves did they use in all?

Add. $4\frac{1}{2} + 2\frac{3}{4}$

$= 4\frac{2}{4} + 2\frac{3}{4}$

$= 6 + \frac{5}{4}$

$= 6 + 1\frac{1}{4}$

$= 7\frac{1}{4}$

Rosa and Yves used $7\frac{1}{4}$ loaves of bread.   How many more loaves did Rosa use than Yves?

Subtract. $4\frac{1}{2} - 2\frac{3}{4}$

$= 4\frac{2}{4} - 2\frac{3}{4}$

$4\frac{2}{4} = (3 + \frac{4}{4}) + \frac{2}{4}$

$= 3 + (\frac{4}{4} + \frac{2}{4})$

$= 3\frac{6}{4}$

$= 3\frac{6}{4} - 2\frac{3}{4}$

$= 1\frac{3}{4}$

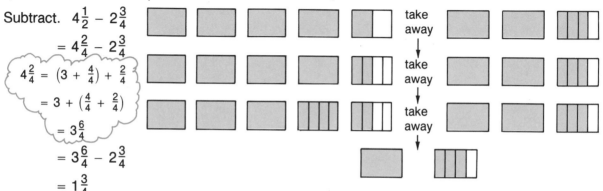

Rosa used $1\frac{3}{4}$ more loaves than Yves.

WORKING TOGETHER

1. Express as a mixed number with the fraction less than one.

   a. $5\frac{4}{3}$ **b.** $7\frac{5}{4}$ **c.** $6\frac{7}{5}$ **d.** $8\frac{9}{5}$

2. Copy and complete.

   a. $5\frac{1}{7} = 4\frac{\square}{7}$ **b.** $6\frac{2}{3} = 5\frac{\square}{3}$

   c. $3\frac{7}{8} = 2\frac{\square}{8}$ **d.** $4\frac{1}{2} = 3\frac{\square}{2}$

3. Add.

   b. $1\frac{3}{5} = 1\frac{\square}{10}$
   $+ 4\frac{3}{10} = + 4\frac{3}{10}$

   a. $1\frac{1}{6} + 2\frac{1}{6}$

   c. $3\frac{3}{4} = 3\frac{\square}{12}$
   $+ 2\frac{2}{3} = 2\frac{\square}{12}$

4. Subtract.

   b. $2 = 1\frac{\square}{5}$
   $- 1\frac{4}{5} = - 1\frac{4}{5}$

   a. $2\frac{3}{4} - \frac{1}{4}$

   c. $3\frac{1}{2} = 3\frac{\square}{10} = 2\frac{\square}{10}$
   $- 1\frac{9}{10} = - 1\frac{9}{10} = - 1\frac{9}{10}$

1. Add.

   a. $2\frac{3}{10} + 1$ b. $1\frac{3}{5} + \frac{4}{5}$ c. $2\frac{2}{3} + 1\frac{1}{6}$

   d. $6\frac{3}{4} + 2\frac{1}{2}$ e. $8\frac{2}{5} + 2\frac{3}{10}$ f. $1\frac{7}{12} + 2\frac{3}{5}$

   g. $5\frac{2}{5} + 1\frac{3}{5}$ h. $3\frac{4}{5} + 4\frac{3}{4}$ i. $2\frac{2}{3} + 1\frac{7}{10}$

2. Subtract.

   a. $3\frac{1}{4} - 1\frac{1}{4}$ b. $7\frac{3}{7} - 2\frac{1}{7}$ c. $3\frac{11}{12} - 2\frac{3}{4}$

   d. $9\frac{3}{4} - 2\frac{1}{3}$ e. $6\frac{1}{2} - 3\frac{3}{5}$ f. $2\frac{1}{4} - \frac{1}{2}$

   g. $4\frac{1}{4} - 2\frac{2}{3}$ h. $5\frac{3}{10} - 1\frac{2}{3}$ i. $6\frac{2}{5} - 3\frac{3}{4}$

3. Anton read $8\frac{1}{2}$ pages before supper. He read $10\frac{3}{4}$ pages after supper. How many pages did he read altogether?

4. From the results of a survey, the average television viewing time per week for teenagers was recorded.

Mon.-Fri. 16:30 h–19:30 h		Sat. 08:00 h–13:00 h	
Girls	Boys	Girls	Boys
$4\frac{1}{10}$ h	$4\frac{2}{3}$ h	$1\frac{1}{5}$ h	$1\frac{3}{10}$ h

   a. On the average, how many hours of television does a boy watch in all?

   b. On the average, how many hours of television does a girl watch in all?

   c. Find the difference in the viewing times.

5. Sandy swam $5\frac{1}{2}$ lengths of the pool in the same time as Elisha swam $3\frac{3}{4}$ lengths. How many more lengths did Sandy swim?

6. Find the sum.

   a. $1\frac{3}{4} + \frac{1}{4} + 2\frac{1}{2}$ b. $1\frac{9}{10} + 3\frac{1}{2} + 2\frac{3}{5}$

   c. $2\frac{5}{12} + 1\frac{2}{3} + 4\frac{1}{2}$ d. $3\frac{3}{4} + \frac{1}{3} + 2\frac{1}{2}$

7. Three students work part-time at a gas station. Their hours are recorded on a time sheet.

Student	Mon.	Tues.	Wed.	Thurs.	Fri.	Sat.
Alan	×	×	×	$3\frac{1}{2}$	$4\frac{3}{4}$	$7\frac{1}{4}$
Joel	$1\frac{1}{2}$	2	×	×	$3\frac{1}{4}$	×
Maya	×	×	$3\frac{3}{4}$	$2\frac{1}{2}$	×	$7\frac{1}{2}$

   a. Find the number of hours each student worked during the week.

   b. How many more hours did Alan work than Joel?

8. Richard drove his race car $47\frac{3}{4}$ laps before a tire blew. Mario's car developed engine trouble after $52\frac{1}{2}$ laps. How many more laps did Mario drive than Richard?

9. The race in exercise 8 is 76 laps long. How many more laps must each driver complete to finish the race?

Try This

The mixed numbers $1\frac{5}{6}$, $90\frac{4}{8}$, and $7\frac{2}{3}$ use each of the digits 0 to 9 once and have a sum of 100. Find other sets of mixed numbers like this.

Multiplying

Mr. Dowswell's farm covers 24 ha. $\frac{3}{4}$ of it is used for growing crops.

How many hectares are used for crops?

 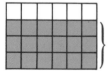

1 ha $\left.\begin{array}{c}\end{array}\right\}$ $\frac{3}{4}$ of 24

The diagram shows that $\frac{3}{4}$ of 24 is 18.

$\frac{3}{4}$ of 24 means $\frac{3}{4} \times \frac{24}{1} = \frac{3 \times 24}{4 \times 1}$

$= \frac{72}{4}$

$= 18$

Mr. Dowswell uses 18 ha for crops.

He ploughs $\frac{2}{3}$ of a field. He plants $\frac{3}{4}$ of the ploughed field in barley.
What fraction of the entire field is planted in barley?

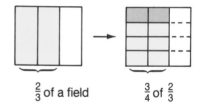

$\frac{2}{3}$ of a field $\frac{3}{4}$ of $\frac{2}{3}$

The diagram shows that $\frac{3}{4}$ of $\frac{2}{3}$ is $\frac{6}{12}$ or $\frac{1}{2}$.

$\frac{3}{4}$ of $\frac{2}{3} = \frac{3}{4} \times \frac{2}{3}$ OR $\frac{3 \times 2}{4 \times 3}$

$= \frac{6}{12}$ $= \frac{\boxed{3} \times \boxed{2}}{\boxed{3} \times \boxed{2} \times 2}$

$= \frac{1}{2}$ $= \frac{1}{2}$

$\frac{1}{2}$ of the entire field is planted in barley.

To multiply mixed numbers, first express them as fractions. Then multiply the numerators and multiply the denominators.

$3\frac{2}{3} \times 1\frac{1}{2} = \frac{11}{3} \times \frac{3}{2}$ OR $\frac{11 \times 3}{3 \times 2} = \frac{11 \times \boxed{3}}{2 \times \boxed{3}}$

$= \frac{33}{6}$ $= \frac{11}{2}$

$= 5\frac{3}{6}$ or $5\frac{1}{2}$

$= 5\frac{1}{2}$

WORKING TOGETHER

1. Find the product.

a. $\frac{1}{5} \times 20$ b. $\frac{3}{4} \times \frac{1}{2}$ c. $\frac{5}{8} \times \frac{2}{3}$

2. Express as fractions. Then multiply.

a. $1\frac{1}{2} \times 2\frac{1}{3}$ b. $3\frac{3}{4} \times 2\frac{1}{5}$ c. $1\frac{2}{5} \times 3\frac{1}{3}$

148

1. Multiply.

  a. $4 \times \frac{1}{2}$ **b.** $\frac{2}{3} \times 6$ **c.** $3 \times \frac{1}{5}$

  d. $\frac{3}{10} \times 25$ **e.** $12 \times \frac{3}{4}$ **f.** $\frac{5}{8} \times 2$

2. Find the product.

  a. $\frac{1}{4} \times \frac{2}{5}$ **b.** $\frac{1}{3} \times \frac{1}{3}$ **c.** $\frac{1}{5} \times \frac{2}{3}$

  d. $\frac{3}{4} \times \frac{3}{4}$ **e.** $\frac{5}{8} \times \frac{4}{5}$ **f.** $\frac{3}{4} \times \frac{8}{15}$

  g. $\frac{1}{3}$ of $\frac{3}{5}$ **h.** $\frac{7}{12} \times \frac{4}{5}$ **i.** $\frac{7}{10}$ of $\frac{2}{5}$

3. Find the amount.

  a. $\frac{1}{3}$ of $420 **b.** $\frac{2}{3}$ of $144 **c.** $\frac{3}{4}$ of $352

4. Marie is buying a record player for $123. She paid $\frac{1}{3}$ in cash and is paying the balance in 4 equal monthly payments.

  a. How much did she pay in cash?

  b. How much is each monthly payment?

5. The regular price of a sweater is $35.

  a. What is the amount of the saving?

  b. What is the sale price?

SWEATER
¼ OFF

6. Multiply.

  a. $8 \times 2\frac{1}{4}$ **b.** $1\frac{2}{3} \times 2\frac{2}{5}$ **c.** $\frac{3}{4} \times 1\frac{7}{10}$

  d. $10 \times 3\frac{1}{5}$ **e.** $\frac{3}{4}$ of $7\frac{1}{2}$ **f.** $3\frac{1}{3} \times 2\frac{1}{10}$

7. A house valued at $116 000 is mortgaged at $\frac{3}{4}$ of its value. What is the amount of the mortgage?

8.

Film Processing $\frac{1}{3}$ off			
135-12	reg. $5.98	135-36	reg. $17.99
135-24	reg. $11.98	Disc	reg. $8.75

  a. Estimate the savings on each processing.

  b. Estimate the sale prices.

9. At a library 128 people signed out books in one day. Of the people $\frac{1}{8}$ were children and $\frac{1}{2}$ were women. How many men signed out books?

10. René has an annual income of $24 600. He budgets $\frac{1}{3}$ of his income for shelter, $\frac{1}{4}$ for food, $\frac{1}{5}$ for clothing, $\frac{1}{10}$ for savings, and the remainder for miscellaneous expenses. How much does he budget for each item annually?

Try This

A woman with 4 sons owned 29 horses. When she died, she asked that $\frac{1}{2}$ of the horses be given to the eldest son, $\frac{1}{5}$ to the next, $\frac{1}{6}$ to the next, and $\frac{1}{10}$ to the youngest. How to do this puzzled the sons until the woman's lawyer rode out to the ranch. After successfully following the woman's instructions, he rode away. How many horses did each son get? How was the lawyer able to do this?

Dividing

Peg cuts 6 sheets of Bristol board into quarters. How many pieces does she have?

$$6 \div \frac{1}{4} = 24$$

Peg has 24 pieces.

Simon cuts 8 sheets of Bristol board into quarters. How many pieces does he have?

$$8 \div \frac{1}{4} = 32$$

Simon has 32 pieces.

They noticed that dividing by $\frac{1}{4}$ is the same as multiplying by 4.

4 is the **reciprocal** of $\frac{1}{4}$. →

To divide by a fraction, multiply by its reciprocal.

To divide mixed numbers, first express them as fractions.

> Two numbers whose product is 1 are **reciprocals** of each other.
>
> $$4 \times \frac{1}{4} = \frac{4 \times 1}{1 \times 4} \qquad \frac{8}{9} \times \frac{9}{8} = \frac{8 \times 9}{9 \times 8}$$
> $$= \frac{4}{4} \qquad\qquad\qquad = \frac{8 \times 9}{8 \times 9}$$
> $$= 1 \qquad\qquad\qquad = 1$$

$$\frac{3}{5} \div \frac{9}{8} = \frac{3}{5} \times \frac{8}{9}$$

$$= \frac{3 \times 8}{5 \times 9} \quad \text{OR} \quad \frac{3 \times 8}{5 \times 3 \times 3}$$

$$= \frac{24}{45} \qquad\qquad = \frac{3 \times 8}{3 \times 5 \times 3}$$

$$= \frac{8}{15} \qquad\qquad = \frac{8}{15}$$

$$3\frac{1}{2} \div 1\frac{2}{3} = \frac{7}{2} \div \frac{5}{3}$$

$$= \frac{7}{2} \times \frac{3}{5}$$

$$= \frac{21}{10}$$

$$\text{or } 2\frac{1}{10}$$

WORKING TOGETHER

1. What is the reciprocal?

   a. $\frac{5}{8}$ b. $\frac{1}{3}$ c. 7   d. $4\frac{1}{2}$

2. Which expression is used to find $\frac{1}{3} \div \frac{1}{4}$?

   a. $\frac{1}{3} \times \frac{1}{4}$ b. $\frac{1}{3} \times \frac{4}{1}$ c. $\frac{3}{1} \times \frac{1}{4}$

3. Copy and complete. Then divide.

   a. $1\frac{2}{3} \div 2\frac{1}{5} = \frac{\square}{3} \div \frac{\triangle}{\bigcirc}$

   b. $1\frac{1}{9} \div 1\frac{1}{7} = \frac{\square}{9} \div \frac{\triangle}{\bigcirc}$

   c. $1\frac{2}{5} \div 1\frac{1}{6} = \frac{\square}{5} \div \frac{\triangle}{\bigcirc}$

APPLICATIONS AND EXERCISES

1. Peg cut 10 sheets of Bristol board into eighths. How many pieces does she have?

2. Repeat exercise 1 for this number of sheets of Bristol board.

   a. 5   **b.** 9   **c.** 11   **d.** 16

3. Is the quotient smaller than 5?

   a. $5 \div \frac{5}{4}$ **b.** $5 \div \frac{3}{8}$ **c.** $5 \div \frac{2}{3}$

   d. $5 \div \frac{8}{3}$ **e.** $5 \div \frac{7}{2}$ **f.** $5 \div \frac{9}{10}$

4. Divide.

   a. $\frac{3}{4} \div \frac{3}{8}$ **b.** $\frac{1}{2} \div \frac{3}{5}$ **c.** $\frac{3}{16} \div \frac{5}{12}$

   d. $\frac{2}{3} \div \frac{2}{3}$ **e.** $2 \div \frac{4}{5}$ **f.** $\frac{2}{3} \div 4$

   g. $\frac{5}{12} \div \frac{1}{3}$ **h.** $1 \div \frac{3}{10}$ **i.** $\frac{1}{4} \div \frac{7}{8}$

5. Choose the best estimate.

5	15	25	30	45	50

   a. $9 \div \frac{5}{7}$ **b.** $17 \div \frac{2}{3}$ **c.** $8 \div \frac{9}{5}$

   d. $39 \div \frac{4}{5}$ **e.** $27 \div \frac{7}{8}$ **f.** $58 \div \frac{5}{4}$

6. Find the quotient.

   a. $1\frac{1}{8} \div \frac{3}{4}$ **b.** $1\frac{1}{2} \div \frac{9}{16}$ **c.** $3\frac{2}{3} \div \frac{5}{2}$

   d. $2\frac{1}{4} \div \frac{7}{8}$ **e.** $2\frac{3}{4} \div \frac{11}{12}$ **f.** $5\frac{2}{5} \div \frac{3}{2}$

   g. $9\frac{1}{3} \div 2\frac{1}{3}$ **h.** $1\frac{2}{3} \div 1\frac{2}{5}$ **i.** $1\frac{1}{5} \div 1\frac{1}{2}$

7. Marcel takes $4\frac{1}{2}$ min to run once around the track. How many laps can he run in 30 min?

8. Bill works in a machine factory. It takes him $\frac{3}{4}$ h to assemble one machine.

   a. How many machines can he assemble in a $7\frac{1}{2}$ h shift?

   b. How many machines can Bill assemble in a $37\frac{1}{2}$ h workweek?

9. On a test José has 15 questions to answer in $\frac{3}{4}$ h.

   a. If the questions are of equal difficulty, what fraction of an hour should he spend on each question?

   b. How many minutes should he spend on each question?

10. The approximate diameter of a circular target can be calculated using this formula.

    $$\text{diameter} = \frac{\text{circumference}}{\frac{22}{7}}$$

    Find the approximate diameter of a target with this circumference.

    a. 330 mm   **b.** 440 mm   **c.** 1.32 m

11. What is the least fraction that $\frac{6}{7}$, $\frac{5}{14}$, and $\frac{10}{21}$ will divide into exactly?

KEEPING SHARP

1. Divide only if the quotient is less than 30. Round to 1 decimal place.

   a. $83.8 \div 12.2$ **b.** $8.4 \div 3.9$ **c.** $124 \div 0.94$ **d.** $268 \div 30.3$ **e.** $0.285 \div 0.01$

   f. $0.79 \div 0.18$ **g.** $32.1 \div 0.158$ **h.** $958 \div 10.05$ **i.** $9.7 \div 0.248$ **j.** $99.8 \div 5.03$

Fractions and Decimals

In one season George Bell hit safely 177 times out of the 600 times he was at bat. What was his batting average?

His batting average was $\frac{177}{600}$.

Batting averages are expressed as quotients. $\frac{177}{600}$ means $177 \div 600$.

 $\boxed{177}\boxed{\div}\boxed{600}\boxed{=}$ $\quad$ (0.295)

$\frac{177}{600} = 0.295$

George's batting average was 0.295.

In one game he hit safely 5 out of 6 times at bat.

 For $\frac{5}{6}$, $\boxed{5}\boxed{\div}\boxed{6}\boxed{=}$ (0.8333333)

$\frac{5}{6} = 0.8\overline{3}$ $\quad$ The bar shows digits that repeat without end.

George's batting average for that game was 0.833 (rounded to the nearest thousandth).

0.295 is a **terminating decimal**. $\quad$ $0.8\overline{3}$ is a **repeating decimal**.

Any fraction or mixed number can be expressed as either a terminating decimal or a repeating decimal. Any terminating decimal or repeating decimal can be expressed as a fraction.

Here are terminating decimals expressed as fractions or mixed numbers.

$0.8 = \frac{8}{10}$ $\qquad$ $0.125 = \frac{125}{1000}$ $\qquad$ $2.75 = 2\frac{75}{100}$ $\qquad$ $1.06 = 1\frac{6}{100}$

$\quad\; = \frac{4}{5}$ $\qquad\qquad\quad\; = \frac{1}{8}$ $\qquad\qquad\quad\; = 2\frac{3}{4}$ $\qquad\qquad\quad\; = 1\frac{3}{50}$

WORKING TOGETHER

1. Express as a decimal.

 a. $1\frac{3}{5}$ $\quad$ **b.** $\frac{1}{3}$ $\quad$ **c.** $\frac{1}{9}$ $\quad$ **d.** $\frac{1}{11}$

2. Which decimals in exercise 1 are repeating decimals?

3. Express using bar notation.

$\quad$ **a.** 0.666... $\quad$ **b.** 0.545 454...

4. Express as a fraction or a mixed number in lowest terms.

$\quad$ **a.** 0.5 $\quad$ **b.** 0.72 $\quad$ **c.** 1.15 $\quad$ **d.** 3.7

APPLICATIONS AND EXERCISES

1. Express as a fraction or a mixed number in lowest terms.

   a. 0.4   **b.** 0.25   **c.** 0.36   **d.** 4.3

   e. 3.125   **f.** 0.43   **g.** 2.99   **h.** 0.3125

2. Is the decimal terminating or repeating?

   a. 1.7   **b.** 5.76   **c.** $5.\overline{2}$ **d.** 0.81

   e. $1.\overline{906}$ **f.** 4.125   **g.** 9.0   **h.** $11.\overline{1}$

3. Express using bar notation.

   a. 0.444...   **b.** 0.727 272...

   c. 5.323 232...   **d.** 28.3111...

   e. 9.615 261 52...   **f.** 7.145 858...

4. Express as a decimal. Which of the decimals are terminating?

   a. $\frac{2}{5}$ **b.** $\frac{1}{2}$ **c.** $\frac{1}{6}$ **d.** $\frac{5}{9}$

   e. $\frac{3}{8}$ **f.** $2\frac{4}{5}$ **g.** $3\frac{1}{3}$ **h.** $\frac{8}{25}$

   i. $\frac{11}{1000}$ **j.** $1\frac{4}{11}$ **k.** $1\frac{9}{20}$ **l.** $1\frac{2}{9}$

5. a. Express $\frac{1}{12}, \frac{2}{12}, \frac{3}{12}, \frac{4}{12}, \frac{5}{12}, \frac{6}{12}$ as decimals.

   b. Which decimals are repeating?

   c. Based on part **a**, predict $\frac{7}{12}, \frac{8}{12}, \frac{9}{12}, \frac{10}{12}, \frac{11}{12}, \frac{12}{12}$ as decimals.

6. Express as a decimal to the nearest thousandth.

   a. $\frac{1}{8}$ **b.** $\frac{5}{16}$ **c.** $\frac{7}{9}$ **d.** $\frac{8}{21}$

7. a. Determine the batting average for each baseball player rounded to the nearest thousandth.

Player	Hits	At bats
Fernandez	22	82
Garcia	26	92
Iorg	18	78
Moseby	21	75

   b. List the players in order from highest to lowest batting average.

   c. How many more hits does Moseby need to have an average over 0.300?

8. The first eight digits of π are 3.141 592 6. Which fraction is closest to this value?

   a. $\frac{22}{7}$ **b.** $\frac{256}{81}$ **c.** $\frac{355}{113}$ **d.** $\frac{432}{137}$

9. a. Express as a decimal using bar notation. $\frac{1}{7}, \frac{2}{7}, \frac{3}{7}$

   b. Based on the results for part **a**, predict the decimals for $\frac{4}{7}, \frac{5}{7},$ and $\frac{6}{7}$.

To find $\frac{2}{5}$ of $0.79,    $\boxed{0.316}$

express the fraction as a decimal and multiply. $\frac{2}{5}$ of $0.79 = $0.32 (rounded to the nearest cent)

1. Find the amount, rounded to the nearest cent.

   a. $\frac{1}{8}$ of $6.85   **b.** $\frac{1}{3}$ of $50   **c.** $\frac{2}{3}$ of $19.49   **d.** $\frac{3}{4}$ of 82¢

Repeating Decimals as Fractions

Bev used a calculator to express fractions as decimals.
The charts below show her results.

Fraction	Decimal
$\frac{1}{9}$	$0.\overline{1}$
$\frac{2}{9}$	$0.\overline{2}$
$\frac{3}{9}$	$0.\overline{3}$
$\frac{4}{9}$	$0.\overline{4}$

Fraction	Decimal
$\frac{12}{99}$	$0.\overline{12}$
$\frac{13}{99}$	$0.\overline{13}$
$\frac{14}{99}$	$0.\overline{14}$
$\frac{15}{99}$	$0.\overline{15}$

For the denominator 9,
she sees this pattern.
- The tenths digit repeats.
- The numerator of the fraction
  is the same as the repeating digit.

For the denominator 99,
she sees this pattern.
- The tenths and hundredths digits repeat.
- The numerator of the fraction is the
  same as the repeating digits.

These patterns can be used to express repeating decimals as fractions or mixed numbers.

Express 0.777... as a fraction.

$$0.777\ldots = 0.\overline{7}$$
$$= \frac{7}{9} \quad \text{Check.}$$

$\boxed{7}\boxed{\div}\boxed{9}\boxed{=}$ (0.7777777)

Express 0.989 898... as a fraction.

$$0.989\,898\ldots = 0.\overline{98}$$
$$= \frac{98}{99} \quad \text{Check by using a calculator.}$$

Express 1.666... as a mixed number.

$$1.666\ldots = 1.\overline{6}$$
$$= 1 + 0.\overline{6}$$
$$= 1 + \frac{6}{9}$$
$$= 1 + \frac{2}{3}$$
$$= 1\frac{2}{3} \quad \text{Check.}$$

Express 2.171 171... as a mixed number.

$$2.171\,171\ldots = 2.\overline{171}$$
$$= 2 + 0.\overline{171}$$
$$= 2 + \frac{171}{999}$$
$$= 2 + \frac{19}{111}$$
$$= 2\frac{19}{111} \quad \text{Check.}$$

WORKING TOGETHER

1. Express as a fraction in lowest terms.
   a. 0.888...
   b. 0.555...
   c. 0.111...
   d. $0.\overline{54}$
   e. 0.636 363...

2. Express as a mixed number with the fraction in lowest terms.
   a. 2.333...
   b. 5.181 818...
   c. $4.\overline{69}$
   d. $6.\overline{153}$

APPLICATIONS AND EXERCISES

1. Express as a fraction in lowest terms.

   a. 0.444... **b.** 0.222... **c.** 0.333...

   d. 0.515 151... **e.** 0.727 272...

2. Express as a fraction in lowest terms.

   a. $0.\overline{27}$ **b.** $0.\overline{45}$ **c.** $0.\overline{57}$

   d. $0.\overline{09}$ **e.** $0.\overline{42}$ **f.** $0.\overline{81}$

   g. $0.\overline{38}$ **h.** $0.\overline{729}$ **i.** $0.\overline{523}$

3. Express as a mixed number with the fraction in lowest terms.

   a. $3.\overline{1}$ **b.** $32.\overline{5}$ **c.** $8.\overline{7}$

   d. $6.\overline{15}$ **e.** $1.\overline{75}$ **f.** $8.\overline{009}$

4. Express $0.\overline{9}$ as a fraction. What do you notice?

5. Copy and use >, <, or = to make a true statement.

   a. $0.\overline{6}$ ◯ 0.6 **b.** $\frac{4}{12}$ ◯ $0.\overline{3}$

   c. $\frac{11}{5}$ ◯ $2.\overline{2}$ **d.** $2.\overline{68}$ ◯ 2.688

6. Which number does not appear to belong?

   a. 0.8, $\frac{8}{10}$, 0.80, $0.\overline{8}$, $\frac{4}{5}$

   b. $3.\overline{3}$, $3\frac{1}{3}$, $\frac{13}{3}$, $\frac{10}{3}$, $3.333...$

   c. 3.09, $\frac{34}{11}$, $3.\overline{09}$, $3\frac{1}{11}$, $\frac{306}{99}$

7. Arrange from greatest to least.

   a. $\frac{1}{4}$, $0.\overline{2}$, 0.282, $\frac{3}{11}$ **b.** 1.55, $\frac{3}{2}$, $1.\overline{5}$, $1\frac{5}{100}$

8. **a.** Find $\frac{5}{11}$ of $22\ 000\ 000.

    b. Use a calculator to express $\frac{5}{11}$ as a decimal and then multiply by \$22 000 000.

   c. Compare the answer from part a with the answer from part **b.** Explain.

9. Calculate accurately.

   a. $0.\overline{6} \times \$3\ 000\ 000$ **b.** $0.\overline{7} \times \$2\ 700\ 000$

   c. $1.\overline{3} \times \$1\ 200\ 000$ **d.** $0.\overline{54} \times \$4\ 400\ 000$

The fractions in group A produce terminating decimals.
The fractions in group B produce repeating decimals.

Try This

Group A		Group B	
$\frac{3}{8}$	$\frac{7}{25}$	$\frac{7}{15}$	$\frac{1}{22}$
$\frac{9}{20}$	$\frac{3}{50}$	$\frac{5}{12}$	$\frac{13}{27}$

1. Verify the above statement.

2. **a.** Express each denominator as a product of prime factors.

   b. What do you notice about the prime factors in each group?

3. State a rule to determine if a fraction will produce a terminating decimal.

4. Use the rule to determine whether the decimal terminates.

   a. $\frac{13}{40}$ **b.** $\frac{11}{200}$ **c.** $\frac{11}{12}$ **d.** $\frac{5}{32}$ **e.** $\frac{7}{125}$ **f.** $\frac{7}{18}$

5. **a.** List three other fractions for group A, and three for group B.

   b. Find a decimal that is neither terminating nor repeating.

1. Find the result.

 a. $2\frac{1}{4} + 1\frac{1}{4}$ **b.** $6\frac{7}{8} - 2\frac{3}{8}$ **c.** $5\frac{2}{3} + 4\frac{1}{4}$

 d. $8\frac{9}{16} - 2$ **e.** $3\frac{7}{10} + 3\frac{3}{4}$ **f.** $9\frac{1}{5} - 6\frac{2}{3}$

 g. $1\frac{3}{4} + 2\frac{7}{12}$ **h.** $4\frac{9}{12} - 3\frac{1}{2}$ **i.** $\frac{3}{10} + 2\frac{1}{2}$

 j. $4\frac{5}{9} + 6\frac{1}{4} + 2\frac{1}{2}$ **k.** $2\frac{1}{3} + 5\frac{1}{2} + 3\frac{7}{10}$

2. Pam works $3\frac{5}{6}$ h before lunch and $4\frac{1}{4}$ h after lunch. How long does she work in all?

3. Colette spends $1\frac{3}{4}$ h each evening doing homework. Her older brother Guy spends $2\frac{1}{2}$ h each evening doing homework. How much longer does Guy spend on homework?

4. Multiply.

 a. $\frac{1}{2} \times \frac{1}{4}$ **b.** $\frac{2}{5} \times \frac{3}{4}$ **c.** $\frac{1}{3}$ of $\frac{5}{8}$

 d. $\frac{5}{6} \times \frac{9}{10}$ **e.** $6 \times \frac{5}{12}$ **f.** $\frac{7}{10}$ of 15

 g. $4\frac{1}{2} \times \frac{2}{3}$ **h.** $2\frac{1}{5} \times 10$ **i.** $3\frac{2}{5} \times 15$

 j. $5\frac{1}{3} \times 1\frac{1}{8}$ **k.** $6\frac{1}{4} \times 1\frac{1}{10}$ **l.** $5\frac{1}{5} \times 1\frac{1}{4}$

5. Find the amount.

 a. $\frac{2}{3}$ of \$12 **b.** $\frac{1}{5}$ of \$200

 c. $2\frac{1}{2} \times \$42$ **d.** $\frac{3}{8}$ of 96¢

 e. $1\frac{3}{4} \times \$80$ **f.** $\frac{7}{10}$ of \$1.20

 g. $\frac{1}{6}$ of \$32 000 **h.** $\frac{3}{4}$ of \$24 000

6. At the farm, eggs are packed in trays of $2\frac{1}{2}$ dozen. Six trays are packed in a box. How many dozen eggs are in a box?

7. What is the reciprocal?

 a. $\frac{5}{11}$ **b.** $\frac{7}{3}$ **c.** 16 **d.** $5\frac{2}{7}$

8. Divide.

 a. $4 \div \frac{1}{2}$ **b.** $6 \div \frac{3}{4}$ **c.** $\frac{8}{4} \div \frac{1}{2}$

 d. $\frac{9}{10} \div \frac{3}{5}$ **e.** $0 \div \frac{1}{3}$ **f.** $2 \div \frac{2}{3}$

 g. $2\frac{1}{2} \div 1\frac{1}{4}$ **h.** $6\frac{1}{4} \div 8\frac{1}{2}$ **i.** $4\frac{1}{5} \div 5$

 j. $1\frac{3}{6} \div 1\frac{1}{2}$ **k.** $7\frac{1}{2} \div 4\frac{1}{2}$ **l.** $1\frac{3}{4} \div 3$

9. A cashier takes about $3\frac{1}{2}$ min to serve a customer.

 a. How many customers can be served in 1 h?

 b. What assumption is made in part **a**?

10. Express as a decimal.

 a. $\frac{2}{5}$ **b.** $\frac{5}{8}$ **c.** $\frac{3}{11}$ **d.** $4\frac{5}{6}$

11. Which decimals in exercise 10 are repeating decimals?

12. Express as a mixed number or a fraction in lowest terms.

 a. 0.25 **b.** 2.45 **c.** 0.6

 d. $0.\overline{9}$ **e.** 1.333... **f.** $1.\overline{85}$

13. Calculate accurately.

 a. $0.\overline{6} \times 1\ 200\ 000$ **b.** $1.\overline{3} \times 30\ 000\ 000$

Rational and Irrational Numbers

Some decimals terminate. **3.65**

Some decimals follow repeating patterns. **7.6363...** or **7.$\overline{63}$**

Decimals that terminate or have repeating patterns can be expressed as fractions. They are called **rational numbers**.

$$3.65 = 3\frac{13}{20} \qquad\qquad 7.\overline{63} = 7\frac{7}{11}$$

Some decimals neither terminate nor follow repeating patterns.

   2.010 110 1...   1.414 213 5...

These decimals cannot be expressed as fractions. They are called **irrational numbers**.

Many square roots are irrational numbers.
Recall that $49 = 7 \times 7$. The principal square root of 49 is 7.
What is the principal square root of 5?
   $4 = 2 \times 2$
   $9 = 3 \times 3$
The principal square root of 5 is between 2 and 3.
By guessing and testing we can approximate $\sqrt{5}$.
But $\sqrt{5}$ is never an exact decimal. It is an irrational number.

In calculations irrational numbers may be left in symbolic form. Otherwise they are approximated.

1. Is the number rational or irrational? Explain.

   a. 0.9   **b.** 33.$\overline{3}$ **c.** 1.3636...   **d.** $\sqrt{2}$ **e.** $\frac{3}{4}$

   f. $\sqrt{16}$ **g.** $\frac{5}{9}$ **h.** 4.198 723...   **i.** $\sqrt{11}$ **j.** $\sqrt{81}$

The most famous irrational number is π.
   $\pi = 3.141\ 592\ 653\ 589\ 793\ 238\ 462...$
Beginning with Archimedes, mathematicians have tried to calculate π more precisely.
Computers now provide the value of π to 2^{23} or 8 388 608 places.

2. Calculate using $\pi \doteq 3.14$.

 a. Which drains faster, 2 drains each 5 cm in diameter or 1 drain 10 cm in diameter?

b. A steel pipe has an inside radius of 4 cm and an outside radius of 5 cm. Calculate the volume of steel in a 2.5 m length of pipe.

Number Systems

The very first use of numbers by our ancient ancestors involved collections of stones or sticks, which were used to represent things like the number of animals in a herd. In comparing two piles of stones, people used the concept of more or less. Gradually, instead of collecting physical objects or tying knots on a rope, they started using symbols.

The earliest type of computing machine was the abacus, developed in China about 5000 years ago.

Each bead above the bar represents 5 units.

Each bead below the bar represents 1 unit.

1. Draw the abacus to show the number.

    a. 603 984

    b. 1563 + 724

100 000 000's, 10 000 000's, 1 000 000's, 100 000's, 10 000's, 1000's, 100's, 10's, 1's

Each column of beads represents a place value. The number shown here is 179.

The basic idea behind the abacus, that of filling one place and overflowing to the next, was adapted by Blaise Pascal in 1642 in his "arithmetic machine." When one wheel made a complete rotation (representing ten numbers), the wheel to its left made $\frac{1}{10}$ of a turn.

Both the abacus and Pascal's "arithmetic machine" work as they do because our number system is based on powers of ten, with each place value being ten times greater than the one to its right.

* Using ten different symbols and one place, we can write 10 different numbers.
  0, 1, 2, 3, 4, 5, 6, 7, 8, 9
* If we use two places, we can write 100 different numbers. 10×10
  0, 1, 2, 3,..., 10, 11, 12, 13,..., 90, 91, 92,..., 98, 99
* If we use three places, we can write $10 \times 10 \times 10$ or 1000 different numbers.

2. How many different numbers are possible using four places?

Our present base 10 number system was invented by the Arabs about 1400 years ago. There is no reason, though, why a base of 12 or 16 or 20 could not have been adopted instead. (Perhaps 10 was chosen because we have ten digits on our hands.) Other cultures used different number systems. The ancient Mesopotamians used a base 60 number system!

Electronic computers were invented about 40 years ago, and a different number system was needed. The electronic switches in a computer can be ON or OFF; therefore only two symbols are needed. 1 is used to represent ON. 0 is used to represent OFF. Because two symbols are used, the number system is called **binary**.

- In the binary number system, using one place, we can write 2 different numbers.
  0, 1
- If we use two places, we can write 4 different numbers. 2×2
  0, 1, 10, 11 ◀ Read as one one.
- If we use three places, we can write $2 \times 2 \times 2$ or 8 different numbers.
  0, 1, 10, 11, 100, 101, 110, 111

3. How many different base 2 numbers are possible using four places?

 4. How many different base 2 numbers are possible using eight places?

5. Continue the pattern and write the numbers from 11 to 16 in the binary system.

Decimal system	0	1	2	3	4	5	6	7	8	9	10
Binary system	0	1	10	11	100	101	110	111	1000	1001	1010

6. Express the binary number as a decimal number.

  a. 11010   **b.** 1000111

$1024_{(base\ 10)} = 1 \times 10^3 + 0 \times 10^2 + 2 \times 10^1 + 4 \times 1$

$1011_{(base\ 2)} = 1 \times 2^3 + 0 \times 2^2 + 1 \times 2^1 + 1 \times 1$
$= 8 + 0 + 2 + 1$
$= 11_{(base\ 10)}$

7. Copy and complete.

2^7	2^6	2^5	2^4	2^3	2^2	2^1
			16	8	4	2

8. Express the decimal number 33 as a binary number.

$17_{(base\ 10)} = 16 + 1$
$= 2^4 + 1$
$= 1001_{(base\ 2)}$

In computer terms, each 0 or 1 is called a **bit** (or ⓑinary digⓘⓣ), and a set of 8 bits is called a **byte**. A **kilobyte** is 2^{10} bytes.
The size of a computer's memory is expressed in kilobytes (or K bytes). This refers to the maximum number of zeros and ones the memory can hold at one time.

 9. How many zeros and ones can a 64 K microcomputer hold at once?

Choose the Operations

Nadia's telephone bill had an operator-assisted long-distance telephone call from Aurora, Ontario, to Red Deer, Alberta, that cost $12.90. The call cost $4.10 for the first 3 min and $1.10 for each additional minute. How long was the telephone call?

Think. Restate the problem.
The call cost $12.90 altogether.
The first 3 min cost $4.10.
How much is the additional charge?
How many additional minutes is that at $1.10/min?

Plan and do. Decide which operations to use.

Total	$12.90
Charge for first 3 min	− 4.10
Additional charge	$ 8.80

Number of minutes at $1.10/min $8.80 ÷ $1.10 = 8

Look back. Nadia said that her call was 8 min long. Is her answer reasonable? Explain.

WORKING TOGETHER

Which operations would you use to solve the problem?

1. You share the cost of a gift equally with your classmates. How much should you pay?

2. Approximately how many textbooks do the students in your school use?

3. Which package of envelopes is the better buy?

Describe how you would solve the problem. Then solve it.

4. For fundraising, the Student Council sold peanuts for 45¢ a bag and almonds for 65¢ a bag. If one class sold 32 bags of almonds and 47 bags of peanuts, how much did they make altogether?

5. For fundraising, the Student Council sold peanuts for 45¢ a bag and almonds for 65¢ a bag. If one class sold 53 bags of peanuts and made $37.50 in all, how many bags of almonds did they sell?

PROBLEMS

Decide which operations you would use to solve the problem. Then solve it.

1. A station-to-station call from Toronto to Miami cost 96¢ for the first minute and 85¢ for each additional minute. How much would it have cost for a 15 min telephone call at these rates?

2. How much extra do you pay for the used car by using the time payment plan?

> $5795
> or
> BUY on TIME
> $900 down
> and
> $150 per month
> for 36 months

3. If Joanne worked only one-third as much, she would receive $36 per week. How much does she receive each week?

4. At West Hill Nursery School, one-fourth of the children are boys, and there are 44 boys in the school. How many children are there?

5. Lorne is the top scorer on the visiting basketball team. If he scored one-third of the points, how many points did the rest of his team score?

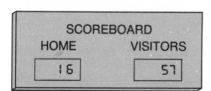

```
         SCOREBOARD
    HOME           VISITORS
    [ 16 ]          [ 57 ]
```

6. In an auditorium $\frac{1}{3}$ of the people present are men, $\frac{1}{4}$ are women, and the rest are children. If there are 1116 people in the auditorium, how many children are there?

7. There are 7 men and 5 women waiting for an elevator. The elevator can safely carry a maximum of 900 kg at one time.

   a. Can the group ride in the elevator safely if the mass of each man is about 85 kg and the mass of each woman is about 60 kg?

   b. What is the maximum number of adults that can ride in the elevator at one time?

8. Of the 72 vehicles in a parking lot, $\frac{2}{3}$ are cars. If $\frac{3}{4}$ of the cars are hardtops, how many cars in the lot are convertibles?

9. A crew of highway workers is painting a solid yellow line, 10 cm wide, along the centre of the road. One litre of the yellow paint covers 20 m². How much paint do the workers need to paint one solid line along 10 km of road?

10. If one can of paint covers about 10 m², how many cans of paint are needed to paint the garden shed?

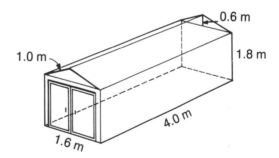

11. How long would it take to give away a million dollars if you gave away $100 every hour?

Problem Solving Review

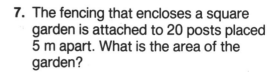

Describe how you would solve the problem.

1. Approximately how many books are in the school library?

2. What is the average daily temperature during the month of June?

Use the information in the amusement-park sign to solve the problems below.

Prices ($)	
Grounds admission only	7.95
Package I (grounds admission + 11 ride tickets—2 A, 3 B, 4 C, 2 D)	11.95
Package II (grounds admisson + 10 ride tickets—good on any ride)	12.95
Unlimited one-day pass	17.95
A ride tickets, each	0.50
B ride tickets, each	0.60
C ride tickets, each	0.70
D ride tickets, each	0.80

3. How much is saved by buying Package I instead of buying the grounds admission and 11 ride tickets separately?

4. What is the maximum amount of money that can be saved by buying Package II?

5. After buying an unlimited one-day pass, how many A rides would Luc have to go on to break even?

6. If you are planning to go on 1 A, 2 B, 1 C and 2 D rides, what is the cheapest method of buying the grounds admission and ride tickets?

Solve.

7. The fencing that encloses a square garden is attached to 20 posts placed 5 m apart. What is the area of the garden?

8. 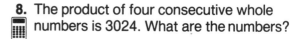 The product of four consecutive whole numbers is 3024. What are the numbers?

9. a. How can 24 metre sticks be arranged to make a rectangle so that the area is as large as possible?

   b. What rectangular arrangement of 34 metre sticks gives the largest possible area?

10. Two numbers are reciprocals of each other. One is four times as great as the other. What are the two numbers?

11. Andrew asked for change for a $10 bill. He requested an equal number of quarters and $1 bills. How many of each did he receive?

12. What is the greatest amount of money you can have in coins and not be able to give change for a dollar?

13. A vertical pole had $\frac{2}{5}$ of its length under water. When the tide rose by 6 m, only half as much of the pole was above water as previously. How tall is the pole?

14. An olive tree drops 1 olive on the first day, 2 on the second day, 4 on the third day, 8 on the fourth day, and so on. If it takes 40 d for the tree to drop all its olives, on which day has the tree dropped half of its olives?

Chapter Checkup

1. Find the GCF of the pair.

  a. $10, 25$ **b.** $12, 30$ **c.** $18, 45$

  d. $42, 70$ **e.** $36, 108$ **f.** $30, 75$

2. Find the LCM of the group.

  a. $2, 4, 5$ **b.** $5, 6, 4$ **c.** $10, 12, 15$

3. Copy and complete.

  a. $\frac{4}{5} = \frac{\square}{20}$ **b.** $\frac{3}{8} = \frac{\square}{24}$ **c.** $\frac{4}{8} = \frac{12}{\square}$

  d. $\frac{3}{4} = \frac{\square}{24}$ **e.** $\frac{40}{16} = \frac{\square}{8}$ **f.** $\frac{32}{20} = \frac{8}{\square}$

4. Express in lowest terms.

  a. 5¢ as a fraction of a dollar

  b. two months as a fraction of a year

  c. 7 h as a fraction of a day

  d. 9 eggs as a fraction of a dozen

5. Copy and use $>$, $<$, or $=$ to make a true statement.

  a. $\frac{3}{5} \bigcirc \frac{4}{5}$ **b.** $\frac{3}{8} \bigcirc \frac{1}{4}$ **c.** $\frac{3}{1} \bigcirc \frac{10}{3}$

  d. $1\frac{3}{4} \bigcirc \frac{11}{8}$ **e.** $2\frac{1}{2} \bigcirc 2\frac{3}{5}$ **f.** $4\frac{2}{3} \bigcirc \frac{14}{3}$

6. A gardener germinated some seeds indoors. Of 40 pea seeds 28 germinated; 36 out of 50 bean seeds germinated; and 75 of 100 tomato seeds germinated. Of which type of seed did the least fraction germinate?

7. Find the result.

  a. $\frac{3}{10} + \frac{1}{10}$ **b.** $\frac{7}{5} - \frac{3}{5}$ **c.** $\frac{7}{8} - \frac{1}{2}$

  d. $\frac{1}{3} + \frac{5}{12}$ **e.** $1\frac{5}{6} + \frac{7}{10}$ **f.** $5\frac{7}{10} - \frac{1}{5}$

  g. $4\frac{1}{2} - 3\frac{2}{3}$ **h.** $2\frac{1}{3} + 1\frac{7}{8}$ **i.** $6 - 4\frac{3}{8}$

8. Express as a fraction.

  a. $2\frac{1}{6}$ **b.** $3\frac{2}{3}$ **c.** $7\frac{3}{5}$ **d.** $6\frac{5}{8}$

9. Find the result.

  a. $\frac{1}{4} \times \frac{1}{2}$ **b.** $4 \div \frac{1}{2}$ **c.** $\frac{3}{4} \div \frac{9}{5}$

  d. $\frac{2}{3} \times \frac{9}{8}$ **e.** $\frac{1}{4}$ of 28   **f.** $1\frac{2}{3} \times \frac{2}{5}$

  g. $2\frac{1}{2} \div \frac{3}{4}$ **h.** $5\frac{1}{2} \times 5\frac{1}{2}$ **i.** $6\frac{2}{3} \div 2\frac{1}{2}$

10. Mr. Chu wanted to complete a job in $1\frac{1}{2}$ h. He worked for $\frac{5}{6}$ h before lunch and $\frac{3}{4}$ h after lunch.

  a. How long did he work in all?

  b. Did he meet his deadline?

  c. How much above or below $1\frac{1}{2}$ h was he?

11. Find the amount.

  a. $\frac{1}{5}$ of $1.25   **b.** $\frac{7}{8}$ of $24   **c.** $\frac{1}{3}$ of 84¢

12. Luke takes $2\frac{1}{4}$ min to run once around the track. How many laps can he run in 20 min?

13. Express as a decimal.

  a. $\frac{3}{4}$ **b.** $2\frac{3}{11}$ **c.** $4\frac{11}{20}$ **d.** $1\frac{7}{8}$

14. Which decimals in exercise 13 are terminating decimals?

15. Express as a mixed number or a fraction in lowest terms.

  a. 0.48   **b.** 1.032   **c.** $0.\overline{45}$ **d.** $4.\overline{126}$

Cumulative Checkup

1. Divide only if the quotient > 300.

    a. $36 \overline{)8260}$ **b.** $29 \overline{)7308}$ **c.** $28 \overline{)10\,304}$

    d. $\frac{250\,263}{621}$ **e.** $\frac{68\,445}{195}$ **f.** $\frac{22\,176}{112}$

2. At a factory, wire 2473 m long was cut into 8 m lengths. Was there any waste?

3. Express as the product of prime factors.

    a. 8   **b.** 12   **c.** 20   **d.** 28

    e. 39   **f.** 42   **g.** 54   **h.** 84

4. Express as a single power.

    a. $\frac{3^7}{3^6}$ **b.** $\frac{5^8}{5^3}$ **c.** $10^6 \times 10^3$

    d. $3^6 \times 3$ **e.** $7^9 \times 7^4$ **f.** $11^{10} \div 11^2$

5. Look for a shortcut. Evaluate.

    a. $4 \times 33 \times 25$ **b.** $32 \times 50 \times 2$

    c. 101×83 **d.** 102×49

    e. 99×43 **f.** 51×25

6. Arrange from least to greatest.

    a. 2.34, 2.43, 4.32, 3.24

    b. 0.999, 0.9, 0.99, 0.09

    c. 8.2, 2.8, 9.1, 1.9

    d. 100.1, 10.01, 10.1, 1.101

7. How much is saved by buying in quantity?

    a. 6 cans of tomato soup for $1.44 or $0.34 each

    b. 2 packages of spaghetti for $3.69 or 1 package for $1.89

8. Find the unit cost to the nearest cent.

    a. 1.38 kg of walnuts for $5.56

    b. 0.45 kg of nails for $1.38

9. a. Calculate the cost of buying one set of gym clothing.

    b. How much change would be received if the items in part **a** were paid for with three $20 bills?

    c. Calculate the cost of buying 3 pairs of socks, 2 T-shirts, 1 pair of running shoes, and 1 pair of shorts.

    d. How much change would be received if the items in part **c** were paid for with a $100 bill?

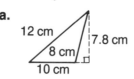
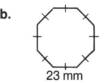
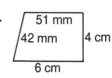

$19.95 $5.98 $2.29 $14.59

10. Copy and complete.

    a. 4 cm = ☐ mm   **b.** 14 mm = ☐ cm

    c. 75 cm = ☐ m   **d.** 9.1 m = ☐ cm

    e. 7.1 cm = ☐ mm   **f.** 0.2 km = ☐ m

11. Find the perimeter.

    a. 12 cm, 7.8 cm, 8 cm, 10 cm

    b. 23 mm

    c. 3 m, 2.8 m, 5 m

    d. 51 mm, 42 mm, 4 cm, 6 cm

12. The perimeter of the figure is 21.6 cm. Find the length of AB.

a.

b.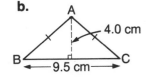

13. Find the area. ☐ represents 1 cm².

a.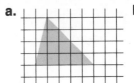

b.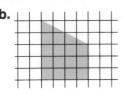

14. Find the area of the parallelogram.

a.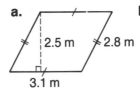

b.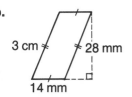

15. A kite is made by forming a cross with two pieces of wood. Find the area of the kite.

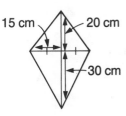

15 cm   20 cm   30 cm

16. What solid can be made from the net?

a.

b.

c.

d.

17. Copy. Complete the chart for regular polyhedrons.

	Type	Faces	Shape of face
a.		4	
b.	octahedron		equilateral triangle
c.		12	
d.			square
e.		20	

18. Identify the solid from the views.

a.

bottom view   side view

b.

bottom view   side view

c.

bottom view   side view

19. Sketch the different faces of the prism. Then find the surface area.

a.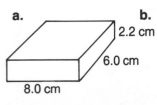

2.2 cm   6.0 cm   8.0 cm

b.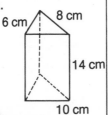

6 cm   8 cm   14 cm   10 cm

20. Find the volume of each shape in exercise 19 to the nearest cubic centimetre.

165

6/Ratios and Rates

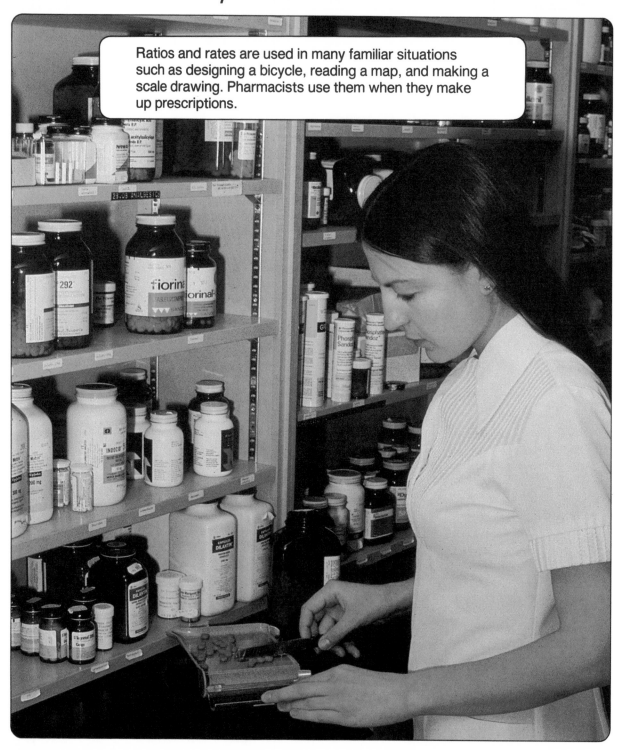

Ratios and rates are used in many familiar situations such as designing a bicycle, reading a map, and making a scale drawing. Pharmacists use them when they make up prescriptions.

Get Set

1. a. What fraction of the balls are baseballs?

  b. What fraction are soccer balls?

  c. What fraction are footballs?

2. Find the GCF.

  a. 24, 36   **b.** 24, 40   **c.** 18, 72

3. Copy and complete.

  a. $\frac{6}{8} = \frac{\blacksquare}{24}$ **b.** $\frac{5}{7} = \frac{15}{\blacksquare}$ **c.** $\frac{\blacksquare}{12} = \frac{5}{6}$

  d. $\frac{4}{\blacksquare} = \frac{20}{5}$ **e.** $\frac{2}{3} = \frac{\blacksquare}{30}$ **f.** $\frac{5}{8} = \frac{\blacksquare}{32}$

4. Copy and complete.

  a.

number of hands	1	3		8	
number of fingers	5		20		55

  b.

number of chairs	1	2		9	
number of legs	4		32		48

  c.

number of days	7		28	63	
number of weeks	1	2			10

5. Which pairs are equivalent?

  a. $\frac{6}{8}, \frac{4}{3}$ **b.** $\frac{5}{10}, \frac{15}{30}$ **c.** $\frac{9}{12}, \frac{2}{3}$

  d. $\frac{1}{3}, \frac{12}{4}$ **e.** $\frac{9}{6}, \frac{3}{2}$ **f.** $\frac{12}{24}, \frac{3}{8}$

6. About how many times does the first number go into the second number?

  a. 5 into 14   **b.** 21 into 100

  c. 42 into 120   **d.** 24 into 75

  e. 50 into 2150   **f.** 35 into 1000

7. Rosemary can run 6 km in 1 h. At this speed, how far can she run in the time?

  a. 2 h   **b.** $\frac{1}{2}$ h   **c.** $1\frac{1}{2}$ h   **d.** $\frac{1}{6}$ h

8. Find the volume.

  a.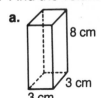

  b.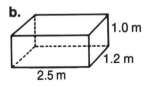

9. How much does one item cost?

  a.
EGGS
$1.32 a dozen

  b.
APPLES
$2.88 a dozen

  c.
LIGHT BULBS
$1.60 pkg. of 4

  d.
GRANOLA BARS
$1.28 box of 8

10. Measure the length to the nearest tenth of a centimetre.

  a.

  b.

  c.

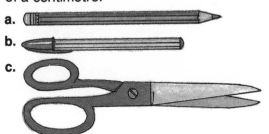

11. Copy and complete.

  a.

cm	100				
m	1	10	100	0.5	20

  b.

cm	100 000	1 000 000	1 500 000
km	1		

  c.

cm					
km	2	12	25	50	12.5

Ratios

Antonia loves physical activity and sports. She has earned eight crests by participating in the Canada Fitness Award program for the last eight years. She has four times as many silver awards as awards of excellence.

AWARD OF EXCELLENCE

GOLD AWARD

SILVER AWARD

The number of silver awards compared to the number of awards of excellence is

4 to 1.

4 to 1 is a comparison of like quantities with the same units. It is called a **ratio**.

4 and 1 are the **terms** of the ratio.

A two-term ratio such as 4 to 1 can also be written as

$4:1$ or $\frac{4}{1}$.

The ratio of the number of awards of excellence
        to the number of gold awards
        to the number of silver awards

        is 1 to 3 to 4.

A three-term ratio such as 1 to 3 to 4 can also be written as $1:3:4$.

WORKING TOGETHER

1. Express the ratio in three ways.

  a. gold awards to silver awards

  b. awards of excellence to gold awards

  c. gold awards to total awards

2. Express the ratio in two ways.

  a. silver awards to gold awards to awards of excellence

  b. gold awards to silver awards to total awards

3. What awards are being compared in the ratio?

  a. $1:3$ **b.** $3:4:1$ **c.** $\frac{1}{8}$

4. a. What awards are being compared in the ratios $3:4$ and $4:3$?

  b. Are these ratios the same? Explain.

APPLICATIONS AND EXERCISES

1. Express the ratio in three ways.

   a. 9 of 10 provinces charge sales tax.

   b. 1 out of every 700 cells is a white blood cell.

   c. 11 out of 15 trees are evergreens.

2. Write the ratio for the comparison.

   a. black to red

   b. black to striped

   c. red to striped

   d. red to black

   e. black to red to striped

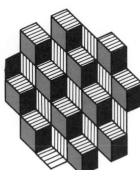

3. Use the diagram in exercise 2 to determine what are being compared.

   a. 22 : 13   b. 22 to 12   c. 12 : 47

   d. 12 : 13 : 22   e. 22 to 12 to 13

4. Costume jewellery is made of 9 parts copper and 1 part zinc. A trumpet is made of 8 parts copper and 2 parts zinc.

   a. What is the ratio of copper to zinc in costume jewellery?

   b. What is the ratio of copper to zinc in a trumpet?

   c. Which has the greater composition of copper?

5. A bag of potting soil contains 4 parts loam, 3 parts peat moss, and 1 part coarse sand.

   a. What is the ratio of loam to coarse sand to peat moss?

   b. What ratio is given by 1 : 3 : 4?

   c. What ratio is given by 3 : 8?

6. Write the ratio of length to width to height for the box.

   a. 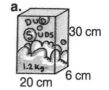 30 cm 6 cm 20 cm

   b. 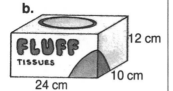 12 cm 10 cm 24 cm

7. Write the ratio.

   a. the length of a side of the square to the length of a side of the triangle to the diameter of the circle

   b. the perimeter of the square to the perimeter of the triangle to the circumference of the circle

      1 cm

3. Express as a ratio.

   a. 1 d to 2 weeks   b. 7 min to 1 h

   c. 1 cm to 1 km   d. 1¢ to $1

Try This

1. One out of every three seats in a theatre is not occupied. There are 108 people seated in the theatre.

   a. How many seats are not occupied?

   b. What is the seating capacity of the theatre?

Equivalent Ratios and Proportions

To make orange juice from concentrate, combine 3 cans of water with every 1 can of concentrate.

The ratio of the number of cans of water to the number of cans of concentrate is

> 3 to 1, 6 to 2, 9 to 3.

3 to 1, 6 to 2, and 9 to 3 represent the same comparison.
They are **equivalent ratios**.

When ratios are equivalent, they can be written in a **proportion**.

$$3:1 = 9:3 \quad \text{OR} \quad \frac{3}{1} = \frac{9}{3}$$

Equivalent ratios are formed by multiplying or dividing the terms of a ratio by the same non-zero number.

When the greatest common factor, the GCF, of the terms is 1, a ratio is in **simplest form**.

$\frac{3}{1}$ is in simplest form.

WORKING TOGETHER

1. Copy and complete.

   a.

   b.

2. To express $\frac{1.2}{1.8}$ in simplest form, multiply each term by 10, then divide each term by the GCF.

3. A shade of green is made by mixing 1.2 L of yellow paint with 800 mL of blue paint.

   a. Write the ratio of millilitres of yellow paint to millilitres of blue paint.

   b. Express the ratio in part **a** in simplest form.

   c. Write the ratio of litres of yellow paint to litres of blue paint.

   d. Express the ratio in part **c** in simplest form.

1. To make lemonade from a concentrate, combine 4 cans of water with every 1 can of concentrate. Copy and complete the table to show equivalent ratios.

concentrate (cans)	2	4			0.5
water (cans)			12	20	

2. To make a shade of mauve, 4 mL of red paint are mixed with 8 mL of blue paint and 6 mL of white paint. Copy and complete the table to show equivalent ratios. Which ratio is in simplest form?

	a.	b.	c.	d.	e.	f.
red paint (mL)	4	2			14	
blue paint (mL)				16		
white paint (mL)	6		9			30

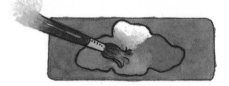

3. Write two equivalent ratios.

   a. 6:5   **b.** 9 to 24   **c.** 2.5:5.0

   d. $\frac{0.9}{0.3}$ **e.** $\frac{350}{42}$ **f.** 8:8:8

   g. 3 to 2 to 5   **h.** 11:22:11

   i. 100:50:25   **j.** $\frac{50\,000}{300}$

   k. 6.3 to 3.6   **l.** 1.2:2.0:3.2

4. Write the simplest form of each ratio in exercise 3.

5. Express as a ratio in simplest form.

   a. 15 s to 1 min   **b.** 2 cm to 1 km

   c. 39 g to 3 kg   **d.** 10 mm to 4.4 cm

   e. 27¢ to $3   **f.** 750 kg to 2.2 t

6. To make 750 mL of maple syrup, 26.25 L of sap are required. Write the ratio of sap to maple syrup in simplest form.

7. The largest fish, the whale shark, has a mass of 40 t and a length of 18 m. The smallest fish, the Marshall Island goby, has a mass of 2 mg and a length of 1 cm.

   a. What is the ratio of their lengths?

   b. What is the ratio of their masses?

8. It takes 2 h to fill a swimming pool with water and 24 min to empty it.

   a. Express this comparison as a ratio in simplest form.

   b. How long would it take to fill the pool $\frac{2}{3}$ full, and how long would it take to empty it?

   c. Express the comparison in part **b** as a ratio in simplest form.

9. A friend asks you to close your eyes and pick an apple from one of the bowls. Which bowl offers the better chance of picking a red apple?

KEEPING SHARP

1. Evaluate.

   a. 1^4 **b.** 5^2 **c.** 8^2 **d.** 2^3 **e.** 4^3 **f.** 3^4

   g. 6^3 **h.** 2^5 **i.** $(9.01)^1$ **j.** $(0.3)^3$ **k.** $(5.2)^2$ **l.** $(1.1)^3$

Solving Proportions

For every 105 L of sap collected,
3 L of maple syrup is produced.

* How much sap must be collected
  to produce 200 L of syrup?

$$\dfrac{\text{amount of sap (L)}}{\text{amount of syrup (L)}} \quad \dfrac{105}{3} \quad \dfrac{\blacksquare}{200}$$

Write a proportion.	No multiple of 3 gives 200. Express $\frac{105}{3}$ in simplest form.	Find the missing term.
$\overset{\displaystyle ?}{\underset{\displaystyle ?}{\dfrac{105}{3} = \dfrac{\blacksquare}{200}}}$	$\overset{\displaystyle \div\,3}{\underset{\displaystyle \div\,3}{\dfrac{105}{3} = \dfrac{35}{1}}}$	$\overset{\displaystyle \times\,200}{\underset{\displaystyle \times\,200}{\dfrac{35}{1} = \dfrac{7000}{200}}}$

To produce 200 L of syrup, 7000 L of sap is required.

* About how much syrup can be produced from 1000 L of sap?

$$\dfrac{\text{amount of sap (L)}}{\text{amount of syrup (L)}} \qquad\qquad \dfrac{35}{1} \qquad\qquad \dfrac{1000}{\blacksquare}$$

Write a proportion.	No multiple of 35 gives 1000. Estimate.	Find the missing term.
$\overset{\displaystyle ?}{\underset{\displaystyle ?}{\dfrac{35}{1} = \dfrac{1000}{\blacksquare}}}$		$\overset{\displaystyle \times\text{ about }30}{\underset{\displaystyle \times\,30}{\dfrac{35}{1} \doteq \dfrac{1000}{30}}}$

About 30 L of syrup can be produced.

WORKING TOGETHER

1. Copy and complete.

a. $\overset{\displaystyle \times\,\blacksquare}{\underset{\displaystyle \times\,\blacksquare}{\dfrac{4}{9} = \dfrac{12}{\bigcirc}}}$

b. $\overset{\displaystyle \times\,\blacksquare}{\underset{\displaystyle \times\,\blacksquare}{\dfrac{0.5}{8} = \dfrac{\bigcirc}{32}}}$

c. $\overset{\displaystyle \div\,4}{\underset{\displaystyle \div\,4}{\dfrac{8}{12} = \dfrac{\triangle}{\bigcirc}}} \,\overset{\displaystyle \times\,\lozenge}{\underset{\displaystyle \times\,\lozenge}{= \dfrac{\blacksquare}{21}}}$

d. $\overset{\displaystyle \times\,\blacksquare}{\underset{\displaystyle \times\text{ about }\blacksquare}{\dfrac{3}{5} \doteq \dfrac{\bigcirc}{39}}}$

172

1. Copy and complete.

a. $\frac{\blacksquare}{3} = \frac{13}{39}$ b. $\frac{3}{4} = \frac{\blacksquare}{100}$ c. $\frac{8}{3} = \frac{48}{\blacksquare}$

d. $\frac{7}{\blacksquare} = \frac{4}{4}$ e. $\frac{\blacksquare}{10} = \frac{9}{18}$ f. $\frac{22}{\blacksquare} = \frac{38}{19}$

2. On a hike, Grant takes 12 steps for every 15 steps that Nancy takes.

a. How many steps does Nancy take when Grant takes 60 steps?

b. How many steps does Grant take when Nancy takes 500 steps?

3. In an election for class president, Tom received 4 votes for every 6 votes that Milos received. Milos received 81 votes.

a. How many votes did Tom receive?

b. How many students voted?

4. Copy and complete.

a. $\frac{0.5}{3} = \frac{\blacksquare}{21}$ b. $\frac{2.5}{1.5} = \frac{100}{\blacksquare}$

c. $\frac{1.6}{24} = \frac{\blacksquare}{12}$ d. $\frac{48}{5} = \frac{9.6}{\blacksquare}$

e. $\frac{0.16}{\blacksquare} = \frac{0.8}{7}$ f. $\frac{7}{\blacksquare} = \frac{4.9}{2.1}$

5. Bronze is made from copper and tin in a fixed ratio. A bronze statue contains 27 kg of copper and 3 kg of tin. How much copper is contained in a statue that has 4 kg of tin?

6. Len's mother works 7 h each day, 4 d each week. Len works $\frac{1}{2}$ h for every 1 h his mother works. How many hours does Len work each week?

7. The ratio of potassium to nitrogen in a plant fertilizer is 4 to 3. The ratio of nitrogen to potash is 1 to 2. A container of this fertilizer has 120 g of nitrogen.

a. How many grams of potash are there?

b. How many grams of potassium are there?

8. In second gear on a bicycle, the ratio of the number of pedal turns to the number of rear-wheel turns is 4 to 7.

a. How many pedal turns are required to make the rear wheel turn 3.5 times?

b. How many rear-wheel turns are made when the pedals are turned once?

9. Copy and complete by estimating.

a. $\frac{15}{4} \doteq \frac{\blacksquare}{15}$ b. $\frac{6}{5} \doteq \frac{\blacksquare}{22}$ c. $\frac{\blacksquare}{75} \doteq \frac{13}{24}$

d. $\frac{100}{\blacksquare} \doteq \frac{3}{7}$ e. $\frac{41}{\blacksquare} \doteq \frac{2}{7}$ f. $\frac{\blacksquare}{31} \doteq \frac{3}{2}$

g. $\frac{3}{5} \doteq \frac{80}{\blacksquare}$ h. $\frac{7}{11} \doteq \frac{93}{\blacksquare}$ i. $\frac{0.8}{50} \doteq \frac{\blacksquare}{90}$

A calculator can be used to help you solve proportions.

To solve $\frac{5}{6} = \frac{\blacksquare}{18}$, press  ($15.$)

To solve $\frac{7}{9} = \frac{28}{\blacksquare}$, press $28 \div 7 \times 9 =$. ($36.$)

1. Use a calculator to solve.

a. $\frac{24}{10} = \frac{36}{\blacksquare}$ b. $\frac{105}{3} = \frac{\blacksquare}{200}$

2. Find the value of each missing term in exercise 9, rounded to the nearest hundredth.

Gears

Wheels called gears turn as their teeth mesh.
As one gear turns, it turns another...and
another...and another.
Gears are useful. They keep printing presses rolling,
wind-up clocks ticking, and ten-speed bicycles moving.

The diagrams show one gear turning another.

32 teeth

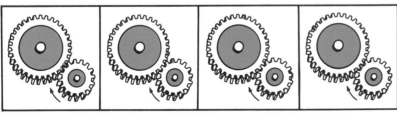

drive wheel   16 teeth

For every 1 full turn of the drive wheel, the other wheel makes $\frac{1}{2}$ turn.

The results of further turns of the gears are recorded.

drive wheel turns other wheel turns	$\frac{1}{\frac{1}{2}}$	$\frac{2}{1}$	$\frac{4}{2}$	$\frac{8}{4}$	$\frac{16}{8}$	$\frac{32}{16}$

The ratio of drive wheel turns to other wheel turns in simplest form is $\frac{2}{1}$.

Compare with this ratio.

$\dfrac{\text{number of teeth on drive wheel}}{\text{number of teeth on other wheel}} = \dfrac{16}{32}$

What do you notice?

$= \dfrac{1}{2}$

WORKING TOGETHER

1. Which ratio compares the number of
   teeth on the drive wheel to the number of
   teeth on the other wheel?

   a. $\frac{1}{3}$ **b.** $\frac{3}{1}$ **c.** $\frac{10}{40}$ **d.** $\frac{30}{40}$

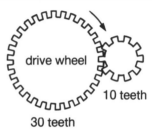

drive wheel

10 teeth

30 teeth

2. Which ratio compares the number of
   turns of the drive wheel to the number of
   turns of the other wheel?

   a. $\frac{1}{3}$ **b.** $\frac{3}{1}$ **c.** $\frac{10}{40}$ **d.** $\frac{30}{40}$

3. Compare the answer from exercise 1 with
   the one from exercise 2. What do you
   notice?

1. **a.** Write the ratio of the number of teeth on the drive wheel to the number of teeth on the other wheel.

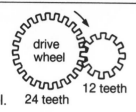

drive wheel

24 teeth   12 teeth

b. When the drive wheel turns once, how many times does the other wheel turn?

c. Write the ratio of the number of turns of the drive wheel to the number of turns of the other wheel.

d. Copy and complete the table.

drive wheel turns	$\frac{1}{2}$	1	3		12	24
other wheel turns				12		

2. Express the comparison as a ratio.

a. 25 teeth on the drive wheel to 75 teeth on the other wheel

b. 50 teeth on the drive wheel to 14 teeth on the other wheel

c. 18 teeth on the drive wheel to 18 teeth on the other wheel

3. Write the ratio of the number of turns of the drive wheel to the number of turns of the other wheel for each gear in exercise 2.

4. **a.** Write the ratio of the number of teeth on the drive wheel to the number of teeth on the other wheel.

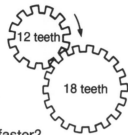

12 teeth

18 teeth

b. Which wheel turns faster?

c. Copy and complete the table.

drive wheel turns	1.5	3	6			21
other wheel turns				12	18	

5. On a gear the ratio of the number of turns of the drive wheel to the number of turns of the other wheel is 2 : 3.

a. Which wheel turns faster?

b. Copy and complete the table.

drive wheel turns	2	6		50		
other wheel turns			30		240	1800

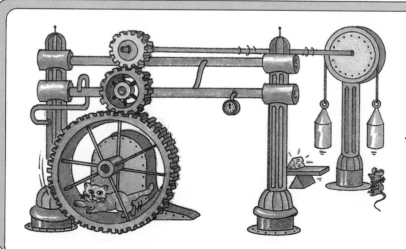

Try This

1. **a.** Which way does each wheel turn, clockwise or counterclockwise?

b. If the cat continues as shown, does he get the mouse?

1. A penny is made of 9 parts copper and 1 part tin. A nickel is made of 1 part nickel and 3 parts copper.

   a. What is the ratio of copper to tin in a penny?

   b. What is the ratio of copper to nickel in a nickel?

2. Write a ratio comparing the first value to the second value. Express the ratio in simplest form.

   a. A square measures 13 cm by 13 cm.

   b. A cake takes 35 min to bake and cupcakes take 20 min.

   c. One pen costs 50¢ and another costs $1.15.

   d. A telephone pole is 16.8 m in height and 28 cm in diameter at the base.

3. Write two equivalent ratios.

   a. 20:12   b. 32:60   c. 72 to 27

   d. $\frac{56}{49}$ e. $\frac{1.2}{0.3}$ f. 4:12:6

4. A recipe for shortbread requires 1 L of flour, 500 mL of butter, and 250 mL of sugar. Copy and complete the table to show equivalent ratios.

	a.	b.	c.	d.	e.
flour (mL)		500		200	
butter (mL)	500				50
sugar (mL)	250		100		

5. Copy and complete.

   a. $\frac{8}{5} = \frac{\square}{20}$ b. $\frac{6}{48} = \frac{1}{\square}$ c. $\frac{2}{4} = \frac{\square}{6}$

   d. $\frac{15}{6} = \frac{25}{\square}$ e. $\frac{27}{12} = \frac{\square}{16}$ f. $\frac{3.2}{1.6} = \frac{10}{\square}$

6. Copy and complete by estimating.

   a. $\frac{3}{8} \doteq \frac{\square}{50}$ b. $\frac{9}{11} \doteq \frac{60}{\square}$

   c. $\frac{9}{5} \doteq \frac{\square}{41}$ d. $\frac{8}{3} \doteq \frac{90}{\square}$

   e. $\frac{1.3}{1.5} \doteq \frac{\square}{4}$ f. $\frac{1.1}{2.5} \doteq \frac{7}{\square}$

7. The ratio of the number of boys to the number of girls in the photography club is 4 to 5. If there are 40 girls in the club, how many boys are there?

8. For every 70 L of sap collected, 2 L of maple syrup is produced.

   a. How many litres of maple syrup can be produced from 1260 L of sap?

   b. How many litres of sap are needed to produce 45 L of maple syrup?

9. Write the ratio.

   a. number of teeth on the drive wheel to number of teeth on the other wheel

   b. number of turns of the drive wheel to number of turns of the other wheel

   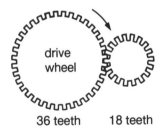

   36 teeth   18 teeth

   c. Which wheel turns faster?

10. Copy and complete the table for the gear in exercise 9.

	a.	b.	c.	d.	e.	f.
drive wheel turns	1	3		18	36	
other wheel turns			18			200

Reciprocals

Does your calculator have a $\boxed{1/x}$ key?

YES		NO

Find the reciprocal of 5.

$\boxed{5}\boxed{1/x}\left(0.2\right)$ $\boxed{5}\boxed{\div}\boxed{=}\left(0.2\right)$

0.2 is the reciprocal of 5.

$$5 \times \frac{1}{5} = 1 \quad \text{and} \quad \frac{1}{5} = 0.2$$

Find the reciprocal of $\frac{3}{4}$.

$\boxed{3}\boxed{\div}\boxed{4}\boxed{=}\boxed{1/x}\left(1.3333333\right)$ $\boxed{3}\boxed{\div}\boxed{4}\boxed{\div}\boxed{=}\left(1.3333333\right)$

$1.\overline{3}$ is the reciprocal of $\frac{3}{4}$.

$$\frac{3}{4} \times \frac{4}{3} = 1 \quad \text{and} \quad \frac{4}{3} = 1.\overline{3}$$

$\boxed{1/x}$ gives the reciprocal of the number in the display.

$\boxed{3}\boxed{\div}\boxed{4}\boxed{=}\boxed{1/x} \neq \boxed{3}\boxed{\div}\boxed{4}\boxed{1/x}$ Why?

---

1. Use your calculator to find the reciprocal.

   a. 8   **b.** 100   **c.** $\frac{1}{4}$ **d.** $\frac{3}{8}$ **e.** $\frac{2}{3}$ **f.** $\frac{5}{6}$ **g.** $1\frac{1}{4}$

The reciprocal key can sometimes be used in place of memory.

Evaluate. $\dfrac{4}{5+3}$

$\boxed{5}\boxed{+}\boxed{3}\boxed{=}\boxed{1/x}\boxed{\times}\boxed{4}\boxed{=}\left(0.5\right)$ $\boxed{5}\boxed{+}\boxed{3}\boxed{\div}\boxed{=}\boxed{\times}\boxed{4}\boxed{=}\left(0.5\right)$

2. Evaluate. Use the reciprocal key instead of memory.
   Remember, a display like $\left(2.9999995\right)$ is considered to equal 3.

   a. $\dfrac{106}{1.5 + 3.8}$ **b.** $\dfrac{198}{18 - 13.6}$ **c.** $\dfrac{45}{6 \times 2.5}$ **d.** $\dfrac{357}{85 \div 5}$

   e. $\dfrac{650}{9.7 + 22.8}$ **f.** $\dfrac{810}{48.5 - 16.1}$ **g.** $\dfrac{364}{13 \times 3.5}$ **h.** $\dfrac{126}{15.12 \div 4.2}$

   i. $\dfrac{256 \times 0.25}{5.9 + 6.9}$ **j.** $\dfrac{15 \times 9}{7.2 - 6.12}$ **k.** $\dfrac{51.5 \times 8}{154.5 \div 6}$ **l.** $\dfrac{13 \times 5}{12.5 \times 5.2}$

Rates

The athlete's heart beats about 65 times in 30 s. For each beat, his heart pumps about 140 mL of blood.

This information can be written as

$\frac{65 \text{ beats}}{30 \text{ s}}$ and $\frac{140 \text{ mL}}{1 \text{ beat}}$.

A comparison of quantities with different units is a **rate**.
Since the quantities are not alike, the units must be included.

$\frac{140 \text{ mL}}{1 \text{ beat}}$ is a **unit rate** because its second term is 1.

This can also be expressed as 140 mL/beat (millilitres **per** beat).

Express $\frac{65 \text{ beats}}{30 \text{ s}}$ as a unit rate.

$$\frac{65 \text{ beats}}{30 \text{ s}} \xrightarrow[\div 30]{\div 30} = \frac{\text{about 2 beats}}{1 \text{ s}} \qquad \text{OR} \qquad \frac{65 \text{ beats}}{30 \text{ s}} \xrightarrow[\times 2]{\times 2} = \frac{130 \text{ beats}}{60 \text{ s}} \qquad \frac{130 \text{ beats}}{1 \text{ min}}$$

Which unit rate do you think is the most useful, about 2 beats/s or 130 beats/min? Why?

The athlete can run 14 km in 2 h. At this rate, how far can he run in 3 h?

$\frac{14 \text{ km}}{2 \text{ h}} = \frac{7 \text{ km}}{1 \text{ h}} = \frac{21 \text{ km}}{3 \text{ h}}$ The rates are equivalent.

The athlete can run 21 km in 3 h.

WORKING TOGETHER

1. Express as a unit rate.

  a. 360 words typed in 6 min

  b. $\frac{210 \text{ beats}}{3 \text{ min}}$ **c.** $\frac{112 \text{ students}}{4 \text{ classrooms}}$

  d. 320 km travelled in 4 h

2. Sonya earns $12 for 2 h of work.

  a. How much does she earn per hour?

  b. At this rate, how much does she earn for $2\frac{1}{2}$ h of work?

APPLICATIONS AND EXERCISES

1. The human heart beats on the average 72 times/min. How many beats are there for the time period?

   a. 10 min   **b.** 35 min   **c.** 1.5 min

2. The table shows the cruising speeds of several planes.

Type of plane	Cruising speed (km/h)
DC-9	826
727	853
747	893
767	849
L-1011	882

   a. If each plane maintains its speed, how far can it travel in 2.5 h?

   b. The L-1011 is destined for Vancouver, 3666 km away. What distance remains after flying for 2.5 h?

3. Express as a unit rate.

   a. $37 for 4 h work   **b.** 12 eggs for 96¢

   c. 7 watermelons for 35 people

4. Eight tickets on the Loop-the-Loop cost $5. How many rides did people take if $960 was collected during the day?

5. Mina typed 350 words in 5 min. At this rate, how many words would she type in 8 min?

6. A computer printer can print about 300 words/min. How many words can it print in the time period?

   a. 1.5 min   **b.** 6 s   **c.** 1 h

7. André is paid an hourly rate. When he works a 40 h week, he receives $340. How much does he receive when he works a 35 h week?

8. Carol travelled 450 km in her car and used 32.4 L of fuel.

   a. At this rate, how much fuel does Carol's car use to travel 100 km?

   b. Fuel consumption is measured in litres per hundred kilometres. Why is this more useful than a unit rate of litres per kilometre or kilometres per litre?

9. Three students can paint a house in 16 h. How long should it take 5 students to paint the house? What assumption are you making?

10. It takes 24 frames of movie film to create 1 s of a cartoon feature.

    a. How many frames are required for a cartoon that plays for 2 h 10 min?

    b. A cartoon movie has 150 000 frames on the film. How long is the cartoon?

Try This

1. It is 10 km to the train station. To just catch the train before it leaves, you must average 60 km/h. The traffic is heavy, so you average only 30 km/h for the first 5 km. What speed must you travel the rest of the way to catch the train?

Comparison Shopping

Which is most economical?

Compare equivalent rates for 4 L of milk.

$$\frac{\$3.19}{4\ L} \qquad \frac{\$2.30}{2\ L} = \frac{\$4.60}{4\ L} \qquad \frac{\$1.20}{1\ L} = \frac{\$4.80}{4\ L} \qquad \frac{70¢}{500\ mL} = \frac{\$1.40}{1\ L} = \frac{\$5.60}{4\ L}$$

Or, compare the costs per litre.

> The cost of one unit or item is the **unit price**.

4 L cost $3.19, which is $3.19 ÷ 4 or $0.7975/L.	2 L cost $2.30, which is $2.30 ÷ 2 or $1.15/L.	1 L costs $1.20, which is $1.20/L.	500 mL costs 70¢, which is $0.70 × 2 or $1.40/L.

The best value is the 4 L bag of milk,
if that much milk can be used before going to waste.

WORKING TOGETHER

1. Which unit price is lower?
   a. 57¢/can or 49¢/can
   b. $0.003/hook or $0.03/hook
   c. $3.75/kg or $3.754/kg

2. Copy and complete the rates.
   a. $\dfrac{\$4.99}{25\ mL} = \dfrac{\blacksquare}{100\ mL}$ b. $\dfrac{\$1.75}{35\ g} = \dfrac{\blacksquare}{70\ g}$

3. Find the unit price.

   a.
   $3.60

   b.
   $2.69

4. a. Which package in exercise 3 is the better buy?
   b. What assumptions are you making?

5. a. Calculate the volume of each wood pile.
   b. Calculate the unit price of each.
   c. Compare the unit prices. Which is the better buy?

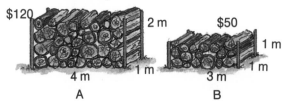

1. Find the unit price to the nearest cent.

   a. 5 kg of bananas for $5.90

   b. 6 lemons for $1.30

   c. 3 loaves of bread for $2.75

2. A can of 3 tennis balls sells for $3.99. A bag of 10 tennis balls sells for $12.75. Which is the better buy?

3. If 2 cans of soup cost 95¢, how many cans can be bought for $5.15?

4. Which package is more economical? Why would you expect this?

   a.   **b.**

5. At Tony's Variety a package of 14 envelopes costs 69¢. At Nixon's School Supplies a package of 45 envelopes costs $1.19.

   a. Which is the better buy?

   b. How much do you save on 1 envelope?

   c. What assumption are you making?

6. **a.** Find the unit price for each product.

   b. Which product is more economical?

7. The inside measurements of two freezers are given.

   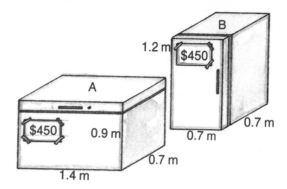

   a. What is the volume of each?

   b. Which freezer is more economical?

   c. What other considerations would affect your choice of freezers?

8. Rob needs 4 batteries for a flashlight. A package of 2 batteries costs $2.18. Packages of 6 are on sale for $5.94.

   a. Find the unit price for each package.

   b. Why might the more expensive batteries be more economical?

9. **a.** Which is more economical?

   b. Why might this be expected?

KEEPING SHARP

1. Evaluate.

   a. 1.75 + 7.34   **b.** 12.04 − 9.45   **c.** 8.1 + 19.08   **d.** 77.4 − 12.15

   e. 4.51 × 10 000   **f.** 12.3 × 100 000   **g.** 5.2 × 1000   **h.** 0.56 × 1 000 000

   i. 5.3 × 1.2   **j.** 6.4 × 2.6   **k.** 1.24 × 0.6   **l.** 4.3 × 0.14

Scale Drawings

Scale 1 : 7500

The ratio 1 : 7500 means that 1 unit on the drawing represents 7500 units of actual length.

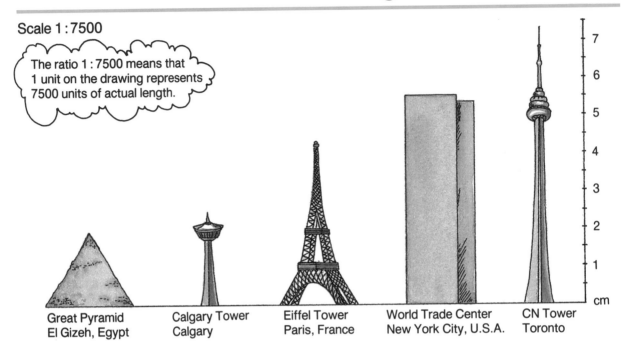

						7
						6
						5
						4
						3
						2
						1
						cm

Great Pyramid
El Gizeh, Egypt

Calgary Tower
Calgary

Eiffel Tower
Paris, France

World Trade Center
New York City, U.S.A.

CN Tower
Toronto

What is the actual height of the Great Pyramid?

Measure the height on the drawing. Then write the ratios.

$$\frac{\text{height on drawing}}{\text{actual height}} = \frac{1.9}{\blacksquare} \left(\frac{\text{cm}}{\text{cm}}\right) \qquad \text{scale} = \frac{1}{7500} \left(\frac{\text{units}}{\text{units}}\right)$$

Write a proportion and find the missing term.

$$\overset{\times\ 1.9}{\overbrace{\frac{1}{7500} = \frac{1.9}{14\,250}}}_{\times\ 1.9}$$

$$\boxed{14\,250 \text{ cm} = 142.5 \text{ m}}$$

The actual height of the Great Pyramid is about 142.5 m.

WORKING TOGETHER

1. The scale of the floor plan of a shopping mall is 1 cm to 4 m. The length of the drawing of one store is 3.6 cm.

   a. What is the actual length of the store in metres?

   b. Check. $\frac{1 \text{ cm}}{4 \text{ m}} = \frac{3.6 \text{ cm}}{\blacksquare \text{ m}}$

2. A model airplane is 15 cm long. The scale of the model is 1 : 200.

   a. Copy and complete the proportion.
   $\frac{1}{200} = \frac{15}{\blacksquare}$

   b. What is the actual length of the plane in metres?

182

APPLICATIONS AND EXERCISES

1. Determine the actual height.

    a. Calgary Tower   **b.** Eiffel Tower

    c. World Trade Center   **d.** CN Tower

2. Place Ville Marie in Montréal is about $\frac{1}{3}$ the height of the CN Tower.

    a. How tall is Place Ville Marie?

    b. How tall would it be on a drawing with the scale 1 cm to 50 m?

3. Express the scale as a ratio.

    a. 1 cm to 1 m   **b.** 1 cm to 1 km

    c. 1 cm to 1 mm   **d.** 1 mm to 10 cm

4. For each scale in exercise 3, decide if the object would be larger or smaller than its scale drawing.

5. To design a car, an automotive engineer draws a blueprint and builds a model.

    a. The model car is 20 cm long. The actual car is to be 4 m long. What is the scale of the model?

    b. The width of the model is 8.7 cm. What is the width of the actual car?

6. Copy and complete.

	Scale	Drawing size	Actual size
a.	1 cm to 10 m		50 m
b.	1 : 50		1750 cm
c.	1 mm to 10 cm	18 mm	
d.	1 : 1250	8.5 cm	
e.	1 cm to 25 m		237.5 m

7. Use the scale 1 mm to 1 m to make a scale drawing of the playing area.

	Playing field	Dimensions
a.	football field	100 m by 90 m
b.	baseball diamond	27 m by 27 m
c.	tennis court	20 m by 10 m
d.	basketball court	26 m by 18 m

8. Use the scale drawings from exercise 7 to find the ratio in simplest form.

    a. the length of the tennis court to the length of the football field

    b. the side of the baseball diamond to the width of the basketball court

    c. the area of the tennis court to the area of the football field

Hardware is a general term used to describe the physical parts of any computer system. All the processing and computing take place in the **central processing unit** or **CPU**. **Peripheral equipment** (peripherals) refers to any equipment, distinct from the CPU, that is plugged into the system. The peripherals are used for input and output of information.

1. Is the peripheral used for input, output, or both?

    a. keyboard   **b.** monitor   **c.** printer

    d. modem   **e.** joystick   **f.** mouse

    g. disk drive   **h.** cassette tape recorder

2. Processing and computing occur in a single **chip**. What are the chip's real dimensions?

Scale 1 : 0.5

183

Map Scales

Road Map of Saskatchewan

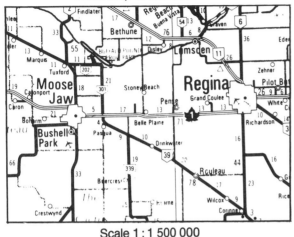

Scale 1 : 1 500 000

The scale 1 : 1 500 000 means that 1 unit on the map represents 1 500 000 units on the ground.
Thus, 1 cm represents 1 500 000 cm
or 1 cm represents 15 km.

Use the road map to determine the driving distance between Regina and Moose Jaw.

On the road map the distance measures 4.7 cm. Write a proportion.

$$\frac{1 \text{ cm}}{15 \text{ km}} = \frac{4.7 \text{ cm}}{\blacksquare \text{ km}}$$

Find the missing term.

$$\frac{1 \text{ cm}}{15 \text{ km}} \; \overset{\times 4.7}{\underset{\times 4.7}{=}} \; \frac{4.7 \text{ cm}}{70.5 \text{ km}}$$

The driving distance from the road map is 70.5 km.

WORKING TOGETHER

Use the provincial map of Saskatchewan.

1. a. Mark the distance between Regina and Moose Jaw along the edge of a piece of paper.

   b. Line up the markings on the paper with the bar scale and determine the distance.

   c. Compare this with the distance from the road map. Which is the better approximation? Why?

2. Approximate the straight-line distance in kilometres.

   a. Swift Current to Moose Jaw

   b. Regina to Saskatoon

   c. Regina to Uranium City

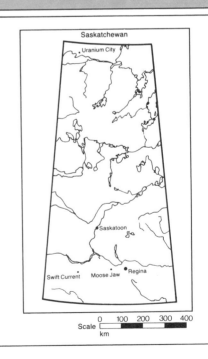

1. Is the scale equivalent to the bar scale?

km

10 0 10 20 30 40

   a. 1 cm to 10 km   **b.** 1 : 10

   c. 1 : 1 000 000

2. **a.** How many kilometres does 1 cm on the map of Saskatoon represent?

   b. Show the scale as a bar scale.

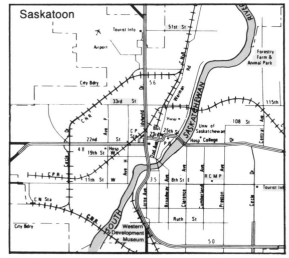

Scale 1 : 150 000

3. Use the map of Saskatoon to find the actual distance.

   a. from 33rd Street to 51st Street along Idylwyld Drive

   b. from the RCMP station to the Tourist Information on 8th Street East

4. What is the distance on the map of Saskatoon for the actual distance?

   a. 12.5 km   **b.** 5 km   **c.** 8.75 km

5. How can you best estimate the driving distance on a map when the roads are curved?

6. **a.** Give one set of directions to drive from the Western Development Museum to the Forestry Farm and Animal Park.

   b. Calculate this distance.

7. On a map of northern Ontario the scale is 1 cm to 20 km. The straight-line distance between Thunder Bay and Sault Ste. Marie is 410 km. What is this distance on the map?

8. Show the scale as a bar scale.

   a. 1 cm to 250 km   **b.** 1 cm to 100 km

   c. 1 : 10 000   **d.** 1 : 50 000

9. The scale on a map is 1 : 30 000.

   a. Find the walking distance when the map distance is 6.5 cm.

   b. Find the map distance when the distance walked is 4.5 km.

10. Canada's longest river, the Mackenzie, is about 4200 km long. Its length measures 35 cm on a map. What is the scale of the map?

Try This

1. Use a map of the capital of your province or territory to plan a tour to five points of interest. List directions and actual distances between the places.

1. Is the rate a unit rate?

   a. 10 tokens for $9.50

   b. 5.9 m in 1 s   **c.** $5.50 for 1 ticket

   d. 2000 characters in 20 s

2. Express as a unit rate.

   a. 300 km travelled in 6 h

   b. 10 h of work for $195

   c. 330 words typed in 5 min

   d. 35 cars sold in 4 d

3. Chantal released a cork in the middle of a stream. Gerard waited downstream and clocked 4 s as the cork passed the 5 m marker. Calculate the rate of flow of the stream in metres per second.

4. A stack of paper 1.2 cm high contains 100 sheets. How many sheets of paper are there in a stack 3 mm high?

5. Alexei rode 20 m in 5 s on his bicycle.

   a. At this rate, how far can he travel in 1 min?

   b. How long would he take to travel 1 km?

6. Find the unit price to the nearest cent.

   a. 2 kg of sugar for $1.39

   b. 24 tins of cat food for $9.99

   c. $1.99 for 2 movie rentals

   d. 3 boxes of juice for $1.39

7. Which package is more economical?

   a. $1.89

   b.  $4.05

8. a. Use this scale drawing of a moose to estimate the height in metres.

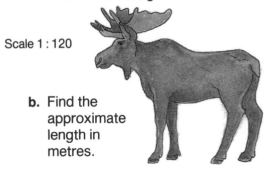

Scale 1 : 120

   b. Find the approximate length in metres.

9. The scale on a drawing of a flea is 1 cm to 1 mm. Express the scale as a ratio.

10. The scale on a floor plan of a house is 1 cm to 3 m. Find the actual length for the measurement on the drawing.

   a. 2 cm   **b.** 10 cm   **c.** 11.1 cm

   d. 1.75 cm   **e.** 0.6 cm   **f.** 15.8 cm

11. A swimming pool is 50 m long and 20 m wide. Make a scale drawing using the scale 1 : 500.

12. Estimate the straight-line distance in kilometres between the places marked.

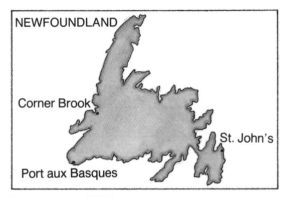

Scale 1 cm to 120 km

Mental Gymnastics

The human mind is the finest, most complex computer on Earth. Studies show that we use it for mental computation and estimation in more than 80% of all real problem solving situations.

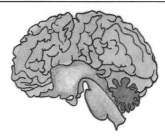

Addition and Subtraction Tricks

- Front-end addition
  $46 + 52 \rightarrow 40 + 50 = 90$
  $ 6 + 2 = 8$
  $ 46 + 52 = 98$

- Partial addition
  $38 + 29 \rightarrow 38 + 20 = 58$
  $ 58 + 9 = 67$

- Partial subtraction
  $95 - 37 \rightarrow 95 - 30 = 65$
  $ 65 - 7 = 58$
  $75 - 49 \rightarrow 75 - 50 = 25$
  $ 25 + 1 = 26$

Multiplication Tricks

- Partial multiplication
  $38 \times 7 \rightarrow 30 \times 7 = 210$
  $ 8 \times 7 = 56$
  $ 38 \times 7 = 266$

- Multiple of 10
  $67 \times 40 \rightarrow 60 \times 4 = 240$
  $ 7 \times 4 = 28$
  $ 67 \times 4 = 268$
  $ 67 \times 40 = 2680$

- Multiple of 100
  $72 \times 500 \rightarrow 70 \times 5 = 350$
  $ 2 \times 5 = 10$
  $ 72 \times 5 = 360$
  $ 72 \times 500 = 36000$

- Multiply by 25
  $54 \times 25 \rightarrow 54 \times \dfrac{100}{4} = \dfrac{5400}{4}$
  (× 100 ÷ 4)
  $= 1350$

- Multiply by 50
  $360 \times 50 \rightarrow 360 \times \dfrac{100}{2} = \dfrac{36\,000}{2}$
  (× 100 ÷ 2)
  $= 18\,000$

- Factor transfer
  $68 \times 5 \rightarrow 34 \times 10 = 340$
  $46 \times 18 \rightarrow 92 \times 9 \text{ or } 90 \times 9 = 810$
  $\phantom{46 \times 18 \rightarrow 92 \times 9 \text{ or }} 2 \times 9 = 18$
  $ 92 \times 9 = 828$

  $27 \times 15 \rightarrow 81 \times 5 \text{ or } 80 \times 5 = 400$
  $\phantom{27 \times 15 \rightarrow 81 \times 5 \text{ or }} 1 \times 5 = 5$
  $ 81 \times 5 = 405$

Division Tricks

- Divide by 25
  $155 \div 25 \rightarrow 155 \div 100 \times 4$
  (÷ 100 × 4)
  $= 1.55 \times 4$
  $= 6.20$

- Divide by 50
  $3880 \div 50 \rightarrow 3880 \div 100 \times 2$
  $= 38.8 \times 2$
  $= 77.6$

- Partial division
  $346 \div 8 \rightarrow 320 \div 8 = 40$
  $ 26 \div 8 = 3 \text{ R2}$
  $ 346 \div 8 = 43 \text{ R2}$

1. Practice mental skills.

a. $58 + 91$	**b.** $78 + 38$	**c.** $71 - 43$	**d.** $146 - 37$	**e.** 42×7
f. 39×9	**g.** 52×30	**h.** 98×300	**i.** 42×600	**j.** 32×25
k. 95×25	**l.** 71×16	**m.** $310 \div 25$	**n.** $480 \div 50$	**o.** $547 \div 7$

Databases

Computers can be programmed to perform a wide variety of tasks, but they are best suited to tasks that involve doing the same thing over and over again. They are incredibly fast and accurate workers, yet never get tired or bored.

1. Which are appropriate tasks for a computer to perform?
   - **a.** print form letters and mailing labels
   - **b.** store and analyse sports statistics
   - **c.** keep track of airline reservations
   - **d.** perform surgery in a hospital
   - **e.** give out tourist information
   - **f.** compose music
   - **g.** keep track of the inventory in a warehouse

Many tasks involve storing and handling large amounts of information. A **database** is an organized collection of facts. Large quantities of data can be stored by computer. However, a database is only useful if any piece of stored information can be retrieved easily and quickly.

The card index or microfiche system in a library is a simple example of a database. One set of cards lists all the titles alphabetically. A second set of cards lists all the authors alphabetically and each author's books by title.

2. How might a third set of cards be organized?

3. What additional information is usually found on each file card?

4. How would you use the card index to find one or more library books dealing with the history of computers?

Information that is stored by computer takes up much less space than card catalogues. More importantly, though, information can be looked up under any category you choose. For example, you could ask for a printout of all the books in the library written by Canadian women in the 1950s, or a listing of all the non-fiction books with the word Pioneer in the title. The search is fast and accurate, and the computer never complains.

People use **database management software** to help them store, sort, and retrieve all kinds of information.

- A record collector might use a microcomputer to keep track of a record collection.

> DAVE'S RECORD COLLECTION
>
> TITLE: TWIST AND SHOUT
> ARTIST(S):   THE BEATLES
> TYPE OF MUSIC: ROCK AND ROLL
> YEAR RELEASED: 1964
> RECORD LABEL: CAPITOL
> PURCHASE PRICE: $3.33
> CONDITION: SCRATCHED ONE SIDE

- Patient records in a hospital might be stored by computer. Dr. Low could ask for a listing of all patients with similar symptoms in order to compare their diagnoses and treatments.

5. How might Dave use the information about his record collection?

6. How can the database from another hospital be used by Dr. Low?

Database companies like Info Globe and Telidon store information in a large central library and charge for each minute that you use their services. You can phone in a request and receive a printout of the information. Or if you have a computer, modem, and special software, you can log onto their computer system and see the information displayed on your own screen.

7. **a.** Explain how you could use an encyclopedia company's database to do research for a project.

   b. Why might a reporter use a newspaper publisher's database to see all of the previously written articles that contain the words computer crime?

Many businesses and government departments have their own databases. Much of the information they store is about people.

Discuss.

8. A person should be told when a record has been made that contains information about that person.

9. A person should be able to check the information in her/his record in any database and have it corrected, if necessary.

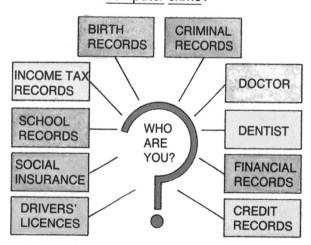

BIRTH RECORDS — CRIMINAL RECORDS — INCOME TAX RECORDS — DOCTOR — SCHOOL RECORDS — WHO ARE YOU? — DENTIST — SOCIAL INSURANCE — FINANCIAL RECORDS — DRIVERS' LICENCES — CREDIT RECORDS

10. Personal data should not be divulged to a third party.

Find the Missing Information

Tom said to Vince, "I have three sons. Guess their ages. I will give you two clues. First, the product of their ages is 36. Second, the sum of their ages is the same as the number of years I've owned the store." How old are Tom's three sons?

Think. Is there enough information to solve the problem?

Plan and do. Vince lists the information from the first clue.

factors of 36:

1 × 1 × 36	2 × 2 × 9	3 × 3 × 4
1 × 2 × 18	2 × 3 × 6	
1 × 3 × 12		
1 × 4 × 9		
1 × 6 × 6		

The second clue is not helpful because Vince does not know how long Tom has owned the store. More information is needed.

I need one more clue.

Okay. My oldest boy just bought his first car.

Look back. Vince guessed that Tom's sons were 1, 2, and 18. Is his answer reasonable?

How long did Tom own his store?

WORKING TOGETHER

 What information is needed? Solve the problem.

1. How many seconds are in a day?

2. How many years is 754 weeks?

3. How many days are in 36 a?

What information is missing? Tell how you would solve the problem.

4. What is the average height of students in your class?

5. How much does it cost to fill the gasoline tank in a school bus?

PROBLEMS

What information is needed to solve the problem? Tell how you would find it and then how you would solve the problem.

1. How many hours are there today from sunrise to sunset in the region where you live?

2. If you start dental school when you are twenty years old, how old might you be when you become a registered dentist?

3. How much would it cost to drive from Fredericton to Edmundston?

4. Will a million $1 bills placed end to end reach Winnipeg from Calgary?

5. How many Swiss francs can you buy with five Canadian dollars?

6. About how much milk does your family use per week?

7. Approximately how many times has your heart beat during your lifetime?

8. What is your greatest speed in metres per second for running 200 m?

9. Which is longer, the width of your hand or your hand span, or the distance around your wrist? How much longer?

10. **a.** How many $1 coins would it take to reach a length of 1 m?

    b. How many $1 coins would it take to cover 1 m²?

Solve the problem if enough information is given. If information is missing, supply it and then solve the problem.

11. How many pages away from halfway is this page?

12. Roger bought 6 cans of cat food at 87¢ each. How much change did he receive from the clerk?

13. Ninety students graduated from King Junior High School. If $\frac{2}{3}$ of the graduating class were boys, how many girls were there?

14. Maria works at a grocery store after school and earns $4.50/h. How much does she earn per week?

15. How much baseboard is needed to go around the perimeter of the room?

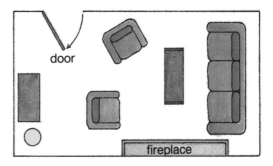

16. Ben bought a record for $7.95 and 2 cassette tapes for $3.95 each. What was the total cost excluding tax?

17. A blue whale can swim at a speed of 20 knots. What is its speed in metres per second?

Problem Solving Review

Tell how you would solve the problem.

1. Approximately how many times do you blink during an average day?

2. How many bricks are needed to build the house?

3. Mr. Gagnon is building stairs from the kitchen to the basement.
   a. How far apart should he place each step?
   b. How many steps will there be?

4. The area of Alberta is 663 741 km². What is the average number of people living on 1 km²?

5. A sheet of paper is torn in half. The two halves are put together and torn in half again. This is repeated 6 times. What is the thickness of the resulting pile of paper?

6. What is the cost of a 6 min dial-direct long-distance call from your house to New York City?

7. a. About how many record albums would it take to go around the perimeter of your classroom?
   b. About how many record albums would it take to cover the floor of your classroom?

8. How long would it take to walk the entire length of the Trans-Canada Highway?

9. How much cooked rice would you get if you cooked 200 mL of uncooked rice?

Solve the problem if enough information is given. If information is missing, supply it and then solve the problem.

10. The sum of two numbers is 99. The ratio of the two numbers is 3 to 8. What are the two numbers?

11. It takes 6 min to saw a log into three pieces. How long would it take to saw the same log into four pieces?

12. A company manufactures metal rods that are 1.5 m long and have a mass of 2.2 kg each. What is the total mass of a box of these metal rods?

13. The Tigers beat the Knights by 10 points. If the Knights had scored twice as many points, they would have beaten the Tigers by 10 points. How many points did each team score?

14. Two trains leave the station in opposite directions at the same time. If train 1 travels at an average speed of 73 km/h and train 2 at 68 km/h, how far apart will they be in 4 h?

15. If gear A turns 3 times, how many times does gear C turn and in what direction?

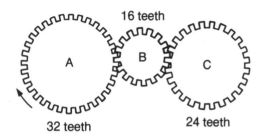

16 teeth

A

B

C

32 teeth

24 teeth

Chapter Checkup

1. Deirdre answered 21 out of 25 problems correctly on a test. Write the ratio.
   a. number correct to total number
   b. number incorrect to total number
   c. number correct to number incorrect

2. Write two equivalent ratios.
   a. 15 to 3   b. 24:32   c. 3.5 to 21.0
   d. $\frac{4.5}{0.4}$ e. 1:3:7   f. 100:25:20

3. A dry mix of concrete is made of 800 g of cement, 1.6 kg of sand, and 3.2 kg of gravel. Write the ratio of cement to sand to gravel in simplest form.

4. Copy and complete.
   a. $\frac{2}{3} = \frac{6}{\blacksquare}$ b. $\frac{25}{15} = \frac{\blacksquare}{3}$ c. $8:\blacksquare = 4:3$
   d. $\frac{14}{21} = \frac{20}{\blacksquare}$ e. $\frac{7}{4.2} = \frac{\blacksquare}{12}$ f. $\frac{0.3}{0.4} = \frac{12}{\blacksquare}$

5. Copy and complete by estimating.
   a. $\frac{7}{3} \doteq \frac{\blacksquare}{11}$ b. $\frac{11}{14} \doteq \frac{\blacksquare}{40}$ c. $\frac{56}{35} \doteq \frac{5}{\blacksquare}$

6.

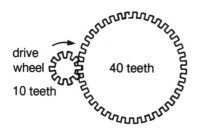

drive wheel 10 teeth   40 teeth

   a. What is the ratio of the number of teeth on the drive wheel to the number of teeth on the other wheel?
   b. Copy and complete the table.

drive wheel turns	1	4			80	100
other wheel turns			3	10		

7. Express each as a unit rate.
   a. 45 km travelled in 30 min
   b. 75 L of punch for 100 people
   c. 12 cans of corn for $9.35

8. Marty's pulse rate is 17 beats/15 s. What is his pulse rate per minute?

9. Carla can pick $1\frac{1}{2}$ baskets of strawberries in 30 min. At this rate, how many baskets can she pick in 2 h?

10. Arif earns $142.50 for working 30 h. How many hours must he work to earn $114?

11. Which package is more economical? Why would you expect this?
   a.
   $1.29
   b.
   $1.19

12. Use the scale drawing of a bee to find the length of a bee in millimetres.

   Scale 2:1

13. Estimate the straight-line distance in kilometres between the cities marked.

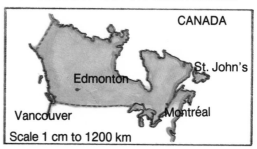

CANADA

St. John's

Edmonton

Vancouver

Montréal

Scale 1 cm to 1200 km

Cumulative Checkup

1. Express as a power.

   a. $3 \times 3 \times 3 \times 3$ **b.** $8 \times 8 \times 8$

   c. $2 \times 2 \times 2 \times 2 \times 2$

   d. $7 \times 7 \times 7 \times 7 \times 7 \times 7 \times 7 \times 7$

2. Evaluate.

   a. $12 - 8 \div 2 + 1$

   b. $(27 + 5) \times 6 - 2^3$

   c. $3^3 + 5 \times 6 - 2^4$

   d. $(16 - 3^2)^2 \div (5 + 2)^2$

   e. $\dfrac{5^2 - 42 \div 6 + 6 \times 4}{7^2 - 7}$

3. Calculate.

   a. 4.7×6.4 **b.** $29.5 \div 2.5$

   c. 368.2×7.8 **d.** $6.8 \div 5$

   e. $54.36 \div 1.2$ **f.** 44.4×0.44

   g. 0.25×0.25 **h.** $99.9 \div 0.09$

4. The product of two numbers is 0.522 06. One of the numbers is 33. What is the other number?

5. On April 1 the price of regular gasoline was 54.6¢/L. On April 30 the price had dropped to 37.4¢/L. How much more did it cost on April 1 than on April 30 to fill a 55 L tank?

6. Find the area of the region. One square represents 1 cm².

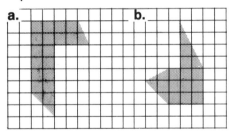

7. Copy and complete to the nearest tenth the chart for circles.

	d	r	C	Area
a.	4 m			
b.	12 cm			
c.		9 mm		
d.		5.1 m		

8. A ring with a diameter of 2.0 cm has 3.5 mm added to its circumference to make it larger. What is its new diameter?

9. A plate just fits inside a square box. If the circumference of the plate is 78.5 cm, what is the perimeter of the box?

10. Classify the regular polyhedron.

   a.   **b.**   **c.**

   d.   **e.**

11. Which regular polyhedron can be made from this net?

   a.   **b.**

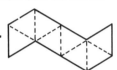

   c.   **d.**

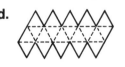

12. Sketch the faces of the prism. Find the surface area.

a.

6 m
2 m
4 m

b.

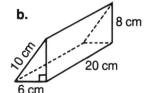

8 cm
10 cm
20 cm
6 cm

13. Find the volume of each prism in exercise 12.

14. Sketch the faces of the pyramid. Find the surface area.

10 m
9 m
9 m

15. A circular swimming pool has a diameter of 6 m and a height of 1.3 m. The pool is filled to a depth of 1.1 m.

  a. Find the surface area of the inside of the pool.

  b. Find the volume of water in the pool.

  c. Express the volume of water from part **b** in kilolitres.

16. Find the GCF.

  a. 15, 24   **b.** 18, 30   **c.** 26, 65

17. Find the LCM.

  a. 5, 7   **b.** 12, 21   **c.** 4, 14

18. A corner store sells only one kind of packaged envelopes. Cindy bought 24 of the envelopes and Annette bought 60 of them. What is the greatest number of envelopes possible for a package?

19. Copy and complete.

  a. $\frac{5}{8} = \frac{\blacksquare}{24}$ **b.** $\frac{28}{20} = \frac{7}{\blacksquare}$ **c.** $\frac{2}{3} = \frac{26}{\blacksquare}$

20. Express as a fraction.

  a. $7\frac{1}{3}$ **b.** $3\frac{2}{7}$ **c.** $4\frac{5}{9}$ **d.** $5\frac{3}{10}$

21. Copy and use >, <, = to make a true statement.

  a. $\frac{5}{7} \bigcirc \frac{6}{7}$ **b.** $\frac{1}{3} \bigcirc \frac{1}{4}$ **c.** $\frac{5}{8} \bigcirc \frac{2}{3}$

  d. $\frac{5}{12} \bigcirc \frac{4}{9}$ **e.** $2\frac{1}{2} \bigcirc \frac{8}{3}$ **f.** $\frac{14}{8} \bigcirc 1\frac{3}{4}$

22. Find each result. Then use the number line to decode the answers.

  E   C   C   I   L   R   A   P   O   R
  ├─┼─┼─┼─┼─┼─┼─┼─┼─┼─┤
  0   1

  a. $\frac{1}{2} + \frac{1}{10}$ **b.** $\frac{3}{4} - \frac{13}{20}$ **c.** $2\frac{1}{10} - 1\frac{4}{5}$

  d. $\frac{8}{15} \times \frac{3}{4}$ **e.** $1\frac{1}{2} - \frac{7}{10}$ **f.** $3\frac{1}{3} \times \frac{3}{10}$

  g. $\frac{3}{5} + \frac{3}{10}$ **h.** $\frac{2}{3} - \frac{7}{15}$ **i.** $3\frac{3}{5} - 2\frac{9}{10}$

  j. $4\frac{1}{3} \div 8\frac{2}{3}$

23. Divide.

  a. $4 \div \frac{1}{2}$ **b.** $\frac{2}{3} \div \frac{5}{9}$ **c.** $2\frac{1}{2} \div \frac{3}{4}$

  d. $6\frac{1}{4} \div 3\frac{1}{3}$ **e.** $4\frac{4}{5} \div 6$ **f.** $6\frac{2}{3} \div 2\frac{1}{2}$

24. Express as a decimal.

  a. $\frac{5}{8}$ **b.** $\frac{5}{6}$ **c.** $\frac{5}{11}$ **d.** $\frac{3}{2}$

25. Which decimals in exercise 24 are repeating?

26. Express as a fraction in lowest terms.

  a. 0.16   **b.** 0.35   **c.** $0.\overline{3}$ **d.** $0.\overline{27}$

7/Percent

Percents express many commercial rates such as sales tax, discounts, commissions, and interest. Real estate agents use percents to describe their commissions and the increase and decrease of house prices.

Get Set

1. Write a decimal and a fraction that tell how much is shaded.

   a. 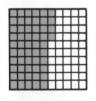 **b.**

   c.

   d. **e.**

2. Write a fraction for the shaded region.

   a. **b.**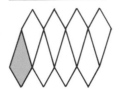

   c.  **d.**

3. Write a fraction for the unshaded region in exercise 2.

4. Copy and complete.

   a. $\frac{1}{2} = \frac{\blacksquare}{100}$ **b.** $\frac{1}{4} = \frac{\blacksquare}{100}$

   c. $\frac{1}{5} = \frac{\blacksquare}{100}$ **d.** $\frac{3}{4} = \frac{\blacksquare}{100}$

   e. $\frac{2}{5} = \frac{\blacksquare}{100}$ **f.** $\frac{4}{5} = \frac{\blacksquare}{100}$

   g. $\frac{1}{10} = \frac{\blacksquare}{100}$ **h.** $\frac{13}{25} = \frac{\blacksquare}{100}$

5. Copy and complete the equivalent fraction in lowest terms.

   a. $\frac{20}{100} = \frac{\blacksquare}{5}$ **b.** $\frac{40}{100} = \frac{\blacksquare}{5}$

   c. $\frac{75}{100} = \frac{3}{\blacksquare}$ **d.** $\frac{48}{100} = \frac{\blacksquare}{25}$

6. Express the fraction in lowest terms.

   a. $\frac{14}{100}$ **b.** $\frac{35}{100}$ **c.** $\frac{80}{100}$ **d.** $\frac{40}{100}$

7. Calculate mentally.

   a. $\frac{1}{4} \times 20$ **b.** $50 \times \frac{1}{2}$ **c.** $70 \times \frac{1}{10}$

   d. 40×7 **e.** 500×6 **f.** 3000×8

   g. $\frac{1}{8} \times 1600$ **h.** $\frac{1}{3} \times 450$ **i.** $\frac{1}{5} \times 4000$

8. Express as a decimal.

   a. $\frac{7}{8}$ **b.** $\frac{3}{4}$ **c.** $3\frac{1}{2}$ **d.** $\frac{5}{8}$

   e. $\frac{2}{3}$ **f.** $\frac{1}{9}$ **g.** $33\frac{1}{3}$ **h.** $\frac{4}{5}$

   i. $\frac{3}{8}$ **j.** $\frac{4}{9}$ **k.** $\frac{3}{5}$ **l.** $\frac{7}{9}$

9. **a.** Find $0.01 \times 21\ 000$. Use the answer to find $0.02 \times 21\ 000$.

   b. Find 0.10×4700. Use the answer to find 0.70×4700.

   c. Find 0.01×550. Use the answer to find 0.07×550.

10. Change months and weeks to years.

    a. 6 months = $\blacksquare$ a   **b.** 1 month = $\blacksquare$ a

    c. 3 months = $\blacksquare$ a   **d.** 7 months = $\blacksquare$ a

    e. 15 months = $\blacksquare$ a   **f.** 13 weeks = $\blacksquare$ a

    g. 26 weeks = $\blacksquare$ a   **h.** 10 weeks = $\blacksquare$ a

197

Meaning of Percent

What part of the floor plan is used for the music room and the guidance office?

The part of the floor plan used for each room can be described in several ways.

Music room

Ratio	**13** out of **100** squares are used.
Fraction	$\frac{13}{100}$ of the squares are used.
Decimal	**0.13** of the squares are used.

Guidance office

Ratio	**9.5** out of **100** squares are used.
Fraction	$\frac{9.5}{100}$ of the squares are used.
Decimal	**0.095** of the squares are used.

A percent can also be used.
Percent means **out of 100**. The symbol for percent is **%**.

13% of the floor plan is used for the music room.

9.5% of the floor plan is used for the guidance office.

WORKING TOGETHER

1. What percent is shaded?

a.   b.

c.

2. Express as a percent.

a. 14 out of 100 b. $\frac{39}{100}$ c. $\frac{4}{100}$

d. $\frac{121}{100}$ e. 0.21   f. 0.09

g. 1.62   h. 0.715   i. 3.00

3. Write the part of the floor plan used for classroom 2.

a. as a fraction   b. as a decimal

c. as a percent

APPLICATIONS AND EXERCISES

1. What percent is shaded?

a. **b.** **c.**

d.

2. Show the percent by shading a 10 by 10 section of grid paper.

a. 1% **b.** 62.5% **c.** $10\frac{1}{2}$% **d.** $33\frac{1}{3}$%

3. Express the decimal as a percent.

a. 0.42 **b.** 0.91 **c.** 0.5 **d.** 0.05

e. 1.0 **f.** 1.09 **g.** 0.672 **h.** 0.018

i. 0.006 **j.** 0.049 **k.** 0.238 **l.** 0.003

4. Express the fraction as a percent.

a. $\frac{77}{100}$ **b.** $\frac{39}{100}$ **c.** $\frac{80}{100}$ **d.** $\frac{8}{100}$

e. $\frac{100}{100}$ **f.** $\frac{211}{100}$ **g.** $\frac{700}{100}$ **h.** $\frac{0.7}{100}$

5. Write a percent that tells what part of the floor plan is used for the space.

a. classroom 1 **b.** the main office

c. the gymnasium

6. In the school band, 17 of 100 members play clarinet. What percent of the band play clarinet?

7. The ratio of the number of Grade 8 students to the number of Grade 7 students is 124 to 100. Express this as a percent.

8. The 100-member band had to order uniforms for 33 members. What percent of the band did not need new uniforms?

9. In the 100-member band, 40 members play woodwind and 49 members play brass instruments. What percent of the band play other kinds of instruments?

10. The sap of a sugar maple is 3 parts maple sugar to 97 parts water. What percent of the sap is water?

11. a. If 52% of the band members are female, what percent are male?

b. If 21% of the instruments need repair and 11% need to be replaced, what percent of the instruments are in satisfactory condition?

KEEPING SHARP

1. Express as a decimal.

a. $\frac{2}{5}$ **b.** $\frac{5}{8}$ **c.** $\frac{2}{3}$ **d.** $\frac{4}{5}$

e. $\frac{1}{3}$ **f.** $\frac{4}{9}$ **g.** $\frac{3}{8}$ **h.** $\frac{7}{9}$

i. $\frac{3}{5}$ **j.** $\frac{1}{8}$ **k.** $1\frac{2}{9}$ **l.** $3\frac{7}{8}$

2. Express as a fraction in lowest terms.

a. 0.25 **b.** 0.75 **c.** $0.\overline{3}$ **d.** 0.625

e. $0.\overline{4}$ **f.** 0.5 **g.** $1.\overline{6}$ **h.** 0.125

i. 0.875 **j.** $22.\overline{2}$ **k.** 1.8 **l.** 0.375

Fractions and Decimals as Percents

Kwame made 9 foul shots in 15 tries. Blair made 5 foul shots in 8 tries. Jason made 2 foul shots in 3 tries. Who had the best shooting percentage?

For Kwame: $\frac{9}{15} = \frac{3}{5}$ (lowest terms)

To find percent, express the fraction as an equivalent fraction with a denominator of 100 or as a decimal.

$$\frac{3}{5} = \frac{\boxed{}}{100} \quad (\times 20)$$

$$\frac{3}{5} = \frac{60}{100}$$
$$= 60\%$$

$$\frac{3}{5} = 0.60$$
$$5 \overline{)3.00} \quad 0.60$$
$$= 60\%$$

Kwame made 60% of his shots.

$\frac{5}{8}$ and $\frac{2}{3}$ cannot be expressed simply with denominators of 100.

The only way to express $\frac{5}{8}$ and $\frac{2}{3}$ as percents is to express the fractions as decimals.

For Blair: $\frac{5}{8} = 0.625$
$$= 62.5\%$$
$$8 \overline{)5.000} \quad 0.625$$

Blair made 62.5% of his shots.

Jason had the best shooting percentage.

For Jason: $\frac{2}{3} = 0.66\overline{6}$
$$= 66.\overline{6}\%$$
$$3 \overline{)2.000} \quad 0.666\ldots$$

Jason made 66.$\overline{6}$% of his shots.

WORKING TOGETHER

1. Find the missing term. Then express the fraction as a percent.

a. $\frac{1}{4} = \frac{\boxed{}}{100}$
   $= \boxed{}\%$

b. $\frac{3}{4} = \frac{\boxed{}}{100}$
   $= \boxed{}\%$

c. $\frac{1}{2} = \frac{\boxed{}}{100}$
   $= \boxed{}\%$

d. $\frac{1}{5} = \frac{\boxed{}}{100}$
   $= \boxed{}\%$

e. $\frac{2}{5} = \frac{\boxed{}}{100}$
   $= \boxed{}\%$

f. $\frac{1}{10} = \frac{\boxed{}}{100}$
   $= \boxed{}\%$

g. $\frac{3}{10} = \frac{\boxed{}}{100}$
   $= \boxed{}\%$

h. $\frac{4}{25} = \frac{\boxed{}}{100}$
   $= \boxed{}\%$

i. $\frac{7}{20} = \frac{\boxed{}}{100}$
   $= \boxed{}\%$

j. $\frac{122}{200} = \frac{\boxed{}}{100}$
   $= \boxed{}\%$

k. $\frac{743}{1000} = \frac{\boxed{}}{100}$
   $= \boxed{}\%$

l. $\frac{3}{50} = \frac{\boxed{}}{100}$
   $= \boxed{}\%$

2. Express the fraction as a decimal. Then express the decimal as a percent.

a. $\frac{1}{8}$ b. $\frac{5}{8}$ c. $\frac{1}{3}$ d. $\frac{4}{9}$

e. $\frac{5}{6}$ f. $\frac{7}{16}$ g. $\frac{10}{9}$ h. $\frac{5}{3}$

3. Write the fraction in lowest terms. Then express this fraction as a percent.

a. $\frac{4}{20}$ b. $\frac{8}{16}$ c. $\frac{27}{36}$ d. $\frac{5}{15}$

e. $\frac{15}{40}$ f. $\frac{147}{147}$ g. $\frac{35}{21}$ h. $\frac{7}{28}$

APPLICATIONS AND EXERCISES

1. What percent is shaded?

   a.   **b.**   **c.**

   d.   **e.**   **f.**

2. Express the fraction as a percent.

   a. $\frac{4}{5}$ **b.** $\frac{9}{20}$ **c.** $\frac{13}{50}$ **d.** $\frac{17}{25}$

   e. $\frac{23}{20}$ **f.** $\frac{17}{5}$ **g.** $\frac{183}{300}$ **h.** $\frac{556}{2000}$

3. Express the fraction as a decimal, then
    as a percent.

   a. $\frac{7}{8}$ **b.** $\frac{7}{9}$ **c.** $\frac{4}{3}$ **d.** $\frac{11}{8}$

   e. $\frac{11}{16}$ **f.** $\frac{5}{12}$ **g.** $\frac{7}{6}$ **h.** $\frac{8}{3}$

4. What percent is shaded?

   a.   **b.**   **c.**

5. What percent is not shaded in exercise 4?

6. Write the fraction in lowest terms. Then
   express this fraction as a percent.

   a. $\frac{30}{80}$ **b.** $\frac{35}{80}$ **c.** $\frac{10}{24}$ **d.** $\frac{150}{90}$

   e. $\frac{20}{40}$ **f.** $\frac{70}{70}$ **g.** $\frac{140}{20}$ **h.** $\frac{45}{60}$

7. **a.** What percent of 20 is 7?
   b. What percent of 25 is 18?
   c. What percent is 30 of 50?
   d. What percent is 140 of 200?

8. **a.** What percent of 8 is 11?
   b. What percent of 12 is 5?
   c. What percent of 3 is 7?
   d. What percent is 4 of 9?

9. Shelley's basketball team won 12 games
   and lost 8 games. What percent of its
   games did Shelley's team win?

10. A baseball player's batting average is
    the ratio of the number of successful hits
    to the number of times at bat, expressed
    as a decimal to the nearest thousandth.

    a. What is the batting average of a
    player who was at bat 140 times and
    made 40 base hits?

    b. Express this as a percent.

11. Calculate the percent of Canada that
    each of the four provinces covers. The
    approximate area of Canada is
    10 000 000 km².

Province	Area (km²)
Alberta	664 000
Québec	1 547 000
Nova Scotia	56 000
Newfoundland	406 000

KEEPING SHARP

1. Evaluate.

   a. $\frac{2}{3} \times \frac{1}{2}$ **b.** $\frac{3}{4} \times \frac{5}{8}$ **c.** $1\frac{1}{5} \times \frac{2}{5}$ **d.** $\frac{1}{3} \times 2\frac{7}{8}$ **e.** $3\frac{1}{2} \times 1\frac{1}{9}$ **f.** $2\frac{1}{6} \times 5\frac{3}{4}$

   g. $\frac{1}{4} \div \frac{1}{3}$ **h.** $\frac{7}{8} \div \frac{3}{5}$ **i.** $3\frac{1}{3} \div \frac{4}{7}$ **j.** $\frac{2}{9} \div 1\frac{1}{2}$ **k.** $2\frac{5}{8} \div 1\frac{1}{4}$ **l.** $3\frac{3}{4} \div 7\frac{1}{2}$

Percents as Decimals and Fractions

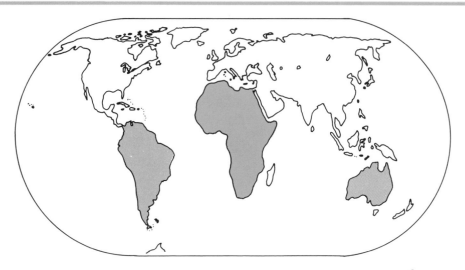

South America is 12% of the land on Earth.

Australia is 5.2% of the land on Earth.

Africa is $22\frac{2}{9}$% of the land on Earth.

To express a percent as a decimal or a fraction, replace % with hundredths. ⟶ **South America**

$$12\% = 12 \text{ hundredths}$$
$$= \mathbf{0.12}$$
$$= \frac{12}{100}$$
$$= \frac{3}{25} \quad \left(\text{lowest terms}\right)$$

Australia

$$5.2\% = 5.2 \text{ hundredths}$$
$$= \mathbf{0.052}$$
$$= \frac{52}{1000}$$
$$= \frac{13}{250} \quad \left(\text{lowest terms}\right)$$

For percents that involve a fraction, first change the fraction to a decimal. ⟶ **Africa** $\quad 22\frac{2}{9}\% = 22.\overline{2}\%$

$$= 0.22\overline{2}$$
$$= \frac{2}{9}$$

WORKING TOGETHER

1. Express as a decimal, then as a fraction.

a. 25%   **b.** 20%   **c.** 30%

d. 3%   **e.** 210%   **f.** 12.5%

g. 62.5%   **h.** 33.$\overline{3}$%   **i.** 44.$\overline{4}$%

j. 66.$\overline{6}$%   **k.** 37$\frac{1}{2}$%   **l.** 12$\frac{1}{2}$%

2. What percent is shaded? Write a fraction in lowest terms equivalent to the percent.

a.   **b.**   **c.**

1. Express the percent as a decimal.

   a. 12%   **b.** 120%   **c.** 1.2%

   d. 114.2%   **e.** 77.$\overline{7}$%   **f.** 66.$\overline{6}$%

   g. 12$\frac{1}{5}$%   **h.** 33$\frac{1}{3}$%   **i.** $\frac{4}{5}$%

2. Express the percent as a decimal.

Continent	Percent of world's population
Asia	60%
Europe	15$\frac{1}{4}$%
Africa	10$\frac{1}{2}$%
North America	8$\frac{1}{5}$%
South America	5$\frac{3}{5}$%
Australia	$\frac{1}{4}$%
Islands	$\frac{1}{5}$%

3. Express the percent as a fraction.

   a. 600%   **b.** 0.6%   **c.** 6%

   d. 37.5%   **e.** 55.$\overline{5}$%   **f.** 11.$\overline{1}$%

   g. 66$\frac{2}{3}$%   **h.** 62$\frac{1}{2}$%   **i.** 15$\frac{1}{4}$%

4. In a school election Takeo received 28% of the votes, Joanna received 46%, and Lee received the remaining votes. Express each percent as a decimal and as a fraction.

5. In a recent year, 66$\frac{2}{3}$% of the Canadian population spoke only English, 20% spoke only French, 13% spoke English and French, and the rest spoke neither English nor French. Express each percent as a decimal and as a fraction.

6. Oceans make up a large part of the Earth's water.

Pacific	46.0%
Atlantic	23.9%
Indian	20.3%
Arctic	2.6%

   a. What percent is occupied by the Earth's remaining bodies of water?

   b. Express each percent as a decimal, then as a fraction.

7. Copy and complete the chart.

	Fraction	Decimal	Percent
a.			1%
b.		0.1	
c.	$\frac{1}{8}$		
d.			20%
e.	$\frac{1}{3}$		
f.		0.375	
g.			62$\frac{1}{2}$%
h.			66.$\overline{6}$%
i.		1.75	
j.	1$\frac{4}{5}$		

Try This

A photocopying machine can make reduced-size copies of pictures.

The machine can reduce a picture to 83$\frac{1}{3}$%, 75%, or 66$\frac{2}{3}$% of its original size.

1. How would you use the machine to make a copy that is 50% of the original size?

100 %

75%

Finding a Percent of a Number I

A new musical group performed
before an audience of 17 000.
12.5% of the audience purchased
souvenirs of the performance.
How many purchased souvenirs?

Find 12.5% of 17 000.

To find a percent of a number, change the
percent to a decimal and multiply.

12.5% of 17 000
= 0.125 × 17 000
= 2125

> 12.5% of 17 000
> $\doteq \frac{1}{8} \times 16\ 000$
> = 2000

2125 seems reasonable.

2125 people purchased souvenirs of the concert.

WORKING TOGETHER

1. Copy and complete the estimation.

   a. 75% of $11.99 $\doteq \frac{3}{4} \times$ $12

   $= 3(\frac{1}{4} \times $12)$

   $= 3(\blacksquare)$

   $= \triangle$

   b. 80% of 1610 $\doteq \frac{4}{5} \times$ ⬤

   $= 4(\frac{1}{5} \times$ ⬤$)$

   $= 4(\blacksquare)$

   $= \triangle$

   c. 62.5% of 238 $\doteq \frac{5}{8} \times$ ⬤

   $= \blacksquare(\frac{1}{8} \times$ ⬤$)$

   $= \blacksquare(\blacksquare)$

   $= \triangle$

2. Change the percent to a fraction.
   Then estimate.

   a. 50% of 4180   **b.** 25% of 3819

   c. 20% of 387   **d.** $33.\overline{3}$% of 241

   e. $37\frac{1}{2}$% of 410   **f.** 150% of 1385

3. Change the percent to a decimal.
   Then estimate.

   a. 40% of $31   **b.** 60% of $24

   c. 20% of 49   **d.** $12\frac{1}{2}$% of 202

4. Which estimates in exercises 2 and 3 are
   high?

5. Calculate. Is the answer reasonable?

   a. 25% of 250   **b.** 62.5% of 41

   c. 30% of 986   **d.** $33.\overline{3}$% of 610

APPLICATIONS AND EXERCISES

1. Estimate.

   a. 50% of 39
   b. 25% of 41
   c. 12.5% of $31.98
   d. 20% of $34.90
   e. 75% of 398
   f. 30% of 99
   g. 40% of 34
   h. 62.5% of 440
   i. 66.6̄% of 75
   j. 33.3̄% of $11.97

2. Which estimates in exercise 1 are low?

3. Calculate each part in exercise 1. Is the answer reasonable?

4. The Moncton Millionaires hockey team won 80% of its 46 games.

   a. Estimate the number of games won.
   b. Calculate the number of games won.

5. About $87\frac{1}{2}$% of the mass of a grapefruit is water.

   a. Estimate the mass of water in a 240 g grapefruit.
   b. Calculate the mass of water in the grapefruit.

6. An antifreeze solution is made by mixing 60% antifreeze with 40% water. How much of each is needed to prepare 5 L of solution?

7. Ernst receives a commission of $12\frac{1}{2}$% for selling records. That is, he earns $12\frac{1}{2}$% of his total sales.

   a. How much does he earn if he sells $480 worth?
   b. How much does he earn if he sells $1350?
   c. How much does he earn if he sells 500 records at $8.50 each?

8. In 1986 the cost of food was about 125% of its cost in 1981.

   a. Estimate the cost of each item in 1986.

   Food Costs in 1981

i.	1 dozen large eggs	$1.26
ii.	1 loaf of bread	$0.85
iii.	1 dozen oranges	$2.11
iv.	1 apple pie	$1.94

   b. Calculate the cost of each item in 1986.

9. a. Estimate the volume of syrup in the can.

   b. Calculate the volume of syrup in the can.

   375 mL   25% syrup

Try This

Last year Kelly's rate of pay was $4.75/h.
This year she received a 33.3̄% increase in wages.

1. a. Estimate her present rate of pay.
   b. Calculate her present rate of pay.

2. Express the ratio of this year's pay to last year's as a percent.

3. Use your answer from exercise 2 to calculate her present rate of pay in another way.

Finding a Percent of a Number II

Mei and Greer both have savings accounts.
Mei earns $59 weekly and saves 6%.
Greer earns $47.60 weekly and saves 28%.
How much are each girl's weekly savings?

Mei's savings

 6% of $59
= 0.06 × $59
= $3.54

> To estimate Mei's savings,
> find 6% of $60.
> First find   0.01 × $60 = $0.60
> Then multiply by 6.
> $0.60 × 6 = $3.60

$3.54 seems reasonable.
Mei's weekly savings are $3.54.

Greer's savings

 28% of $47.60
= 0.28 × $47.60
= $13.33

> To estimate Greer's savings,
> find 30% of $50.
> First find   10% × $50 = 0.1 × $50
>   = $5
> Then multiply by 3.
> $5 × 3 = $15

$13.33 seems reasonable.
Greer's weekly savings are $13.33.

WORKING TOGETHER

1. Find 100%.

  a. 91   **b.** 17   **c.** 3296 **d.** 4.31

2. Find 10%.

  a. 82   **b.** 450   **c.** 43.1 **d.** 8

3. Use the answers from exercise 2 to find
20% of each.

4. Find 1%.

  a. 73   **b.** 6   **c.** 142   **d.** 9.5

5. Use the answers from exercise 4 to find
7% of each.

6. Estimate.

  a. 5% of 12   **b.** 3% of 58

  c. 32% of 479   **d.** 47% of 69

  e. 98% of 361   **f.** $63\frac{1}{2}$% of 72

7. Which estimates in exercise 6 are high?

8. Calculate each part in exercise 6. Is the
answer reasonable?

206

APPLICATIONS AND EXERCISES

1. Find the percent of $540.

    a. 3% **b.** 7% **c.** 20% **d.** 60%

2. Find the percent of $3200.

    a. 4% **b.** 8% **c.** 90% **d.** 200%

3. Andrea has 280 customers on her paper route. 90% of them paid last collection day. How many paid?

4. Estimate.

    a. 70% of 48   **b.** 38% of 720

    c. 5% of 375   **d.** 91% of 61

    e. 40% of 205   **f.** $2\frac{1}{2}$% of 9

    g. 7.8% of 183   **h.** 18% of $1\frac{1}{4}$

    i. 80.9% of 111   **j.** 2% of 30.9

    k. 78% of 74   **l.** 27% of 39

5. Calculate each part in exercise 4. Is the answer reasonable?

6. In a test of 78 problems, Marc answered 68% correctly. How many problems did he answer correctly?

7. **a.** Hans receives $8\frac{3}{4}$% commission for selling lawn mowers. Estimate his commission for the total sales.

      i. $72   **ii.** $124   **iii.** $73.80

    b. Calculate each commission in part **a.**

8. In an election, 71% of the eligible voters voted. 25 300 people were eligible to vote. How many did vote?

9. Of the records sold by Maria's Music Store, 44.4% were rock, 21.2% were classical, and 24.4% were jazz. 2780 records were sold during the summer. How many of each type were sold?

10. In a survey of 270 Grade 9 students, 58% liked rock music. How many did not like rock music?

11. About 23% of Canada's population are under the age of 15.

    a. If Canada's population is 25 318 000, about how many people are under 15?

    b. In a city of 54 000 people, about how many people would you expect to be under 15?

Try This

1. Marion is paid a graduated **commission**. Each month, Marion earns $12\frac{1}{2}$% of sales on the first $500, 15% on sales from $500 to $1000, and 18% on sales over $1000. Find Marion's earnings for each month.

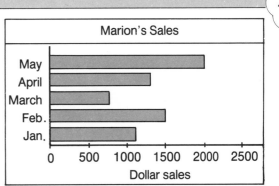

Marion's Sales

Percents and Circle Graphs

This circle graph shows the various holiday destinations of Canadians. If 830 000 Canadians travelled last year, how many travelled within Canada?

Canadian Holiday Locations

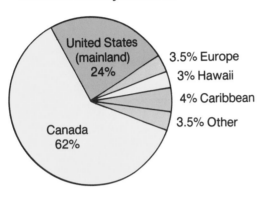

Find 62% of 830 000.

$$62\% \text{ of } 830\,000$$
$$= 0.62 \times 830\,000$$
$$= 514\,600$$

514 600 seems reasonable.
514 600 Canadians travelled within Canada.

> 60% of 800 000
> **Step 1** 10% of 800 000
> $= 0.1 \times 800\,000$
> $= 80\,000$
> **Step 2** 80 000 × 6
> $= 480\,000$

WORKING TOGETHER

1. Use 1% of 800 000. Estimate the number of Canadian tourists.

   a. Hawaii   **b.** Caribbean

   c. Europe and other countries

2. Calculate the number of Canadian tourists in exercise 1.

3. **a.** Use a fraction to estimate the number of Canadians who visited the United States.

   b. Calculate the number who visited the United States.

4. This circle graph shows how Sharon's time is spent during one year.

   Sharon's Activities

   75% Education

   Vacation 5%   20%   Part-time job

   a. Estimate the number of weeks Sharon spends doing each activity.

   b. Calculate the number of weeks for each activity.

APPLICATIONS AND EXERCISES

1. A family spent $1580 in all.

   a. Estimate the money spent.

      i. accommodation   **ii.** entertainment

      iii. souvenirs   **iv.** food

   b. Calculate each expense.

   c. What are two ways to calculate the amount of money spent on gas?

   d. Use one way to calculate the amount of money spent on gas.

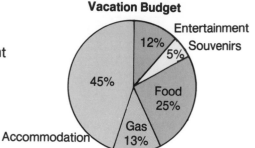

Vacation Budget

2. **a.** Which region has the greatest area?

   b. About what fraction of Canada's area is in Central Canada?

   c. Order the regions from the greatest area to the least.

   d. The area of Canada is about 9 922 330 km². Find the area of each region.

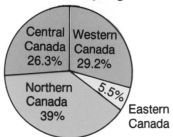

Canada's Area by Regions

3. The Canadian government spent $107 682 million in one year.

   a. Estimate the money spent.

      i. health and welfare   **ii.** defence
      iii. other expenses   **iv.** grants

   b. Calculate each amount in part **a**.

   c. Calculate the money spent on the public debt.

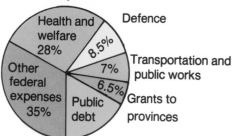

Federal Expenditures

How many students is 25% of 32 students?

[32] [×] [25] [÷] [100] [=] (8.)   OR   [32] [×] [25] [%] (8.)

Using [%] saves the steps [÷] [100] [=] or five key presses!

Does [25] [×] [32] [%] give the same result? Why?

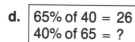

1. Use the given answer to find the missing answer. Check.

   a. | 20% of 35 = 7
   35% of 20 = ?

   b. | 80% of 15 = 12
   15% of 80 = ?

   c. | 40% of 25 = 10
   25% of 40 = ?

   d. | 65% of 40 = 26
   40% of 65 = ?

PRACTICE

1. What percent is shaded?

   a. red

   b. yellow

   c. orange

   d. white or gray

2. Express the fraction as a percent.

   a. $\frac{41}{100}$ **b.** $\frac{56}{100}$ **c.** $\frac{7.9}{100}$ **d.** $\frac{0.4}{100}$

3. Express the decimal as a percent.

   a. 0.91   **b.** 0.08   **c.** 0.7

   d. 0.325   **e.** 0.005   **f.** 5.0

4. Express the percent as a decimal.

   a. 71%   **b.** 70%   **c.** 7%

   d. 0.7%   **e.** $41\frac{1}{2}$%   **f.** $13\frac{3}{4}$%

5. What percent is shaded?

   a.   **b.**   **c.**

6. Use a fraction to estimate.

   a. 20% of 100   **b.** 50% of 900

   c. 25% of 440   **d.** 80% of 50

7. Choose the best estimate.

   a. 30% of 86

   | 2.7 | 27 | 270 |

   b. 96% of 90

   | 9 | 90 | 900 |

   c. 61% of 17

   | 10 | 100 | 100 |

   d. 137% of 37

   | 5.6 | 56 | 560 |

8. Calculate.

   a. 0.4% of 510   **b.** 32.4% of 85

   c. $42\frac{1}{2}$% of 780   **d.** $73\frac{3}{4}$% of 96

9. During a flu epidemic 40% of the 385 students in the school were absent.

   a. How many were present?

   b. How many would you expect to be absent in a class of 28 students?

10. This circle graph shows recent statistics on the ethnic origin of the population of New Brunswick. Calculate the size of each group if the population of New Brunswick is 720 000.

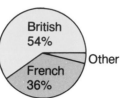

11. Copy and complete.

	Fraction	Decimal	Percent
a.	$\frac{3}{5}$		
b.	$\frac{7}{20}$		
c.		0.07	
d.		0.055	
e.			136%
f.	$\frac{5}{8}$		
g.			$60\frac{1}{2}$%
h.	$3\frac{1}{2}$		
i.	$2\frac{4}{9}$		

12. **a.** What percent is 20 out of 25?

   b. What percent of 50 is 35?

   c. What percent is 13 out of 16?

   d. What percent of 80 is 60?

   e. What percent of 22 is 8?

The Percent Key

The keys of a calculator show the functions that a person uses most frequently. Because people need to calculate percentages so often, most calculators include a %‍ key. The following examples show how %‍ is used.

20 × 50 %	calculates 50% of 20 (or 20% of 50).
20 + 50 %	adds 50% of 20 to 20.
20 − 50 %	subtracts 50% of 20 from 20.
20 ÷ 50 %	shows 20 out of 50 as a percent, or shows the number that 20 is 50% of.

1. Carry out the above calculations mentally. Then use the key press.

2. Estimate. Then use %‍ to calculate.
   a. 75% of 30　　b. 12% of 45　　c. 65% of 250　　d. 110% of 60
   e. 5% of 50　　f. 30% of 50　　g. 75% of 50　　h. 90% of 50

3. Estimate an increase of 25%. Then use %‍ to calculate.
   a. 40　　b. 75　　c. 135　　d. 150　　e. 200　　f. 240

4. Estimate a decrease of 75%. Then use %‍ to calculate.
   a. 60　　b. 90　　c. 125　　d. 180　　e. 250　　f. 280

5. Estimate. Then use %‍ to calculate.
   a. 30 out of 40　　b. 15 out of 60　　c. 90 out of 150　　d. 25 out of 80
   e. 12 out of 50　　f. 25 out of 110　　g. 17 out of 30　　h. 125 out of 500
   i. the ratio of 43 to 76　　j. the ratio of 30 to 20

6. Solve using %‍.
   a. 90 out of 600 voters did not vote. What percent did not vote?
   b. A hockey team won 65% of its 40 games. How many games were won?
   c. A basket of food cost $26.75 in 1986. In 1987 the cost increased by 8%. How much did the same basket cost in 1987?
   d. The cost of a $120.50 coat was reduced by 30%. What was the reduced price of the coat?
   e. There are 800 g of sunflower seeds in a 2.5 kg bag of birdseed. What percent of the mixture is sunflower seeds?

Finding a Number When a Percent of It Is Known

On the average, boys reach 90% of their
final height by the time they are 12.5 a.

Andrew is almost thirteen years old.
His height is 153 cm. Approximately what
will his final height be?

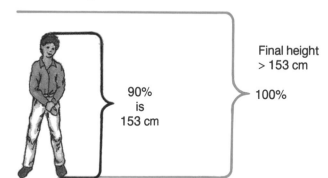

90% is 153 cm

Final height > 153 cm

100%

 90% of his final height is 153 cm.

1% of his final height is $\frac{153}{90}$ or 1.7.

100% of his final height is 1.7 × 100.
His final height is 170 cm.

Check.
  90% of 170
= 0.9 × 170
= 153

170 > 153   The answer seems reasonable.
Andrew's final height should be about 170 cm.

WORKING TOGETHER

1. Copy and complete. Check the answer.

  a. 15% of the number is 30.

    1% of the number is $\frac{30}{\triangle}$ or ⬤.

    100% of the number is ⬤ × 100.
    The number is ▨.

  b. 70% of the number is 21.

    1% of the number is $\frac{21}{\triangle}$ or ⬤.

    100% of the number is ⬤ × 100.
    The number is ▨.

2. Decide if the missing number is larger or
smaller than the given number.

  a. 20% of the number is 40.

  b. 200% of the number is 16.

  c. 2% of the number is 8.

3. Choose the correct answer.

  a. 100% of ▨ is 17.

    | 1 | 17 | 35 | 100 |

  b. 1% of ▨ is 5.

    | 1 | 5 | 100 | 500 |

  c. 50% of ▨ is 40.

    | 20 | 40 | 50 | 80 |

  d. 20% of ▨ is 15.

    | 3 | 15 | 20 | 75 |

1. Copy and complete.

   a. 10% of the number is 56.

   1% of the number is $\frac{56}{\triangle}$ or ⊙.

   100% of the number is ⊙ × 100 or ▣.

   b. 2% of the number is 8.

   1% of the number is $\frac{8}{\triangle}$ or ⊙.

   100% of the number is ⊙ × 100 or ▣.

   c. 98% of the number is 196.

   1% of the number is $\frac{196}{\triangle}$ or ⊙.

   100% of the number is ⊙ × 100 or ▣.

   d. 150% of the number is 24.

   1% of the number is $\frac{24}{\triangle}$ or ⊙.

   100% of the number is ⊙ × 100 or ▣.

2. Check each answer in exercise 1.

3. Decide if the missing number is larger or smaller than the given number. Find the missing number. Then check the answer.

   a. 15% of the number is 25.

   b. 300% of the number is 66.

   c. 18 is 20% of the number.

   d. 84 is 6% of the number.

   e. 180% of the number is 72.

   f. 102 is 17% of the number.

4. A boy reaches 50% of his adult height by the time he is two years old. Pedro was 88.5 cm tall on his second birthday. What will his approximate adult height be?

5. On the average, girls reach 90% of their final height by the time they are 10.5 a.

   a. Tina is almost eleven and her height is 144 cm. Approximate her final height.

   b. Amy is 10.5 a and her height is 130 cm. Approximate her final height.

6. It is recommended that no more than 30% of a person's income be spent on housing. The rent for an apartment is $480 per month. What is the minimum monthly income a person should have to rent this apartment?

7. The owner of a record store buys records from the manufacturer at $4.95 each. This is 60% of the price the customer pays for each record. What is the retail price?

8. An antiseptic solution for cuts is 75% rubbing alcohol and 25% water. How much of this solution can be made using 250 mL of rubbing alcohol?

9. At a mine in Newfoundland 19% of an ore is iron. How many tonnes of ore are required to yield 15 t of iron?

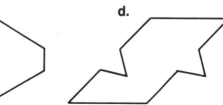

1. Where can you make one straight cut so that the two pieces will form a square?

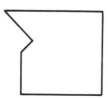

2. For each piece, estimate its percent of the whole square.

Try This

Discount

Merete is buying a pair of skis that regularly sells for $234.98. By what amount is the price reduced if she purchases the skis now? What is the sale price?

The amount the price is reduced is the **discount**.

A 20% discount means the price of the skis is reduced by 20% of their regular price.

Discount = 20% of the regular price
= 20% of $234.98
= 0.20 × $234.98
= $46.996
= $47.00

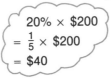
20% × $200
= $\frac{1}{5}$ × $200
= $40

The price is reduced by $47.

Sale Price = Regular Price − Discount
= $234.98 − $47.00
= $187.98

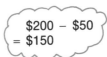
$200 − $50
= $150

The sale price is $187.98.

WORKING TOGETHER

1. Find the discount and the sale price.

   a. Regular price $32.50
   Discount 15%

   b. Regular price $24.98
   Discount 25%

2. 40% discount on ski equipment is $128.

   a. Copy and complete to find the regular price. Check the answer.
   40% of regular price is $128.
   1% of regular price is $\frac{128}{\triangle}$ or ⬡.
   100% of regular price is ⬡ × 100 or ◼.
   The regular price is ◼.

   b. Find the sale price of the ski equipment.

APPLICATIONS AND EXERCISES

1. Estimate the discount.

   a. Skates—Regular price $38.59
   Discount 18%

   b. Bicycle—Regular price $142.98
   Discount 25%

   c. Stereo—Regular price $246.59
   Discount $10\frac{1}{2}$%

2. Calculate the discount and the sale price of the items in exercise 1.

3. A store gives a 25% discount on equipment purchased by a hockey team. Calculate the cost to outfit 20 players.

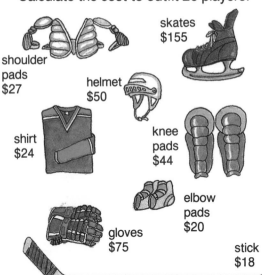

shoulder pads $27

skates $155

helmet $50

shirt $24

knee pads $44

gloves $75

elbow pads $20

stick $18

4. Calculate the regular price.

   a. 20% discount is $35.

   b. 35% discount is $140.

   c. 18% discount is $9.

   d. 12% discount is $7.20.

5. Calculate the sale price for each discount in exercise 4.

6. Barry bought a ski jacket at a discount of 20%. With this discount he saved $28.50.

   a. Calculate the regular price of the ski jacket.

   b. What was the sale price?

7. Lucia receives a 10% discount on her purchases at Hartley's Sports Store. What is the regular price of the item?

   a. running shoes, discount $2.50

   b. track suit, discount $4.22

   c. jacket, discount $6.98

8. **a.** Calculate the sale price for each item in exercise 7.

   b. Express the sale price as a percent of the regular price.

   c. How can you calculate the sale price directly?

Try This

1. The price of a dirt bike was reduced to 80% of the original price during the first week of a sale. For each of the second and third weeks the price was again reduced to 80% of the previous week's price. After the three discounts, the bike sold for $1536.

   What was the original price of the bike?

Sales Tax

How much did the skateboard cost in Ontario?

When the skateboard was purchased, an
extra charge was added to the price.

This extra charge is the **sales tax**.

In Ontario the sales tax was 7%.
This means that, for every $1.00 spent on
a taxable item in Ontario, 7¢ was added as tax.

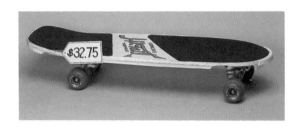

To calculate the sales tax, multiply.

7% of price
= 7% of $32.75
= 0.07 × $32.75
= $2.2925
= $2.29

> 7¢ for every dollar
> 7¢ × 30
> = 210¢ or $2.10

The sales tax was $2.29.

Total Cost = Regular Price + Sales Tax
           = $32.75 + $2.29
           = $35.04

The skateboard cost $35.04 in Ontario.

Province	Sales tax (1987)
British Columbia	7%
Alberta	0%
Saskatchewan	5%
Manitoba	6%
Ontario	7%
Québec	9%
New Brunswick	11%
Nova Scotia	10%
Prince Edward Island	10%
Newfoundland	12%

WORKING TOGETHER

1. Can the expression be used to find the
   total cost of a $25 taxable item in Québec?

   a. $25 + 0.09 × $25   **b.** 0.09 × $25

   c. 1.09 × $25   **d.** 0.9 × $25

2. A pair of skates was priced at $41.95 in
   New Brunswick.

   a. Find 11% of $41.95.

   b. Find the total cost.

3. A new car was priced at $12 000 in
   Newfoundland.

   a. Find 12% of $12 000.

   b. Find the total price.

   c. Compare the result from part **b** with
   112% of $12 000.

4. In which province might you have been to
   use this calculator sequence for finding
   the cost of an item?
   32.75 × 0.05 + 32.75 = (34.3875)

1. Estimate the sales tax paid in Newfoundland for the item.

a. $12   b. $23.95

c. $59.95   d. $62.95

2. Calculate the sales tax for each item in exercise 1.

3. What would have been the total cost of a $55 ski jacket in each province of Canada?

4. Copy and complete. In which province might these prices have been paid?

	Item	Price	Price + 6% tax
a.	mini-bike	$485.00	
b.	baseball glove	$ 48.60	
c.	bicycle	$169.95	
d.	puck	$ 0.75	
e.	tennis racket	$ 29.95	

5. Tanya bought these items at Fong's Variety in Halifax: shampoo $2.45, gum 35¢, suntan lotion $3.49, batteries $2.78, garbage bags $3.99, insect repellent $2.98.

a. Find the total before sales tax.

b. How much did Tanya pay?

6. Olga Johannsen bought a camera for $219. Her bill came to $243.09.

a. How much was the sales tax? Express this as a percent of the original price.

b. In which province might she have made this purchase?

7. The following purchases were made at a sports store: adult ski mitts $26, ski suit $210, and ski boots $125; child's scarf and toque $12, ski suit $55, and sport socks $8. Children's items are non-taxable. Find the total cost in this province.

a. Québec   b. Manitoba

c. Saskatchewan

The computer language that a programmer decides to use depends on the kind of task the computer is to perform.

COBOL (**Co**mmon **B**usiness **O**riented **L**anguage) is used mainly in business, where large quantities of information are handled and few mathematical or scientific calculations are required.

BASIC (**B**eginner's **A**ll-Purpose **S**ymbolic **I**nstruction **C**ode) is the language most beginners use to handle numbers and words. It is "built into" most microcomputers, so there is no need to load special software.

Suppose you typed the following BASIC statements.
LET A = 2.5
LET B = 4000
LET C = 0.006
LET D = 12

1. Predict the output for the BASIC command.

a. PRINT A + D

b. PRINT "A + D"

c. PRINT "A TIMES B IS " A ✳ B

d. PRINT D " SQUARED IS " D ∧ 2

e. PRINT A ✳ D ∧ 2

f. PRINT (A ✳ D) ∧ 2

g. PRINT "B DIVIDED BY C IS " B/C

h. PRINT " A/D = " A/D

i. PRINT " B TO THE 4TH IS " B ∧ 4

Simple Interest

Tess deposits $180 in a savings account. If she makes no more deposits or withdrawals, how much will her money earn in 3 months?

The bank pays Tess a certain amount of money for the use of her money. This amount is called **interest**.

A formula can be used to find simple interest.

Interest = Principal × Rate × Time

- Amount deposited
- %
- Expressed in years

$$= \$180 \times 9\frac{1}{2}\% \times \frac{3}{12}$$
$$= \$180 \times 9.5\% \times \frac{1}{4}$$
$$= \$180 \times 0.095 \times 0.25$$
$$= \$4.275$$
$$= \$4.28$$

$$\$200 \times 10\% \times \frac{1}{4}$$
$$= \$200 \times 0.1 \times \frac{1}{4}$$
$$= \$20 \times \frac{1}{4}$$
$$= \$5$$

Her money earns $4.28 in interest.

Total amount = Principal + Interest
$$= \$180 + \$4.28$$
$$= \$184.28$$

Tess's money will be worth $184.28 after 3 months.

WORKING TOGETHER

1. Express the time as a fraction of a year. Express the fraction as a decimal.

   a. 3 months   **b.** 9 months   **c.** 4 months

   d. 13 weeks   **e.** 39 weeks   **f.** 16 weeks

2. Can the expression be used to find the interest on $800 for one year at 11%/a?

   a. $800 \times 0.1 \times 11$ **b.** $800 \times 0.11 \times 1$

3. Can the expression be used to find the interest on $700 for 3 months at 9%/a?

   a. $700 \times 0.25 \times 9$ **b.** $700 \times 0.09 \times 0.25$

4. Carlos borrowed $100 for 9 months. The interest rate is 13%/a.

   a. How much is the interest?

   b. What amount will he repay the bank at the end of 9 months?

5. Trish borrowed $250 for 6 months. The interest rate is $9\frac{1}{4}\%$/a.

   a. How much is the interest?

   b. What amount will she repay at the end of 6 months?

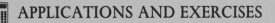 **APPLICATIONS AND EXERCISES**

1. Express as a fraction of a year, then as a decimal rounded to the nearest thousandth.
   a. 5 months   b. 8 months   c. 7 months
   d. 26 weeks   e. 15 weeks   f. 4 weeks

2. Write the expression to find the interest on the deposit.
   a. $700 for 6 months at 10%
   b. $600 for 9 months at $9\frac{1}{2}$%
   c. $1200 for 3 months at $11\frac{3}{4}$%

3. a. Calculate each interest in exercise 2.
   b. Calculate the total amount at the end of the given time in exercise 2.

4. Regan borrowed $5000 to buy a car. If the interest rate is 12%/a, how much will she owe at the end of one year?

5. Derek borrowed $800 to buy a stereo. He agreed to repay the principal and interest of $9\frac{1}{2}$%/a at the end of one year. What amount does he repay?

6. Calculate the interest.

	Principal	Rate per annum	Time
a.	$ 748	$12\frac{1}{2}$%	9 months
b.	$1500	$11\frac{1}{4}$%	3 months
c.	$ 300	$13\frac{1}{2}$%	13 weeks

7. A credit card company charges interest of $1\frac{3}{4}$% per month.

Item	Amount ($)
clothes	56.95
records	12.98
books	18.57
sporting goods	34.79
train fare	26.00

If the above charges were not paid within 1 month, find the interest charge and the total amount due.

8. Pierre deposited $100 in a savings account. At the end of one year he received $9.50 in interest. Express the ratio of interest to principal as a percent. What was the bank's interest rate?

9. A bank pays interest of 8%/a. How much money would be in a bank account for the interest at the end of the year to be $52?

10. Mr. Schmidt borrowed $10 000 at a rate of 12%/a. Then he lent it to a company at a rate of 16%/a.
    a. What amount does he pay in one year for borrowing the money?
    b. What amount does he receive in one year for lending the money?
    c. How much does he gain?

1. Find the quotient.
   a. $\frac{3}{4} \div \frac{5}{8}$ b. $\frac{9}{10} \div \frac{1}{5}$ c. $\frac{5}{6} \div \frac{5}{9}$ d. $\frac{15}{16} \div \frac{5}{8}$ e. $\frac{11}{12} \div \frac{5}{6}$
   f. $8 \div \frac{2}{3}$ g. $2\frac{3}{4} \div 22$ h. $1\frac{2}{3} \div \frac{5}{8}$ i. $6\frac{3}{4} \div \frac{9}{12}$ j. $11 \div 1\frac{3}{8}$

Gain and Loss

Grassie's house was priced at $75 000.
Its value increased by 15% in the spring,
then decreased by 8% in the fall.
The house sold at the fall price.
What was the selling price?

The original price was $75 000.

The **increase** in price was 15% of $75 000.

15% of $75 000
= 0.15 × $75 000
= $11 250   ←— gain

New Price = Original Price + Gain

= $75 000 + $11 250
= $86 250

The **decrease** in price was 8% of $86 250.

8% of $86 250
= 0.08 × $86 250
= $6 900   ←— loss

Final Price = New Price − Loss

= $86 250 − $6900
= $79 350

The selling price was $79 350.

WORKING TOGETHER

1. A $7 book dropped in price by 20%.
   a. Find the decrease in price.
   b. Find the new price.

2. A 90 cm plant increased in height by 5%.
   a. Find the height gained.
   b. Find the new height.

3. A $100 ring increased in value to $140. Write the ratio of the increase to the original value. Then express this ratio as a percent.

4. A mass of 10 kg decreased to 3 kg. Write the ratio of the decrease to the original mass. Then express this ratio as a percent.

1. Last year Mr. Dugan bought a new car for $12 500. After one year its value decreased by 11%. Find the present value of the car.

2. In 1971 a new gold coin was worth $35. Fifteen years later the same coin had increased to 11 times that value.

   a. Express the increase in value as a percent.

   b. How much was the coin worth in 1986?

3. Two puppies each had a mass of 7 kg. One puppy gained 12% of its mass in a week and 12% more the next week. The other puppy gained 24% of its mass in two weeks. Which puppy gained more?

4. A basket of groceries that cost $50 in 1971 cost 290% more in 1981. By 1987 the cost of the same basket of groceries had increased by another 42%.

   a. How much did these groceries cost in 1987?

   b. What % increase was this over the 1971 cost?

5. When macaroni is cooked, it increases in volume by 300%. How much cooked macaroni is made from the uncooked amount?

   a. 220 mL   b. 1 L   c. 4 scoops

6. When Jeanne was one month old, her mass was 4 kg and her height was 60 cm. When she was 12 a, her mass was 40 kg and her height was 150 cm.

   a. Express the increase in height as a percent.

   b. Express the percent increase in mass.

   c. Which had the greater increase, mass or height?

7. Bacon shrinks when cooked. An uncooked slice is 25 cm long and has a mass of 20 g. When cooked, the slice is 13 cm long and its mass is 6 g.

   a. Express the decrease in length and the decrease in mass as percents.

   b. Which is greater?

Try This

A retail store buys goods from a wholesaler and then tries to sell the goods for more than they cost. The difference between the wholesale and the retail price is called **profit**. The percent by which the wholesale price is increased is called **markup**.

Out of the profit the retailer must pay wages, rent, insurance, and so on.

1. Copy and complete the table.

	Wholesale price	Markup rate	Profit	Retail price
a.	$ 1.50	30%		
b.	$ 40.00	100%		
c.	$ 50.00	250%		
d.	$200.00			$600.00
e.	$ 50.00		$ 25.00	

PRACTICE

1. Copy and complete. Check the answer.

   a. 8% of a number is 24.
   1% of the number is △.
   100% of the number is ▣.

   b. 55% of a number is 110.
   1% of the number is △.
   100% of the number is ▣.

   c. 240% of a number is 48.
   1% of the number is △.
   100% of the number is ▣.

2. Decide if the missing number is larger or smaller than the given number. Find the missing number. Check the answer.

   a. 6 is 25% of the number.

   b. 50% of the number is 241.

   c. 130% of the number is 13.

   d. 2.82 is 1% of the number.

   e. 70 is 200% of the number.

3. On the average, boys reach 98% of their final height by the time they are 17.75 a and girls by the time they are 16.5 a.

   a. John is almost eighteen and his height is 180 cm. Approximate his final height.

   b. Marta is almost seventeen and her height is 160 cm. Approximate her final height.

4. An ore mined at Flin Flon, Manitoba, contains about 2% copper. How many tonnes of ore are required to yield 1000 kg copper?

5. A bakery sells day-old baked goods at a 20% discount. Find the sale price.

   a. a loaf of bread, regular price $1.15

   b. a dozen rolls, regular price $1.30

6. Calculate the regular price.

   a. 30% discount is $60.

   b. 25% discount is $200.

   c. 15% discount is $300.

   d. 18% discount is $54.

7. Calculate the sale price for each discount in exercise 6.

8. Estimate the total cost of the item if the sales tax is 7%

   a. $3.45

   b. $14.99

   c. 70¢

   d. $8.69

9. Calculate the total cost of each item in exercise 8.

10. A bicycle is priced at $175. The sales tax is 11%. What is the total cost?

11. Vladimir Chekhov bought a pair of $24 blue jeans. His bill came to $25.20.

    a. How much was the sales tax? Express this as a percent.

    b. In which province did he make this purchase?

12. Unpaid phone bills over $50 are subject to a late payment charge of $1\frac{1}{2}$% per month. Find the late payment charge for the unpaid amount at the end of 1 month.

    a. July, $68.40

    b. October, $107.10

    c. January, $43.93

    d. March, $52.00

Origami

Origami is the Japanese art of paper folding. Reference books show how to make many beautiful and intricate paper figures. To make an attractive figure, the paper must be folded accurately.

To make the fish, follow these steps.

1. Fold diagonal CD of a square. Unfold.

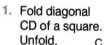

2. Bring AC and BC to CD and crease.

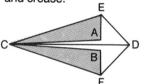

3. Bring ED to CD and crease.

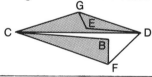

4. Bring FD to CD and crease.

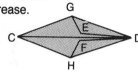

5. Bring E and F to the outside edges and fold each corner part way back.

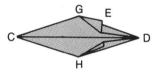

6. Turn the paper over and fold corner C.

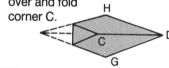

7. Fold the model so that G meets H. Crease CD.

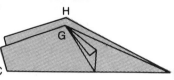

8. Fold the tail. Draw the details.

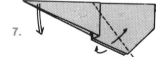

Follow these steps to make a puppy.

1.
2.
3.

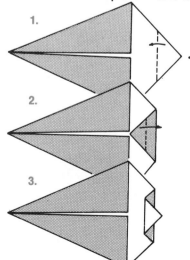

4.
5.
6.

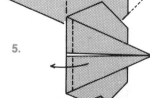
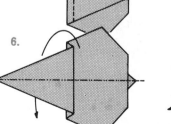

7.
8.
9.

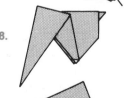
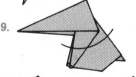

10.
11.

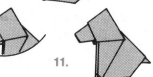

BASIC Programming I

In BASIC programs, the instructions have line numbers so that the computer can follow them in order. **To change** an instruction, type a new line using the same line number. **To delete** an instruction, retype only the line number. **To add** another instruction, use a new line number to show where to insert it. When you type LIST, the computer puts all the lines in order.

```
]10 REM MULTIPLY TWO NUMBERS
]20 INPUT "WHAT IS FIRST NUMBER? ";F
]30 INPUT "WHAT IS SECOND NUMBER? ";S
]40 PRODUCT = F * S
]50 PRINT PRODUCT
]60 END
]RUN
WHAT IS FIRST NUMBER? █
```

Line 10 in this program is a REMark statement, and is used to remind us what the program does. The computer ignores it. In line 20, INPUT tells the computer to pause after the **prompt** and wait for a number to be entered.

> whatever is inside the quotation marks

F is a **variable** that represents any number you choose. When you type RUN, the computer carries out the commands, one at a time, in order by line number.

1. Predict the product if you enter 13 for F and 4 for S.

2. How does the following change in line 50 affect the output?
   50 PRINT F " X " S "=" PRODUCT

3. Modify the program to multiply three numbers.

A **loop** can be created by adding a new line.   55   GOTO 20
This tells the computer to go back to line 20 and ask for more input, so it never gets to line 60. The program would have to be interrupted by pressing BREAK or CTRL C.

```
]NEW
]10 REM CONCERT TICKET PRICE
]20 INPUT "WHAT IS YOUR NAME? ";N$
]30 INPUT "HOW OLD ARE YOU? ";AGE
]35 PRINT
]40 IF AGE > 12 GOTO 70
]50 PRINT "$2.00 PLEASE, ";N$
]60 GOTO 80
]70 PRINT "$5.00 PLEASE, ";N$
]80 END █
```

A computer can also work with variables that represent words. The letters are followed by a $, which tells the computer that you are choosing a word instead of a number.

When the computer gets to line 40, it compares the number you entered for AGE with 12. If the number is not greater than 12, the computer continues to the next line.

4. Predict the output if you enter Mel for N$ and 12 for AGE.

Writing a computer program is like problem solving.
The first step is to understand the purpose of the program. What kind of information is available? What kind of output is needed?

The second step is to plan and do. In programming, this is often done by drawing a **flow chart**, then **coding** the program, and RUNning it on a computer. The programmer must break down the problem into simple steps, and questions that can be answered YES or NO.

The final step is to look back, to test the program with different sets of data, and to remove any **logical** or **syntax errors** (**debug** the program).

This flow chart shows the thinking that goes into planning a BASIC program to print the 6 times table.

M represents the multiplicand.
P represents the product.

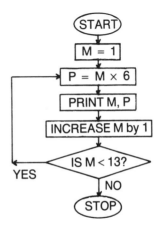

5. a. Write a BASIC program for this flow chart. Include REM statements to describe the program.

b. Test and debug the program.

c. Add some PRINT statements so that the output will include a title and the table is printed with double spacing.

Miss Newton's class had a physical fitness test. Any students who scored from 1 to 20 were placed in the Beginner group. Those who scored between 21 and 40 were placed in the Intermediate group. Those with scores over 40 were placed in the Advanced group.

6. Draw a flow chart for a program that accepts input for the name of a student and her/his score, and outputs the student's name and group.

7. Write a BASIC program that accepts input for the numerator and denominator of a fraction, and outputs the fraction both as a decimal and as a percent. Your program should give a warning message if zero is input as the denominator. Why?

More Than One Combination

In the Richmond Heights soccer league there are four teams—
the Spitfires, the Titans, the Vikings, and the Cougars.
How many arrangements of the four teams' standings
are possible for the end of the season?

Think. The arrangements need to be counted systematically.

Plan and do. The captain of the Cougars used a chart.

Team	Finishing position					
C	1	1	1	1	1	1
S	2	2	3	3	4	4
T	3	4	2	4	2	3
V	4	3	4	2	3	2

The captain of the Titans used a **tree diagram.**

```
     1st  2nd  3rd  4th   Outcome
            V — C      T,S,V,C
         S<
            C — V      T,S,C,V
            S — C      T,V,S,C
   T ── V<
            C — S      T,V,C,S
            V — S      T,C,V,S
         C<
            S — V      T,C,S,V
```

There are 6 different ways that a team can finish in first place.
Since there are 4 teams, there must be 6 × 4 or 24 combinations.

Look back. If there were only 2 teams, there would be
2 teams to pick from for 1st place and 1 team left for 2nd place.
If there were only 3 teams, there would be
3 teams to pick from for 1st place, 2 teams for 2nd, and 1 team for 3rd.
For 4 teams, there are 4 teams to pick from for 1st place,
3 teams for 2nd place, 2 teams for 3rd place, and 1 team for 4th.

This suggests a pattern: if 2 teams, 2 × 1 or 2 combinations
if 3 teams, 3 × 2 × 1 or 6 combinations
if 4 teams, 4 × 3 × 2 × 1 or 24 combinations.

WORKING TOGETHER

1. If you use the pattern suggested above, how many different combinations would there be for 5 teams?

2. Is the pattern suggested above reasonable? Check by completing a chart or a tree diagram for 2 teams, 3 teams, 4 teams, and 5 teams.

PROBLEMS

Copy and complete the tree diagram. Solve the problem.

1. Pat bought 3 shirts, 2 pants, and 2 pairs of shoes. How many new outfits does Pat have?

Shirt	Pants	Shoes	Outfit
		1	1,1,1
	1	2	1,1,2
1		1	1,2,1
	2	2	1,2,2
	1	1	2,1,1
2		2	2,1,2
	2		

2. Lily, Sarah, Matthew, and Guy are on a relay team. In how many ways can the runners be positioned if boys and girls must alternate?

1st	2nd	3rd	4th	Order
L	M — S — G			L,M,S,G
	G — S — M			L,G,S,M
M	L — G — S			M,L,G,S
	S			

Copy and complete the chart. Solve the problem.

3. How many different ways can a restaurant, shoe store, pet store, and bookstore be arranged side by side in a shopping mall? The pet store cannot be located next to the restaurant.

Restaurant first	Shoe store first	Book store first
RSPB	SRBP	BPSR
RSBP	~~SRPB~~	~~BPRS~~
~~RPSB~~	~~SPRB~~	BRSP
~~RPBS~~	SPBR	~~BRPS~~

Solve.

4. **a.** How many different ways can Aram, Betty, Cam, and Dalia sit at four desks, one behind the other?

   b. What if Aram and Dalia are not to sit in front of or behind each other?

5. How many numbers can be formed using the digits 7, 8, and 9, if the digits are not repeated?

   a. 1-digit numbers

   b. 2-digit numbers

   c. 3-digit numbers

   d. 4-digit numbers

6. Solve problem 5 again, this time allowing for repeating digits.

7. How many telephone numbers with the same first three digits are possible?

8. How many different dinner combinations does the restaurant serve? With their steak, chicken, or fish dinners, there is a choice of mashed potatoes, baked potatoes, or french fries. With the fish or chicken dinners, there is also a choice of one vegetable—peas, beans, or carrots. Each dinner comes with soup or a green salad, and a roll.

9. How many different ways can you draw a fourth circle that just touches three given circles? One such circle is drawn.

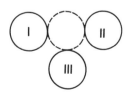

Problem Solving Review

Sales Tax Table ($6\frac{1}{2}\%$)

Transaction	Tax	Transaction	Tax	Transaction	Tax	Transaction	Tax	Transaction	Tax	Transaction	Tax
0.01–0.10	.00	3.77–3.92	.25	7.62– 7.76	.50	11.47–11.61	.75	15.31–15.46	1.00	19.16–19.30	1.25
0.11–0.20	.01	3.93–4.07	.26	7.77– 7.92	.51	11.62–11.76	.76	15.47–15.61	1.01	19.31–19.46	1.26
0.21–0.35	.02	4.08–4.23	.27	7.93– 8.07	.52	11.77–11.92	.77	15.62–15.76	1.02	19.47–19.61	1.27
0.36–0.51	.03	4.24–4.38	.28	8.08– 8.23	.53	11.93–12.07	.78	15.77–15.92	1.03	19.62–19.76	1.28
0.52–0.67	.04	4.39–4.53	.29	8.24– 8.38	.54	12.08–12.23	.79	15.93–16.07	1.04	19.77–19.92	1.29
0.68–0.83	.05	4.54–4.69	.30	8.39– 8.53	.55	12.24–12.38	.80	16.08–16.23	1.05	19.93–20.07	1.30
0.84–0.99	.06	4.70–4.84	.31	8.54– 8.69	.56	12.39–12.53	.81	20.08–20.23	1.31	20.08–20.23	1.31
1.00–1.15	.07	4.85–4.99	.32	8.70– 8.84	.57	12.54–12.69	.82	16.39–16.53	1.07	20.24–20.38	1.32
1.16–1.30	.08	5.00–5.15	.33	8.85– 8.99	.58	12.70–12.84	.83	16.54–16.69	1.08	20.39–20.53	1.33
1.31–1.46	.09	5.16–5.30	.34	9.00– 9.15	.59	12.85–12.99	.84	16.70–16.84	1.09	20.54–20.69	1.34
1.47–1.61	.10	5.31–5.46	.35	9.16– 9.30	.60	13.00–13.15	.85	16.85–16.99	1.10	20.70–20.84	1.35
1.62–1.76	.11	5.47–5.61	.36	9.31– 9.46	.61	13.16–13.30	.86	17.00–17.15	1.11	20.85–20.99	1.36
1.77–1.92	.12	5.62–5.76	.37	9.47– 9.61	.62	13.31–13.46	.87	17.16–17.30	1.12	21.00–21.15	1.37
1.93–2.07	.13	5.77–5.92	.38	9.62– 9.76	.63	13.47–13.61	.88	17.31–17.46	1.13	21.16–21.30	1.38
2.08–2.23	.14	5.93–6.07	.39	9.77– 9.92	.64	13.62–13.76	.89	17.47–17.61	1.14	21.31–21.46	1.39
2.24–2.38	.15	6.08–6.23	.40	9.93–10.07	.65	13.77–13.92	.90	17.62–17.76	1.15	21.47–21.61	1.40
2.39–2.53	.16	6.24–6.38	.41	10.08–10.23	.66	13.93–14.07	.91	17.77–17.92	1.16	21.62–21.76	1.41
2.54–2.69	.17	6.39–6.53	.42	10.24–10.38	.67	14.08–14.23	.92	17.93–18.07	1.17	21.77–21.92	1.42
2.70–2.84	.18	6.54–6.69	.43	10.39–10.53	.68	14.24–14.38	.93	18.08–18.23	1.18	21.93–22.07	1.43
2.85–2.99	.19	6.70–6.84	.44	10.54–10.69	.69	14.39–14.53	.94	18.24–18.38	1.19	22.08–22.23	1.44
3.00–3.15	.20	6.85–6.99	.45	10.70–10.84	.70	14.54–14.69	.95	18.39–18.53	1.20	22.24–22.38	1.45
3.16–3.30	.21	7.00–7.15	.46	10.85–10.99	.71	14.70–14.84	.96	18.54–18.69	1.21	22.39–22.53	1.46
3.31–3.46	.22	7.16–7.30	.47	11.00–11.15	.72	14.85–14.99	.97	18.70–18.84	1.22	22.54–22.69	1.47
3.47–3.61	.23	7.31–7.46	.48	11.16–11.30	.73	15.00–15.15	.98	18.85–18.99	1.23	22.70–22.84	1.48
3.62–3.76	.24	7.47–7.61	.49	11.31–11.46	.74	15.16–15.30	.99	19.00–19.15	1.24	22.85–22.99	1.49

Use this sales tax table to solve the following problems.

1. Marlene bought a skirt for $19.75. How much did she pay?

2. Rolph bought some articles at a store for 98¢, 66¢, 79¢, and 59¢. How much change did he get from a $5 bill?

3. If you paid $23.16 for a pair of jeans, and the sales tax was $1.41, what was the price of the jeans?

4. A $23 jacket is reduced in price to $14.99. How much less is the sales tax now?

5. Nicole bought school supplies and paid 64¢ sales tax. What is the least and the most she could have paid?

6. a. The price of a ski jacket is $39.50. How much does it cost including tax?

   b. The price of a pair of skis is $75. What is the cost including sales tax?

Solve.

7. A shirt sells for $9.00 more than a tie. The price of both shirt and tie is $24.50, excluding sales tax. How much does the tie sell for?

8. In how many different ways can 6 people stand in line for a movie, if they stand in single file?

9. The loaded moving van leaves the Jeffersons' old house and travels 80 km before the Jeffersons leave and follow the van in their car. If the van averages 72 km/h and the car averages 88 km/h, how many hours will it take the car to catch up with the van?

10. Murray shares a paper route with his sister by delivering on alternate days. If they deliver the same number of papers daily and their weekly total is 350, how many papers does Murray deliver each week?

Chapter Checkup

1. What percent is shaded? Write a fraction in lowest terms equivalent to the percent.

   a.   b.

2. Express the decimal as a percent.

   a. 0.65   b. 0.6   c. 0.06

   d. 0.006   e. 6.06   f. 6.0

3. Express the percent as a decimal.

   a. 30%   b. 3%   c. 300%

   d. 0.3%   e. $13\frac{3}{4}\%$ f. $42\frac{1}{5}\%$

4. Express the fraction as a percent.

   a. $\frac{17}{100}$ b. $\frac{1}{4}$ c. $\frac{3}{5}$ d. $\frac{9}{20}$

5. Copy and complete.

	Fraction	Decimal	Percent
a.		0.18	
b.			40%
c.	$\frac{3}{5}$		
d.			$67\frac{1}{2}\%$
e.	$1\frac{1}{8}$		

6. Estimate.

   a. 50% of 109   b. 25% of 42

   c. 11% of 71   d. 19% of 15

   e. $12\frac{1}{2}\%$ of 80   f. 8.2% of 24

   g. 10% of $2\frac{3}{5}$ h. 2% of 1790

7. Calculate the values in exercise 6.

8. There were 4 candidates for class president.

   a. What percent of the votes did Anna receive?

   b. If 36 students voted, how many voted for each candidate?

   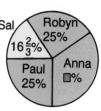

9. About 5% of the oranges in a shipment were spoiled. Predict the number unspoiled in a crate of 40 oranges.

10. In 4 L of snowmobile fuel, 5% is oil and the rest is gasoline. How many litres of gasoline are in the fuel?

11. Anita scored 16 out of 20 on a spelling test and 19 out of 25 on a math test. What percent did she receive on each?

12. Decide if the missing number is larger or smaller than the given number. Then find the missing number and check.

    a. 23 is 50% of the number.

    b. 36% of the number is 9.

    c. 196 is 98% of the number.

13. At a restaurant Mr. Sorensen left a tip of $4.50 for the waiter. This was 15% of his bill. How much was the bill?

14. Find the sale price of the item if there is a 25% discount.

    a. sweetheart charm, regular $7.95

    b. identification bracelet, regular $26

    c. birthstone ring, regular $129.99

15. Mrs. Vail borrows $700 for 6 months, at 16%/a. What amount does she pay the bank at the end of 6 months?

Cumulative Checkup

1. Evaluate.

a. $\sqrt{36}$ **b.** $\sqrt{1}$ **c.** $\sqrt{49}$

d. $\sqrt{256}$ **e.** $\sqrt{900}$ **f.** $\sqrt{6400}$

2. Multiply or divide.

a. 28.4×100 **b.** 0.001×27.45

c. $0.825 \times 100\,000$ **d.** $3.14 \div 0.001$

e. $19.2 \div 10\,000$ **f.** $0.018 \div 0.01$

g. 0.001×0.001 **h.** $38.47 \div 10\,000$

3. The perimeter of the figure is 15 cm. Find the length of AB.

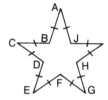

4. Copy. Complete the chart for parallelograms.

	Base	Height	Area
a.	7 cm	9 cm	
b.	2.5 m	2.5 m	
c.	24 mm	3 cm	
d.	510 cm	3 m	

5. Copy. Complete the chart for triangles.

	Base	Height	Area in smaller units	Area in larger units
a.	2 m	50 cm		
b.	19 mm	3 cm		
c.	0.5 km	600 m		

6. Calculate the area of the shaded region to the nearest tenth.

a. 14 cm   **b.** 6.9 cm, 8.0 cm

7. Find the volume.

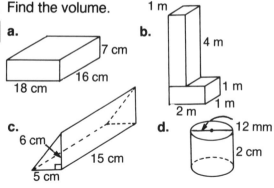

a. 18 cm, 16 cm, 7 cm

b. 1 m, 4 m, 1 m, 1 m, 2 m

c. 6 cm, 5 cm, 15 cm

d. 12 mm, 2 cm

8. Copy and complete.

	a.	b.	c.	d.	e.
Volume	4 cm³	400 cm³			5 m³
Capacity			3 L	2 kL	

9. A coffee pot has a diameter of 14 cm and a height of 20 cm. About how many litres to the nearest tenth of coffee can the pot hold?

10. Copy and complete.

a. $5\text{ kg} = \square\text{ g}$ **b.** $4100\text{ g} = \square\text{ kg}$

c. $0.9\text{ kg} = \square\text{ g}$ **d.** $790\text{ g} = \square\text{ kg}$

e. $3.1\text{ t} = \square\text{ kg}$ **f.** $4750\text{ kg} = \square\text{ t}$

11. Find the LCM of the group.

a. 2,3,4   **b.** 6,8,10   **c.** 3,6,9

d. 12,18,21   **e.** 18,24,30   **f.** 3,26,39

12. Wieners are sold in packages of 10. Hot dog buns are sold in packages of 8. What is the least number of packages of each you would have to buy to get the same number of wieners as buns?

13. Arrange from greatest to least.

a. $\dfrac{7}{8}, \dfrac{11}{12}, \dfrac{2}{3}$ **b.** $\dfrac{8}{5}, \dfrac{13}{10}, \dfrac{5}{3}$ **c.** $\dfrac{2}{3}, \dfrac{19}{33}, \dfrac{8}{11}$

14. Find the result.

   a. $\frac{5}{6} - \frac{2}{3}$ **b.** $\frac{9}{10} - \frac{7}{15}$ **c.** $\frac{2}{5} + \frac{2}{3}$

   d. $\frac{5}{8} + \frac{7}{12}$ **e.** $10\frac{2}{3} - 2\frac{1}{4}$ **f.** $5\frac{3}{10} + 3\frac{1}{2}$

15. Express as a mixed number.

   a. $\frac{21}{4}$ **b.** $\frac{19}{5}$ **c.** $\frac{31}{7}$ **d.** $\frac{27}{2}$

16. What is the reciprocal?

   a. $\frac{7}{11}$ **b.** $\frac{1}{8}$ **c.** 11   **d.** $5\frac{1}{3}$

17. Divide.

   a. $\frac{4}{7} \div \frac{8}{21}$ **b.** $\frac{1}{5} \div \frac{9}{20}$ **c.** $16 \div \frac{4}{5}$

   d. $18 \div \frac{9}{7}$ **e.** $\frac{3}{8} \div 12$ **f.** $\frac{5}{2} \div 16$

18. One week, Mark spent $\frac{1}{2}$ of his pay on food, $\frac{1}{3}$ on paying various bills, and the remaining $100 for miscellaneous expenses.

   a. What fraction of his pay went for miscellaneous expenses?

   b. What was his total pay for the week?

19. Express the ratio in three ways.

   a. 3 out of 5 students are girls.

   b. 9 out of 13 golf clubs are irons.

   c. 3 out of 1000 births are twins.

20. A recommended mixture for concrete is 1 part cement, 2 parts sand, and 3 parts crushed stone. Give the ratio.

   a. cement to sand

   b. crushed stone to sand

   c. cement to sand to crushed stone

21. Copy and complete.

   a. $\frac{7}{5} = \frac{\blacksquare}{50}$ **b.** $\frac{9}{11} = \frac{45}{\blacksquare}$ **c.** $\frac{8}{7} = \frac{\blacksquare}{42}$

   d. $\frac{1.5}{1.6} = \frac{4.5}{\blacksquare}$ **e.** $\frac{14}{24} = \frac{\blacksquare}{60}$ **f.** $\frac{1.4}{1.6} = \frac{\blacksquare}{4}$

22. On a gear the ratio of the number of turns of the drive wheel to the number of turns of the other wheel is $5:4$.

   a. Which wheel turns faster?

   b. Copy and complete the table.

drive wheel (turns)	5	10			100		
other wheel (turns)				24		120	220

23. Express as a unit rate.

   a. 48 km driven in 30 min

   b. 85 L of punch for 125 guests

   c. 24 boxes of juice for $9.75

24. Aaron earns $187.50 for working 30 h. How much can he earn in 8 h?

25. At Jaime's Stationery a set of 12 markers costs $10.75. At White's Variety a set of 8 markers costs $6.95. Which is the better buy?

26. The scale on a map is $1:250\,000$. The straight-line distance between two towns measures 8.7 cm on the map. What is the actual distance between the towns?

27. Express the scale as a ratio.

   a. 1 mm to 100 cm   **b.** 1 mm to 1 m

   c. 1 mm to 1 km   **d.** 1 cm to 1 mm

28. For each scale in exercise 27, decide if the object is larger or smaller than its scale drawing.

8/Geometry

An understanding of lines, angles, triangles, quadrilaterals, and circles is necessary to design and construct buildings.

Get Set

1. Is the figure a line, line segment, or ray?

a.   **b.**   **c.**

2. Name three pairs of intersecting line segments.

3. Draw.

   a. a right angle

   b. an angle less than a right angle

   c. an angle greater than a right angle

4. Guess and test to find the missing number.

   a. $\square + 25 = 90$ **b.** $90 - \square = 72$

   c. $65 + \square = 180$ **d.** $180 - \square = 29$

   e. $x + 5 = 12$ **f.** $x + 45 = 90$

5. Name the polygon.

   a.   **b.**

   c.   **d.**

   e.   **f.**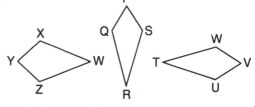

6. Sketch the polygon. Draw, then count, the number of diagonals.

   a. pentagon   **b.** octagon   **c.** nonagon

7. Classify the triangle.

   a.   **b.**   **c.**

8. Classify the quadrilateral.

   a.   **b.**   **c.**

   d.   **e.**   **f.**

9. Draw a circle.

   a. radius 3 cm   **b.** diameter 8 cm

10. Use tracing paper to identify the pairs of congruent figures. List the matching vertices and sides.

   a.

   b.

   c.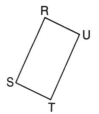

233

Lines, Line Segments, and Rays

Hydro wires suggest **lines**.

A hydro pole suggests a **line segment**.

The light beams from the light suggest **rays**.

Line AB or BA continues without end.
Its symbol is $\overleftrightarrow{AB}$ or $\overleftrightarrow{BA}$.

Line segment DE or ED is part of a line. It has
two end points, D and E. Its symbol is $\overline{DE}$ or $\overline{ED}$.

Ray FG is part of a line. It has one end point and
continues without end in one direction. Its symbol is $\overrightarrow{FG}$.

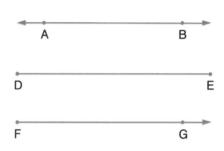

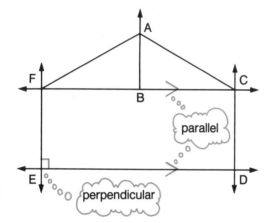

Two lines that intersect and make a
90° angle are **perpendicular lines**.

$\overleftrightarrow{EF}$ is perpendicular to $\overleftrightarrow{ED}$. $\overleftrightarrow{EF} \perp \overleftrightarrow{ED}$

Two lines that never meet are **parallel lines**.

$\overleftrightarrow{FC}$ is parallel to $\overleftrightarrow{ED}$. $\overleftrightarrow{FC} \parallel \overleftrightarrow{ED}$

WORKING TOGETHER

1. In the classroom what suggests these
   line segments?

   a. parallel

   b. perpendicular

   c. intersecting but not perpendicular

2. Name two.

   a. parallel lines

   b. parallel rays

   c. perpendicular
   line segments

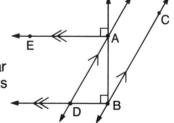

APPLICATIONS AND EXERCISES

1. Which part of the picture suggests the following?

   a. a line

   b. a line segment

   c. a ray

   d. parallel lines or line segments

   e. perpendicular lines or line segments

2. a. How many lines parallel to $\overleftrightarrow{AB}$ can be drawn through point X?

   b. How many lines perpendicular to $\overleftrightarrow{AB}$ can be drawn through point X?

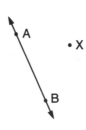

5. Draw and name.

   a. two parallel rays

   b. two perpendicular lines

   c. ray AB parallel to line XY

   d. $\overleftrightarrow{EF}$ perpendicular to $\overline{GH}$

   e. $\overline{MN} \perp \overrightarrow{OP}$ **f.** $\overrightarrow{GH} \parallel \overleftrightarrow{IJ}$

3. Copy and use $\perp$ or $\parallel$ to make a true statement.

   a. $\overleftrightarrow{AB} \odot \overleftrightarrow{DC}$

   b. $\overleftrightarrow{AD} \odot \overleftrightarrow{DC}$

   c. $\overleftrightarrow{CB} \odot \overleftrightarrow{BA}$

   d. $\overleftrightarrow{DA} \odot \overleftrightarrow{CB}$

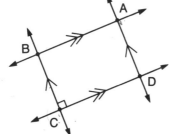

6. Name the pairs of parallel faces in the polyhedron.

   a.

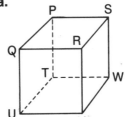

   b.

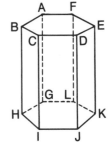

4. Classify figure ABCD in exercise 3.

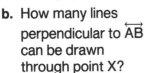

The way in which lines and angles are drawn on paper can cause our eyes to "play tricks" on us. This is an **optical illusion.**

Try This

1. a. Are $\overline{AB}$ and $\overline{CD}$ parallel?

   b. How can the answer be checked?

Angles

The roof truss is made by joining pieces of lumber at different angles. Angles are measured in **degrees (°).**

∠ABC or ∠CBA is 90° and is a **right angle.**

∠ABD or ∠DBA is less than 90° and is an **acute angle.**

∠EBC or ∠CBE is 180° and is a **straight angle.**

∠EBD or ∠DBE is less than 180° but greater than 90° and is an **obtuse angle.**

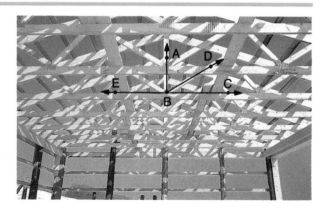

Measuring an Angle

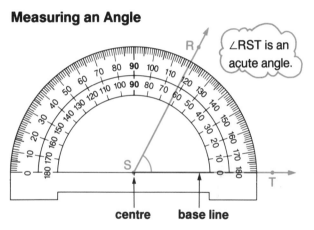

∠RST is an acute angle.

The measure of ∠RST is 62°.

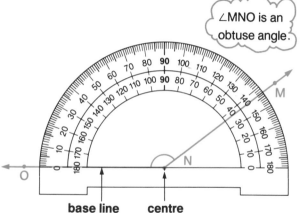

∠MNO is an obtuse angle.

The measure of ∠MNO is 143°.

WORKING TOGETHER

1. Draw ∠XYZ with measure 135°.

   a. Draw a ray, $\overrightarrow{YZ}$.

   b. Place the centre of the protractor on the end point, Y, of the ray. Line up the base line of the protractor with the ray.

   c. Move your pencil from 0° on the ray to 135°. Mark a dot. Label it X.

   d. Draw $\overrightarrow{YX}$.

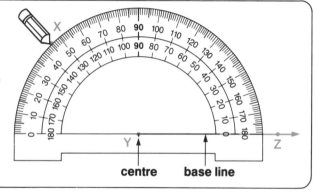

APPLICATIONS AND EXERCISES

1. Copy and complete the chart.

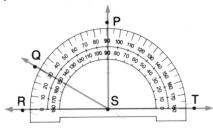

	Name	Size	Classification
a.	∠PST or ∠TSP		
b.	∠QST or ∠TSQ		
c.	∠RST or ∠TSR		
d.	∠RSP or ∠PSR		
e.	∠RSQ or ∠QSR		
f.	∠QSP or ∠PSQ		

2. Estimate the size of the angle.

a.   **b.**

c.   **d.**

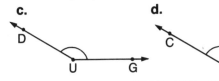

3. Measure the angles in exercise 2.

4. Use a protractor to draw an angle with this measure.

   a. 31°   **b.** 112°   **c.** 156°   **d.** 173°

5. Use a straightedge to sketch an angle with about this measure.

   a. 45°   **b.** 30°   **c.** 60°   **d.** 85°

   e. 120°   **f.** 150°   **g.** 170°   **h.** 135°

6. Measure the angles in exercise 5. Draw an angle if the sketch is more than 5° off.

7. Two angles that have the same measure are congruent angles. Measure to find pairs of congruent angles in the figure.

a.

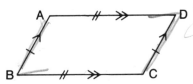

b.

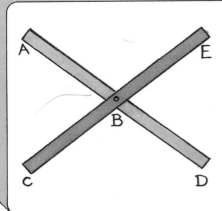

Try This

1. a. Attach two strips of cardboard together with a paper fastener. Steady the strips in a definite position.

   b. Use a protractor to measure each angle.

   c. Compare the measures.

     i. ∠ABC and ∠EBD   **ii.** ∠ABE and ∠CBD

     iii. ∠ABE and ∠EBD   **iv.** ∠DBC and ∠ABC

2. a. Repeat exercise 1 with the strips in a different position.

   b. What do you notice?

Pairs of Angles

∠BAC and ∠CAD are **adjacent angles**.
Adjacent angles share a vertex and a
ray but do not overlap.

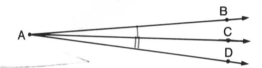

Two angles that have a sum of 90° are **complementary angles**.

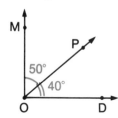

∠MOP and ∠POD are
complementary angles.

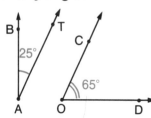

∠BAT and ∠COD are
complementary angles.

Two angles that have a sum of 180° are **supplementary angles**.

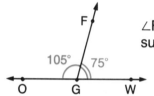

∠FGO and ∠FGW are
supplementary angles.

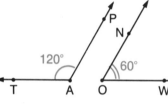

∠TAP and ∠NOW are
supplementary angles.

When two lines intersect, the **opposite angles** are equal.

∠MAT and ∠CAB are
opposite angles.
∠MAT = ∠CAB
    = 70°

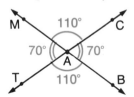

∠MAC and ∠TAB are
opposite angles.
∠MAC = ∠TAB
    = 110°

WORKING TOGETHER

1. Calculate the unknown angle measure x°.

   a.
   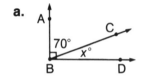

   b.

   c.

   d.
   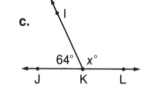

2. **a.** Draw two lines, $\overleftrightarrow{EF}$ and $\overleftrightarrow{GH}$, that intersect at I.

   b. Name one pair of opposite angles. Find their measure.

   c. Name one pair of adjacent angles. Calculate the unknown angle measure.

238

1. Classify the pair of angles as complementary, supplementary, or opposite angles.

a.

b.

c.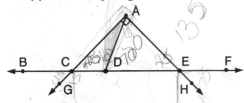

d.

2. Name two pairs.

a. adjacent angles   **b.** opposite angles

c. complementary angles

d. supplementary angles

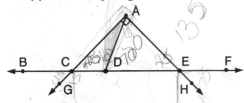

3. What is the measure of the complementary angle of this angle?

a. 30°   **b.** 65°   **c.** 42°   **d.** 8°

4. What is the measure of the supplementary angle of this angle?

a. 30°   **b.** 145°   **c.** 98°   **d.** 159°

5. Calculate the unknown angle measures $x°$ and $y°$.

a.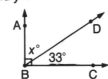

b.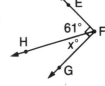

c.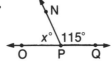

d.

e.

f.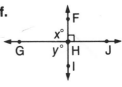

6. Calculate the unknown angle measure $x°$.

a.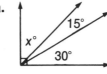

b.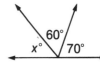

c.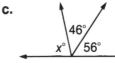

d.

e.

f.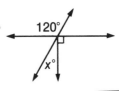

KEEPING SHARP

1. Calculate the circumference of the circle.

a. diameter 30 mm   **b.** diameter 10 cm   **c.** radius 4 m

2. Find the perimeter of the figure.

a.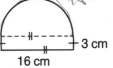

b.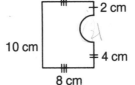

c.

239

Parallel Lines and Their Angles

How are parallel lines used in the photograph?

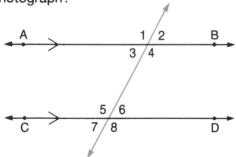

Alternate interior angles are equal and form a **Z pattern**.

Corresponding angles are equal and form an **F pattern**.

Co-interior angles have a sum of 180° and form a **E pattern**.

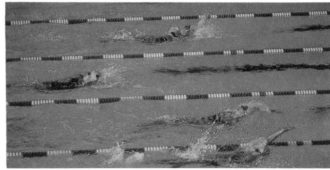

When a line intersects two parallel lines, eight angles are formed. The line is called a **transversal**.

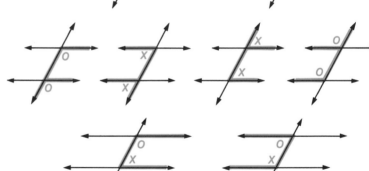

WORKING TOGETHER

1. Trace the diagram and extend the lines. Measure each angle, then copy and complete the table.

Angle	1	2	3	4	5	6	7	8
Measure								

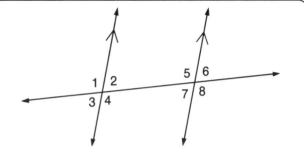

2. List the pairs of alternate interior angles and their measures.

3. List the pairs of corresponding angles and their measures.

4. List the pairs of co-interior angles and their measures.

APPLICATIONS AND EXERCISES

1. Name two pairs of alternate interior angles.

a.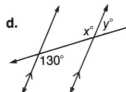

b.

2. Name four pairs of corresponding angles and two pairs of co-interior angles in each part of exercise 1.

3. Calculate the unknown angle measures $x°$ and $y°$.

a.

b.

c.

d.

4. Calculate the measure of the angle.

a. $\angle BCH$ **b.** $\angle ABF$ **c.** $\angle HCD$

d. $\angle EBD$ **e.** $\angle GCD$ **f.** $\angle FBD$

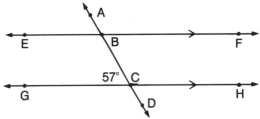

5. Calculate the unknown angle measures $x°$ and $y°$.

a.

b.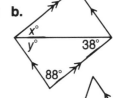

c.

d.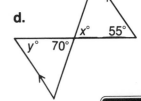

1. Arrange the steps in a logical order. Connect them with arrows to draw a flow chart.

a.

| Put the key away. | STOP | Take out the door key. | Walk in. | Unlock the door. | Is the door locked? | START |

b.

| Look out the window. | START | Wear a raincoat. | Will it rain later? | Take a raincoat. | STOP |

Is it raining?   Go without a raincoat.   Listen to the weather forecast.

2. Draw a flow chart for the situation.

a. crossing a busy intersection   **b.** buying a pair of jeans

241

Triangles

Triangles are classified in two ways.
–by their congruent parts
–by the measure of the largest angle

Congruent parts

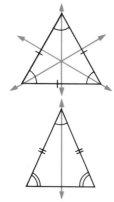

Equivalent triangle
3 congruent sides
3 congruent angles
3 lines of symmetry

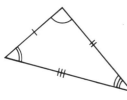

Isosceles triangle
2 congruent sides
2 congruent angles
1 line of symmetry

Scalene triangle
0 congruent sides
0 congruent angles
0 lines of symmetry

Largest angle

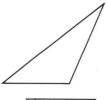

Acute-angled triangle
largest angle < 90°

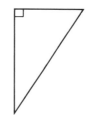

Obtuse-angled triangle
largest angle > 90°

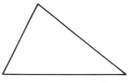

Right-angled triangle
largest angle = 90°

The vertices of the triangle can be torn off and
placed together so that the sides touch.
A straight angle is formed.
The sum of the angle measures is 180°.

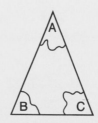

WORKING TOGETHER

1. Classify the triangle in two ways.

a.

b.

c.

2. Calculate the unknown angle measures.

a.

b.

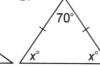

c.

1. Measure the sides and classify the triangle.

a.

b.

c.

d.

2. Measure the largest angle, then classify the triangle.

a.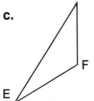

b.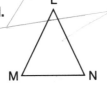

c.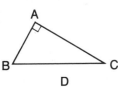

d.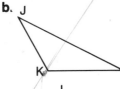

3. Classify the triangle in two ways.

a. **b.** **c.**

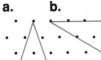

4. Copy each triangle in exercise 3. Then fold to show the lines of symmetry.

5. Calculate the unknown angle measure $x°$.

a.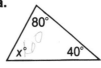

b.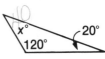

c.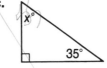

d.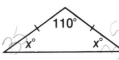

e.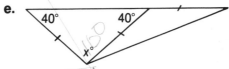

6. One angle in a triangle measures 47°, the other 68°. Calculate the measure of the remaining angle. Then classify the triangle.

7. Calculate the unknown angle measures.

a. **b.**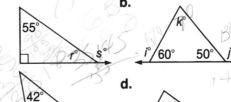

c. **d.**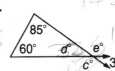

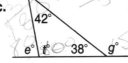

Try This

1. Copy the regular hexagon onto triangular dot paper. Draw all the diagonals. How many are there?

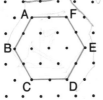
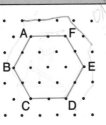

2. How many of these triangles can be found in your diagram?

a. equilateral **b.** isosceles

c. right-angled **d.** scalene

243

Quadrilaterals

A quadrilateral is a closed four-sided figure.

Special Quadrilaterals and Their Properties

A **parallelogram** has 2 pairs of parallel sides.

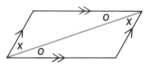

If you draw in a **diagonal**, the alternate interior angles are equal.

    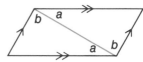

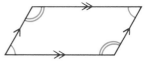

The **opposite angles** of a parallelogram are equal.

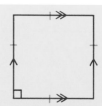

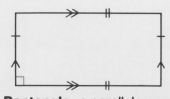 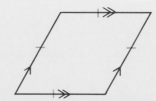

Rectangle–a parallelogram with one right angle

Rhombus–a parallelogram with four equal sides

Square–a parallelogram with four equal sides and one right angle

WORKING TOGETHER

1. What properties does the quadrilateral have?

   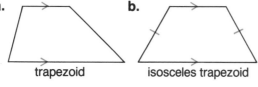

   a. trapezoid   b. isosceles trapezoid

   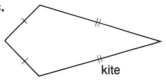

   c. kite

2. Use a straightedge.

   a. Draw any quadrilateral.

   b. Draw a diagonal. How many triangles are formed?

   c. What is the sum of the measures of the angles in each triangle?

   d. What is the sum of the measures of the angles of the quadrilateral?

   e. Measure each angle of the quadrilateral with a protractor. Is the sum reasonable?

APPLICATIONS AND EXERCISES

1. Answer.

a. Is every rhombus a parallelogram?

b. Is every square a rectangle?

c. Is every parallelogram a rectangle?

d. Is every rectangle a parallelogram?

e. Is every square a rhombus?

f. Is every rhombus a square?

g. Is any kite a parallelogram?

h. Is every rectangle a square?

i. Is every trapezoid a parallelogram?

2. Classify the quadrilateral in two ways.

a.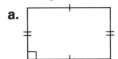

b.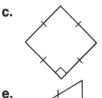

c.

d.

e.

f.

3. Calculate the unknown angle measures.

a.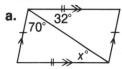

b.

c.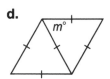

d.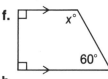

e.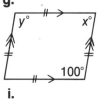

f.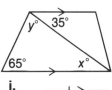

g.

h.

i.

j.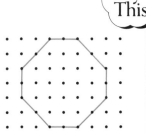

4. Trace an example of each quadrilateral on the preceding page. Then fold to show the lines of symmetry of each quadrilateral.

Try This

1. a. Draw a pentagon, hexagon, heptagon, and octagon on square dot paper. Draw the diagonals from one vertex.

b. Copy and complete.

Name	Sides	Diagonals	Triangles formed	Sum of interior angles
pentagon	5	2	3	540°
hexagon	6	3		
heptagon	7			

2. What is the sum of the interior angles?

a. in a decagon **b.** in a dodecagon **c.** in a polygon with 20 sides

PRACTICE

1. Classify the angle.

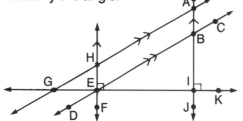

    a. ∠CBI   **b.** ∠GHE   **c.** ∠HEI

    d. ∠FEH   **e.** ∠AHE   **f.** ∠BIE

2. Copy and use ⊥ or ∥ to make true statements for the diagram in exercise 1.

    a. $\overline{GI}$ ○ $\overleftrightarrow{HF}$ **b.** $\overleftrightarrow{HF}$ ○ $\overleftrightarrow{AJ}$

    c. $\overleftrightarrow{DC}$ ○ $\overline{HA}$ **d.** $\overleftrightarrow{EI}$ ○ $\overleftrightarrow{AI}$

3. What is the measure of the complementary angle for this measure?

    a. 22°   **b.** 64°   **c.** 50°   **d.** 45°

4. What is the measure of the supplementary angle for this measure?

    a. 22°   **b.** 136°   **c.** 162°   **d.** 90°

5. Calculate the unknown angle measures $x°$ and $y°$.

    a.   **b.**

    c. 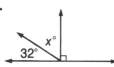   **d.**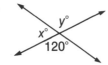

    e.    **f.**

6. Calculate the unknown angle measures $x°$ and $y°$.

    a.    **b.**

    c. 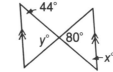   **d.**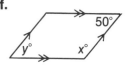

    e.    **f.**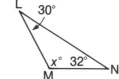

7. Draw a triangle of this type on triangular dot paper.

    a. equilateral   **b.** scalene

    c. obtuse-angled   **d.** right-angled

    e. acute-angled isosceles

8. Classify the triangle. Then calculate the unknown angle measure $x°$.

    a. 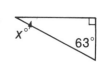   **b.**

    c.   **d.**

9. Classify the quadrilateral. Then calculate the unknown angle measures $x°$ and $y°$.

    a.   **b.**

246

Curve Stitching

- From a point 0 draw two line segments each 6 cm long.
- Divide each into 0.5 cm sections.
- Starting at 0, label one line segment A, B, C,...
- Starting at the other end of the other line segment, label it A, B, C,...
- Use a straightedge to join each pair of points with matching letters.

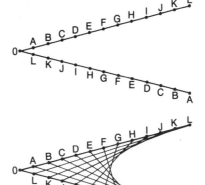

The resulting curve is a **parabola**.

This method of curve drawing is sometimes called **curve stitching**.

1. Use the curve-stitching method to draw a parabola for this angle.

   a. right angle   **b.** obtuse angle   **c.** larger obtuse angle

2. Explain the effect that an increase in the measure of the angle has on the resulting parabola.

3. Use the pattern to create a design. You might use colored pencils on paper or colored thread on cardboard.

a.

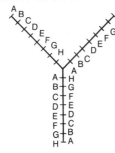

b.

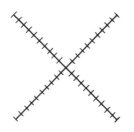

c.

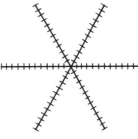

d.

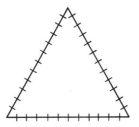

e.

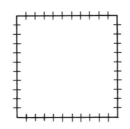

f.

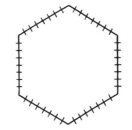

Congruent Line Segments and Angles

Most automobiles are manufactured on an assembly line. The parts that are used must be identical in size and shape to fit any car on the line.

In geometry, figures that have the same size and shape are **congruent figures**.

Compasses and a straightedge can be used to draw a figure congruent to another.

Copying a line segment

Draw $\overrightarrow{AB}$. Set compasses to the distance JK. Mark the same distance from A. Label C.

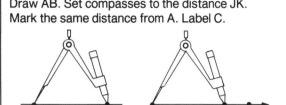

$\overline{AC}$ and $\overline{JK}$ are congruent.

Copying an angle

Draw $\overrightarrow{RS}$. With centre A, draw an arc. Label XY.
With centre R, same radius, draw another arc. Label T.

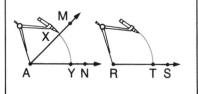

With centre T, radius XY, draw an arc. Label Q.

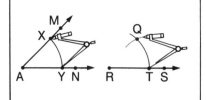

Draw $\overrightarrow{RQ}$.

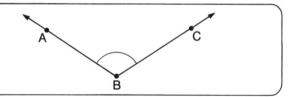

$\angle$MAN and $\angle$QRS are congruent.

WORKING TOGETHER

1. Trace $\angle$ABC. Use compasses and a straightedge. Construct an angle congruent to $\angle$ABC.

1. a. Estimate which line segments are congruent.

b. Use compasses to determine which line segments are congruent.

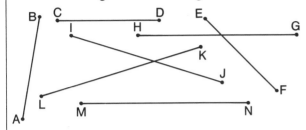

2. Use compasses and a straightedge to construct the line segment.

a. $\overline{AB}$ congruent to $\overline{EF}$

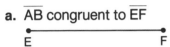

b. $\overline{CD}$ twice the length of $\overline{EF}$

c. $\overline{XY}$ three times the length of $\overline{EF}$

3. Use compasses and a straightedge to construct on angle congruent to the given angle.

a. 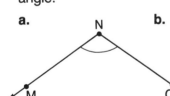 **b.**

4. Use a protractor to draw the angle.

a. 45° **b.** 90° **c.** 60° **d.** 120°

5. Use compasses and a straightedge to copy each angle in exercise 4. Measure each copy to check.

6. Use compasses and a straightedge to construct an angle with measure three times ∠BOX.

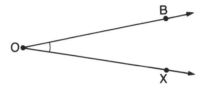

7. Use compasses and a straightedge to construct an angle whose measure is the sum of ∠ONE and ∠TWO.

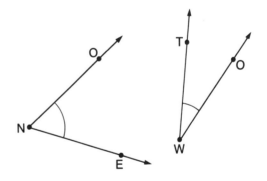

---

1. Use a Mira and a straightedge to construct a congruent figure.

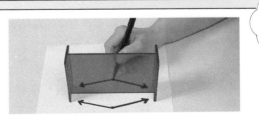

a. 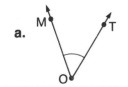 **b.**  **c.** **d.**

Constructing Congruent Triangles

Is it necessary to know all three sides and angles to accurately construct a congruent triangle?

Try three sides.

Try two sides and a contained angle.

Try two angles and a contained side.

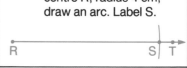

1	Draw X⃗Z⃗. With centre X, radius 2 cm, draw an arc. Label Y.	**1**	Draw N⃗P⃗. With centre N, radius 3 cm, draw an arc. Label O.	**1**	Draw R⃗T⃗. With centre R, radius 4 cm, draw an arc. Label S.

2	With centre X, radius 3 cm, draw an arc. With centre Y, radius 2 cm, draw an arc. Label W.	**2**	Use a protractor to draw an angle of 25° at N. With centre N, radius 2 cm, draw an arc. Label M.	**2**	Use a protractor to draw an angle of 30° at R and an angle of 20° at S. Label Q.

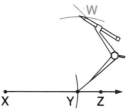
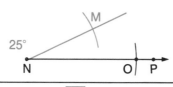
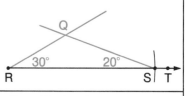

3	Draw W̅X̅ and W̅Y̅.	**3**	Draw M̅O̅.	**3**	Use tracing paper. Is △QRS ≅ △GHI?

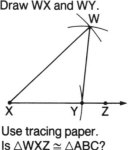
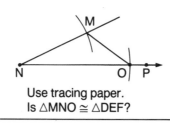

Use tracing paper.
Is △WXZ ≅ △ABC?

Use tracing paper.
Is △MNO ≅ △DEF?

The three conditions above are sufficient for constructing congruent triangles.

WORKING TOGETHER

1. Use compasses, a ruler, and a protractor to construct the following.

   a. △PAT, ∠PAT = 74°, PA = 8 cm, AT = 7 cm

   b. △HTO, ∠HTO = 60°, ∠OHT = 70° HT = 7 cm

1. Use compasses, a ruler, and a protractor to construct a congruent triangle.

a.

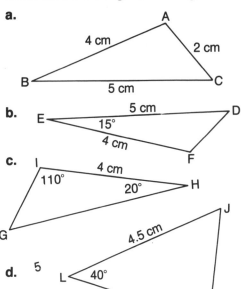

b.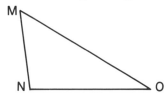

c.

d.

2. Use tracing paper to check the accuracy of your constructions in exercise 1.

3. Use compasses and a ruler to construct the triangle.

a. equilateral △BCD, each side 11 cm

b. isosceles △SOD, SO = OD = 7 cm, SD = 5 cm

c. scalene △TED, TE = 10 cm, ED = 8 cm, TD = 7 cm

4. Use compasses, a ruler, and a protractor to construct the triangle.

a. △RAT, RA = 7 cm, AT = 5 cm, ∠RAT = 80°

b. △MAP, MA = 8 cm, ∠PMA = 50°, ∠PAM = 80°

c. △DOG, OG = 6 cm, ∠DOG = 110°, ∠DGO = 30°

d. △BAT, BT = 8 cm, BA = 7 cm, ∠TBA = 120°

e. △FOG, FG = 10 cm, ∠OFG = 42°, ∠FGO = 71°

5. Construct a triangle congruent to △MNO.

6. a. Construct different triangles using different combinations of these lines as sides.

_____   _____

_____

_____

b. Which combinations of three lengths cannot be used to construct a triangle? Why?

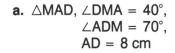

Try This

1. Construct the triangle.

a. △MAD, ∠DMA = 40°, ∠ADM = 70°, AD = 8 cm

b. △CAT, ∠CAT = 30°, ∠ATC = 80°, ∠TCA = 70°

c. △BOX, BO = 5 cm, OX = 6 cm, ∠OBX = 40°

2. What do you notice about each construction above?

3. What three conditions are not sufficient to construct a congruent triangle?

Congruent Triangles

△ABC is congruent to △DEF.
   △ABC ≅ △DEF

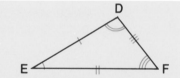

Corresponding sides match.   AB ≅ DE, BC ≅ EF, and AC ≅ DF
Corresponding angles match.   ∠ABC ≅ ∠DEF, ∠ACB ≅ ∠DFE, and ∠BAC ≅ ∠EDF

Three matching parts are often enough to show two triangles congruent.
Two triangles are congruent if any of the following cases is true.

- Three sides of one triangle are
  congruent to three sides of the other.

  AB ≅ DE, BC ≅ EF, AC ≅ DF
  △ABC ≅ △DEF   **SSS** — side-side-side

  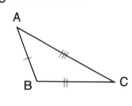
  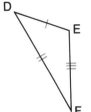

- Two sides and the **contained angle**
  of one triangle are congruent to two
  sides and the **contained angle** of the other.

  MN ≅ QR, ∠NMO ≅ ∠PQR, MO ≅ PQ
  △MNO ≅ △QRP   **SAS** — side-angle-side

  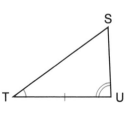
  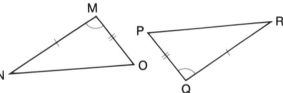

- Two angles and the **contained side**
  of one triangle are congruent to two
  angles and the **contained side** of the other.

  ∠STU ≅ ∠XVW, TU ≅ VW, ∠TUS ≅ ∠VWX
  △STU ≅ △XVW   **ASA** — angle-side-angle

  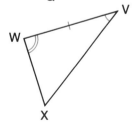

WORKING TOGETHER

1. a. △JKL ≅ △MNP. Why?
   b. △ABC ≅ △DEF. Why?

2. Match the sides and the angles.

   a. JK ≅ ☐   **b.** ∠JKL ≅ ☐   **c.** ∠LJK ≅ ☐

   d. BC ≅ ☐   **e.** AB ≅ ☐   **f.** ∠ABC ≅ ☐

   g. ∠BAC ≅ ☐   **h.** ∠NPM ≅ ☐   **i.** FD ≅ ☐

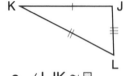

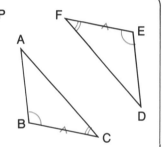

1. **a.** List the corresponding sides that make the triangles congruent. Then write the congruence statement.

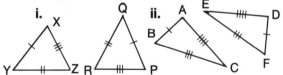

i. **ii.**

   b. List the congruent angles.

2. **a.** List the corresponding sides and the contained angle that make the triangles congruent. Then write the congruence statement.

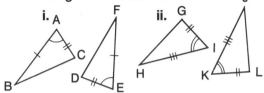

i. **ii.**

   b. List the other congruent angles and sides.

3. **a.** List the corresponding angles and contained sides that make the triangles congruent. Then write the congruence statement.

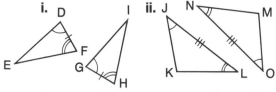

i. **ii.**

   b. List the other congruent angles and sides.

4. List the three matching parts for the pair of triangles. Then write the congruence statement using SSS, SAS, or ASA.

a. **b.**

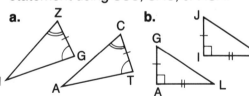

c.

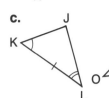

5. Write the congruence statement using SSS, SAS, or ASA.

a.

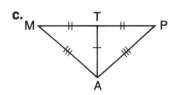

b.

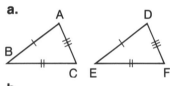

c.

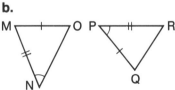
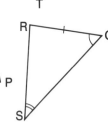

Pascal's Triangle

```
              1
            1   1
          1   2   1
        1   3   3   1
      1   4   6   4   1
    1   5  10  10   5   1
  1   6  15  20  15   6   1
```

Try This

This array can be extended indefinitely.

1. Identify some patterns that are satisfied by the numbers of this array.

253

Bisecting Angles and Line Segments

In a baseball diamond, the pitcher's mound is located on the bisector of the angle formed by the base lines.

Compasses and a straightedge can be used to bisect an angle.

Draw an arc on ∠ABC. Label M and N.	With centre M, draw an arc.	With centre N, same radius, draw an arc. Label D.	Using a straightedge, draw $\overrightarrow{BD}$.
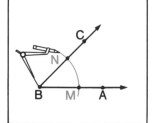	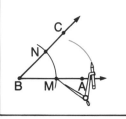	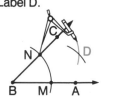	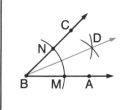

∠CBD ≅ ∠ABD.   ∠ABC is divided into two congruent angles. $\overrightarrow{BD}$ is the **bisector** of ∠ABC.

Compasses and a straightedge can be used to bisect a line segment.

With centre L, draw an arc more than halfway across.	With centre M, same radius, draw an arc. Label P and Z.	Using a straightedge, draw $\overleftrightarrow{PZ}$. Label Q.	$\overline{LQ}$ and $\overline{MQ}$ are congruent. $\overline{PQ}$ and $\overline{LM}$ are perpendicular.
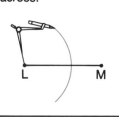	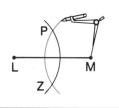	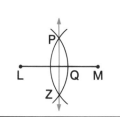	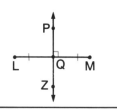

$\overline{QL}$ ≅ $\overline{QM}$.   ∠PQL and ∠PQM are 90°. $\overleftrightarrow{PZ}$ is the **perpendicular bisector** or **right bisector** of $\overline{LM}$.

WORKING TOGETHER

1. a. Use a protractor to draw an angle with measure 115°. Use compasses and a straightedge to bisect the angle.

b. Use compasses and a straightedge to bisect a line segment with length 5 cm.

2. a. Use a protractor to draw an angle with measure 66°. Use a Mira to bisect the angle.

b. Use a Mira to right bisect a line segment with length 9 cm.

APPLICATIONS AND EXERCISES

1. Use a ruler to draw the line segment. Then use compasses and a straightedge to construct the perpendicular bisector. Check your results with a Mira.

   a. 6 cm　　**b.** 9 cm　　**c.** 70 mm

2. Use compasses and a straightedge.

   a. Use a ruler to draw $\overline{AB}$ with length 12 cm.

   b. Construct the perpendicular bisector.

   c. Find a point N such that $\overline{AN} = \frac{1}{4}\overline{AB}$.

   d. What other fractions of $\overline{AB}$ can be constructed?

3. **a.** Use compasses and a ruler to construct △MNO with MN = 10 cm, NO = 8 cm, and OM = 6 cm.

   b. Construct the right bisector of each side. Extend these lines until they intersect each other. Label this point P.

   c. Using P as centre and radius PM, draw a circle.

   d. What do you notice?

4. Use compasses and a straightedge to construct a line segment with length $4\,\overline{CD} - \frac{1}{2}\overline{AB}$.

   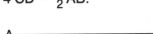

5. **a.** Use a protractor to draw the angle.

   　i. 64°　**ii.** 90°　**iii.** 112°　**iv.** 153°

   b. Use compasses and a straightedge to bisect each angle.

6. **a.** Use a protractor to draw an angle measuring 120°. Use compasses and a straightedge to divide the angle into four congruent angles.

   b. Calculate the measure of each of the four congruent angles.

   c. Use a protractor to check the measure of each angle.

7. **a.** On tracing paper use a protractor to draw an angle with measure 110°. Fold the paper to find the bisector.

   b. On tracing paper draw a line segment with length 12 cm. Fold the paper to find the right bisector.

8. Draw a straight angle. Then use compasses and a straightedge to construct the angle.

   a. 90°　**b.** 45°　**c.** $22\frac{1}{2}°$　**d.** 135°

9. **a.** Use compasses and a straightedge to construct an equilateral triangle with sides 10 cm.

   b. What is the measure of each angle?

   c. Use compasses and a straightedge to divide one angle into four congruent angles.

   d. Calculate the measure of each of the smaller angles.

Try This

1. Use compasses and a straightedge to construct this angle.

   a. $67\frac{1}{2}°$　　**b.** $112\frac{1}{2}°$　　**c.** 120°　　**d.** 150°　　**e.** $157\frac{1}{2}°$

Constructing Parallel Lines

Following the building plan, steelworkers install the steel beams parallel to one another.

Compasses and a straightedge can be used to draw the parallel lines on the building plan.

With centre P, radius LM, draw an arc.	With centre M, radius LP, draw an arc to cut the previous arc. Label Q.	Draw $\overleftrightarrow{PQ}$. $\quad\overleftrightarrow{PQ} \parallel \overleftrightarrow{LM}$
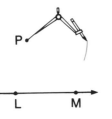	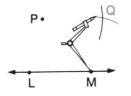	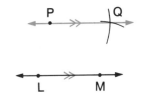

A Mira can also be used to construct a parallel line.

Place the Mira across $\overleftrightarrow{AB}$ but not on P, so that the reflection of one side of the line maps onto the other side of the line.	Mark the image of P. Label P'.	Draw $\overleftrightarrow{PP'}$. $\quad\overleftrightarrow{PP'} \parallel \overleftrightarrow{AB}$
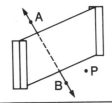	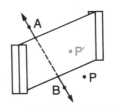	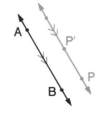

WORKING TOGETHER

1. Draw line segment DE and point F not in the line segment. Use compasses and a straightedge to construct a line segment through F parallel to $\overline{DE}$.

2. Draw line segment AB and point C not in the line segment. Use a Mira to construct a line segment through C parallel to $\overline{AB}$.

APPLICATIONS AND EXERCISES

1. Trace the diagram. Use compasses and a straightedge.

   a. Construct a line through P parallel to $\overleftrightarrow{AB}$.

   b. Construct a line through P parallel to $\overleftrightarrow{DE}$.

   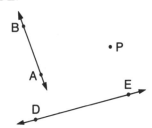

2. Use compasses and a ruler.

   a. Construct an equilateral △MAD with sides 8 cm.

   b. Construct a line through M parallel to AD.

   c. What are the measures of the angles at M?

3. Use a protractor and a ruler.

   a. Construct an isosceles △PAM with PA = 6 cm, AM = 6 cm, and ∠PAM = 70°.

   b. Construct a line through M parallel to PA.

   c. Compare the measures of the angles of the triangle and the angles at M.

4. a. Use compasses and a straightedge to copy the figure.

   b. Use a Mira or compasses to complete rectangle ABCD.

5. a. Use compasses and a straightedge to copy the figure.

   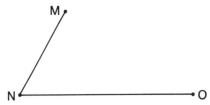

   b. Use a Mira or compasses to complete parallelogram MNOP.

6. Use compasses and a ruler to construct the figure.

   a. parallelogram with sides 8 cm and 4 cm

   b. rhombus with sides 5 cm

   c. parallelogram with sides 6 cm and 3 cm

   d. rectangle with base 5 cm and height 3 cm

What do parallel lines have in common with the following expressions?

1. Calculate.

   a. $16 \times 14 \div 8 - 17$

   b. $(43 + 65) \div 9 - 1$

   c. $14 \times 8 - 19 \times 5 - 6$

   d. $400 - 38 \times 9 - 47$

   e. $29 \times 7 - 24 \times 8$

   f. $269 - (78 - 35) \times 6$

   g. $\frac{(258 + 9) \div 3 - 12}{7}$

   h. $\frac{33 + 44 \times 5}{23}$

   i. $\frac{49 - 312 \div 13 + 8}{3}$

Constructing a Perpendicular to a Line

A plumb line helps a paperhanger find the perpendicular from a point to a horizontal line.

In a triangle, the perpendicular from a vertex to the opposite side is an **altitude**.

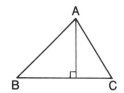

Compasses and a straightedge can be used to construct a perpendicular from a point to a line.

With centre P, draw an arc to cut $\overleftrightarrow{LM}$ in two places. Label X and Y.	With centres X and Y and equal radii, draw arcs to meet somewhere other than P. Label Z.	Draw $\overleftrightarrow{PZ}$. $\overleftrightarrow{PZ} \perp \overleftrightarrow{LM}$
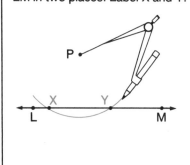	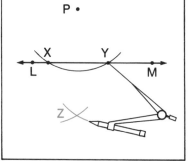	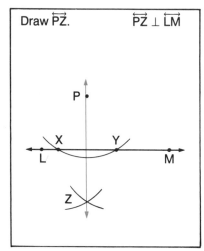

WORKING TOGETHER

1. Draw line XY and point A not in $\overleftrightarrow{XY}$. Use compasses and a straightedge to construct the perpendicular from A to $\overleftrightarrow{XY}$.

2. Investigate how to do exercise 1 using a Mira.

3. **a.** Use a protractor and a ruler to construct △PET with PE = 8 cm, ∠TPE = 70°, and ∠TEP = 50°.

   b. Use compasses and a straightedge to construct the three altitudes of △PET.

1. Trace the diagram. Use compasses and a straightedge to construct the perpendicular from P to $\overleftrightarrow{AB}$.

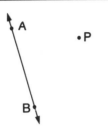

2. Trace the diagram. Use compasses and a straightedge to construct the perpendicular from X to $\overline{CD}$ and from X to $\overline{EF}$.

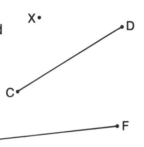

3. Trace the diagram.

   a. Use compasses and a straightedge to construct the perpendicular from D to $\overline{CB}$ and from D to $\overline{AB}$.

   b. Measure the perpendicular distance from D to $\overline{CB}$ and from D to $\overline{AB}$.

   c. What do you notice?

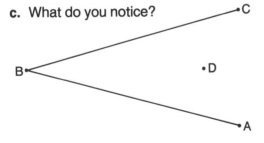

4. Use compasses and a ruler to construct.

   a. △DOT, DO = 8 cm, DT = 10 cm, OT = 6 cm

   b. △MUD, MU = 5 cm, MD = 5 cm, UD = 3 cm

   c. △PAT, PA = 4 cm, PT = 4 cm, AT = 5 cm

5. Use compasses and a straightedge to construct all the altitudes of each triangle in exercise 4. What do you notice about the altitudes?

   a. in the right-angled triangle

   b. in the acute-angled triangle

   c. in the obtuse-angled triangle

6. Trace the map.

   a. Find the perpendicular distances from Tom's camp to each road.

   b. How much closer is Tom's camp to Hwy 60 than to Lake Clear Road?

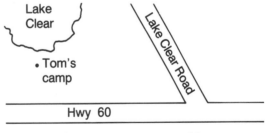

Scale: 1 cm represents 1 km

1. Find the area.

   a.

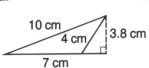

   b.

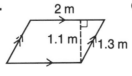

   c.

   d.

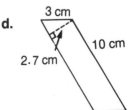

259

Circle Designs

The compasses setting used to draw a circle also separates the circle into six equal arcs.

A regular hexagon is drawn by connecting each point to the one next to it.

An equilateral triangle is drawn by connecting every other point.

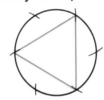

A six-petal flower is drawn by drawing arcs from each point until the pattern is complete.

Circles can also be separated into twelve equal arcs.

Divide the circle into six arcs. Connect the opposite points.	Bisect one angle.	Divide the circle into six more equal arcs.	Draw arcs from each point until the twelve-petal flower is complete.
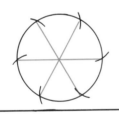			

WORKING TOGETHER

1. Use compasses and a straightedge to divide the circle into six equal arcs. Construct the design.

   a.    b.

2. Construct a circle with centre O and radius 6 cm.

   a. Draw a diameter RS.

   b. Use compasses and a straightedge to construct the perpendicular bisector of RS. Label the points that intersect the circle P and Q.

   c. Join P, S, Q, and R. Classify the polygon.

1. Construct a circle with centre O and radius 8 cm.

   a. Draw a diameter AB.

   b. Use compasses and a straightedge to construct the perpendicular bisector of $\overline{AB}$. Label the points that intersect the circle C and D.

   c. Bisect each angle at the centre O.

   d. Draw the bisectors to intersect the circle.

   e. Connect the points on the circle.

   f. What polygon has been constructed?

2. Use the method in exercise 1 to construct a regular polygon with 16 sides.

3. Use the method in exercise 1 to make this design.

   a.

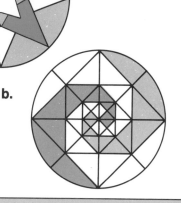

   b.

4. Divide a circle into six equal arcs. Then make this design.

   a.    b.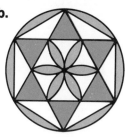

5. Construct a circle with a radius congruent to $\overline{AB}$.

   A •————————————• B

   a. Draw concentric circles (circles with the same centre and different radii) inside your circle.

   b. Create a design using concentric circles.

6. Use compasses to draw the design.

   a. 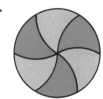   b.

   c. 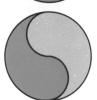   d.

Try This

1. a. Use compasses and a ruler to construct this diagram.

   b. Find the area of the **lune** (the shaded area).

PRACTICE

1. Use compasses and a straightedge.

  a. Construct a line segment congruent to $\overline{DE}$.

  b. Construct an angle congruent to ∠MON.

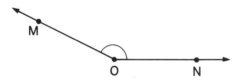

2. Use compasses, a ruler, and a protractor to construct the triangle.

  a. a scalene triangle with sides measuring 6 cm, 9 cm, and 14 cm.

  b. an isosceles triangle with sides measuring 6 cm and 6 cm and the contained angle measuring 40°

  c. a scalene triangle with two angles measuring 30° and 50° and the contained side measuring 7 cm

  d. an equilateral triangle with all sides 7 cm

3. Use compasses, a ruler, and a protractor to construct a triangle congruent to △ABC.

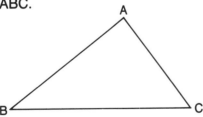

4. a. Use a protractor to draw the angle.

    i. 90°   **ii.** 60°   **iii.** 170°

  b. Use compasses and a straightedge to bisect each angle.

5. Copy $\overline{LM}$. Then divide it into four equal parts.

6. Trace △TED. Use compasses and a straightedge to construct the three altitudes.

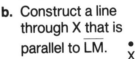

7. Trace △TED in exercise 6. Use compasses and a straightedge to construct the three angle bisectors. Label their point of intersection P. (This is the **incentre** of the triangle.)

8. Trace $\overline{LM}$ and the point X.

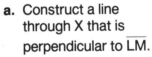

  a. Construct a line through X that is perpendicular to $\overline{LM}$.

  b. Construct a line through X that is parallel to $\overline{LM}$.

9. a. Use compasses and a straightedge to construct a square with sides the length of AB.

  b. Construct a rhombus with sides the length of AB.

10. Use compasses and a straightedge to construct the circle design.

Squares and Square Roots

Squaring and finding the square root are **inverse operations**.

$7^2 = 49$ $\sqrt{49} = 7$

Many calculators square numbers without a special key.

Press $5\boxed{\times}\boxed{=}$.   What is the result?
Press $9\boxed{\times}\boxed{=}$.   What is the result?
Predict the result of $8\boxed{\times}\boxed{=}$.

1. Square.
   a. 14   b. 23   c. 35
   d. 39   e. 46   f. 52

Calculators can be used to find square roots by trial and error.

$\sqrt{289}$ Try 15. $\boxed{15}\boxed{\times}\boxed{=}$ (225.) too low
              Try 17. $\boxed{17}\boxed{\times}\boxed{=}$ (289.) ✓

2. Find the square root of the number.
   a. 324   b. 529   c. 4356   d. 784   e. 2025   f. 2704

Many calculators have special keys, $\boxed{x^2}$ and $\boxed{\sqrt{}}$, for performing these inverse operations.

Press $\boxed{7}\boxed{x^2}$.   What is the result?
Press $\boxed{100}\boxed{\sqrt{}}$ What is the result?

3. Perform the operation indicated.
   a. $\sqrt{169}$ b. 25^2 c. $\sqrt{256}$ d. $\sqrt{2209}$ e. 36^2 f. 41^2
   g. 57^2 h. $\sqrt{5476}$ i. 4.5^2 j. $\sqrt{72.25}$ k. 6.7^2 l. $\sqrt{104.04}$

Both $\boxed{x^2}$ and $\boxed{\sqrt{}}$ operate on the number that is in the display.

4. a. Predict the result of $\boxed{8}\boxed{x^2}\boxed{\sqrt{}}$. Check.
   b. Do you think $\boxed{8}\boxed{\sqrt{}}\boxed{x^2}$ gives the same result? Check. Explain the result.

5. a. Press $\boxed{2}\boxed{\sqrt{}}\boxed{\sqrt{}}\boxed{\sqrt{}}\boxed{\sqrt{}}$ ... What is happening to the display?
   b. How many times do you press $\boxed{\sqrt{}}$ before the same number appears after each press?

BASIC Programming II

A computer is ideally suited for performing repetitive tasks. It can be programmed to do the same thing over and over again without loss of speed and accuracy. You can use a GOTO statement to set up a loop, and a **counter** to keep track of how many times the computer goes around the loop. Any variable can be a counter.

In line 20 the counter starts at 1. Line 60 tells the computer to increase the value of the counter by 1 before going through the loop again. SPC(9) means leave 9 spaces blank.

```
10   REM SQUARE NUMBERS
20   LET C = 1
30   INPUT "NUMBER? ";N
40   SQ = N ∧ 2
50   PRINT SPC(9) N, SQ
60   LET C = C + 1
70   IF C < 11 THEN GOTO 30
80   END
```

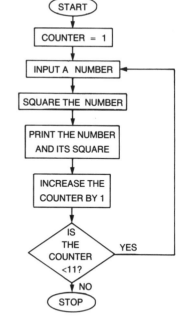

1. Predict the output of the program above if the input is consecutive even numbers from 2.

Another way of obtaining the same result is to replace lines 20, 60, and 70 with these lines. →
FOR and NEXT statements are always used together.

```
20   FOR C = 1 TO 10
60   NEXT C
70
```

2. Predict the output of the program.

a.
```
10 FOR C = 1 TO 100
20 PRINT "WHO ARE YOU?"
30 NEXT C
40 END
```

b.
```
10 FOR N = 10 TO 50 STEP 5
20 PRINT N
30 NEXT N
40 END
```

c.
```
10 SUM = 0
20 FOR I = 1 to 10
30 SUM = SUM + I
40 PRINT I, SUM
50 NEXT I
60 END
```

3. Modify the square number program to print the squares and cubes of the first 12 natural numbers. Format the output to look like this. →

NUMBER	SQUARE	CUBE
1	1	1
2	4	8
3	9	27

4. Ontario sales tax is 7%. Design a program to calculate and print an Ontario sales tax chart listing the tax for amounts of $1, $2, $3,..., to $20.

5. Suppose that Burger Palace agrees to pay Mike $5/h and agrees to pay Beth 1¢ the first hour, 2¢ the second hour, 4¢ the third hour, doubling each hour. After each works 36 h, who earns more? How much more?

Sometimes, instead of using an INPUT line to receive data from the keyboard, a programmer uses **READ** and **DATA** statements within the program.

Mrs. Lee wishes to calculate the average mark for each of her 30 students, each of whom has five subjects.

```
10   REM AVERAGE MARK
20   FOR I = 1 TO 30
30   READ NAME$
40   READ A, B, C, D, E
50   AV = (A + B + C + D + E)/5
60   PRINT NAME$, AV
70   NEXT I
80   END
101  DATA ERNST, 70, 60, 58, 92, 83
102  DATA TRACEY, 92, 45, 78, 81, 64
          ⋮
130  DATA HEIDI, 82, 77, 69, 78, 92
```

DATA statements can be placed anywhere in the program, but for convenience in changing data, they are usually placed after the END statement.

There are 30 lines of DATA for the 30 students.

6. Predict the output for Ernst, Tracey, and Heidi.

When there is a lot of information, for example, marks for all the students in a school, it is often stored in a **file** on a **disk** or a **tape**. The READ statement can be adjusted to instruct the computer to look for the data in the specific **storage device**.

7. Predict the output of the program. →

```
10   READ SIDE
20   IF SIDE = 0 GOTO 60
30   PRINT "LENGTH" SIDE, "AREA = " SIDE * SIDE
40   GOTO 10
50   DATA 5, 9, 20, 17, 32, 196, 0
60   END
```

8. Design a program to calculate and print the volume of rectangular solids. Instruct the program to READ 10 sets of DATA. Observe the outcome when you include only 5 DATA statements. The computer responds with an error message. OUT OF DATA ERROR

9. Design a program to compare pairs of numbers and to print the relationship between them using <, >, or = . Include a counter to tell the computer how many pairs of numbers to process.

Look for a Pattern

There are 12 teams in a ringette league. Each team plays each of the other teams twice. How many games are played?

Think. The problem could probably be solved by acting it out or drawing a diagram. Is there a shorter way?

Plan and do. Consider similar-but-simpler problems. List the results in a table. Then look for a pattern.

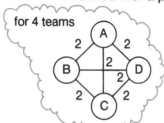

for 4 teams

If the pattern is continued as shown, 12 teams would play 132 games.

Number of teams	Number of games
2	2
3	6
4	12
5	20

$\big\}$ + 4
$\big\}$ + 6
$\big\}$ + 8

Look back. What if there were 50 teams?
Look for a rule between the columns.
Then generalize the rule.
Use the rule to check.

For 50 teams, there would be 2450 games.

| 4 | 4×3 |
| 5 | 5×4 |

$n \qquad n \times (n - 1)$
$12 \qquad 12 \times 11 = 132 \checkmark$
$50 \qquad 50 \times 49 = 2450$

WORKING TOGETHER

1. How many toothpicks are needed to make 10 triangles in a row, if sides are shared?

a. Use the similar-but-simpler situations below. Copy and complete the table.

Number of triangles	Number of toothpicks
1	
2	
3	

b. Continue the pattern to find how many toothpicks are needed for 10 triangles.

c. Generalize the rule. **d.** How many toothpicks are needed for 25 triangles?

e. What if the sides cannot be shared?

PROBLEMS

Look for a pattern in the similar-but-simpler situations. Then solve.

1. What is the maximum number of pieces you can cut a pie into with ten straight cuts?

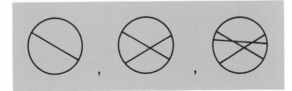

2. How many squares are there in a 10 × 10 grid?

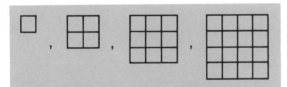

3. How many line segments with end points on the circle are in this figure?

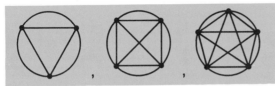

4. What is the sum of these fractions?

$$\frac{1}{1 \times 2} + \frac{1}{2 \times 3} + \frac{1}{3 \times 4} + \frac{1}{4 \times 5} + \cdots$$
$$\cdots + \frac{1}{13 \times 14} + \frac{1}{14 \times 15}$$

$$\frac{1}{1 \times 2} + \frac{1}{2 \times 3}, \quad \frac{1}{1 \times 2} + \frac{1}{2 \times 3} + \frac{1}{3 \times 4},$$
$$\frac{1}{1 \times 2} + \frac{1}{2 \times 3} + \frac{1}{3 \times 4} + \frac{1}{4 \times 5}$$

Generalize the rule. Then solve.

5. If the pattern continues, what is the sum of the numbers in row 100?

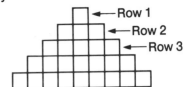

6. How many blocks are there in the 32nd row?

7. **a.** If the pattern continues, how many toothpicks are needed to make 333 squares?

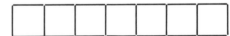

   b. What if sides cannot be shared?

8. If the number of bacteria each hour doubles that of the previous hour, how many bacteria will there be after 10 h? Assume there was one to begin with.

9. What is the sum of the measures of the interior angles of a polygon with 22 sides?

Solve.

10. How many different paths can you take from A to B by following the grid lines?

Problem Solving Review

Solve.

1. A wall measuring 4.5 m by 2.4 m is to be covered with jute fabric. The fabric is 0.5 m wide. How many metres of jute fabric are needed?

2. What is the fraction? The sum of the numerator and the denominator is one less than a square number. The numerator subtracted from the denominator is one more than a square. The product of the terms is one less than a square.

3. For the powers of 3, the pattern of the last digits is shown below. What is the last digit of the product for 3^{25}?

    $3 \times 3,$ 9
    $3 \times 3 \times 3,$ 7
    $3 \times 3 \times 3 \times 3,$ 1
    $3 \times 3 \times 3 \times 3 \times 3,$ 3

4. A record store sells cassette tapes for $3.50 each and albums for $7.99 each. On Friday 25 cassette tapes and 40 albums were sold. On Saturday 33 cassette tapes and 61 albums were sold.

    a. What was the total value of cassette tapes and albums sold on Friday and Saturday?

    b. How much money would the store collect, including sales tax, in your province?

5. Using an existing fence for one side, a rectangular area is to be fenced. 96 m of new fencing is available. What are the dimensions of the largest area that the new fencing can enclose?

6. Maureen, Vic, and Jennifer take turns while playing a game. Vic takes the first turn, Maureen the second, and Jennifer the third.

    a. Who takes the tenth turn?

    b. Who takes the fiftieth turn?

7. Eight people went to a party.

    a. How many handshakes were there if they all shook hands with each other?

    b. How many handshakes would there be if there were 8 couples?

8. Count one, then wait 1 s. How long will it take to count to a billion?

9. Two sides of a scalene triangle are 4 cm and 15 cm long. What is the perimeter of the triangle?

10. How many times a day do the two hands of a clock form a 64° angle?

11. If the snowmobile is worth 10% less each year, in how many years is it worth half its original value?

Chapter Checkup

1. Copy and complete with || or ⊥ to make a true statement.

a. $\overline{AE} \bigcirc \overline{FH}$ **b.** $\overline{AF} \bigcirc \overline{BG}$

c. $\overline{GH} \bigcirc \overline{HD}$ **d.** $\overline{CG} \bigcirc \overline{DH}$

e. $\overline{CG} \bigcirc \overline{GH}$ **f.** $\overline{DG} \bigcirc \overline{EH}$

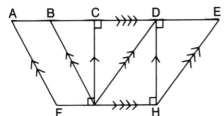

2. What is the measure of the complementary angle for this angle?

a. 7° **b.** 19° **c.** 88° **d.** 77°

3. What is the measure of the supplementary angle for this angle?

a. 120° **b.** 18° **c.** 45° **d.** 152°

4. Calculate the unknown angle measures.

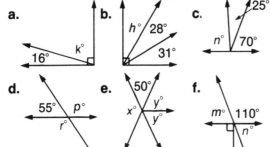

5. Classify the triangle. Then calculate the unknown angle measure x°.

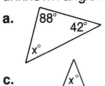

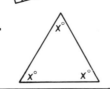

6. Classify the quadrilateral. Then calculate the unknown angle measures x° and y°.

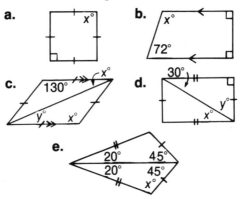

7. Use compasses and a straightedge to construct the line segment.

a. one congruent to $\overline{AB}$

A • ———————— • B

b. one twice the length of $\overline{AB}$

c. one half the length of $\overline{AB}$

8. a. Draw an acute angle.

b. Use compasses and a straightedge to copy the angle.

c. Estimate, then measure, the size.

9. Use compasses and a ruler to construct a scalene triangle with sides measuring 2 cm, 3 cm, and 4 cm.

10. a. Use compasses, a ruler, and a protractor to construct an isosceles triangle with two angles measuring 70° each and the contained side measuring 8 cm.

b. Bisect each angle of the isosceles triangle. Extend the angle bisectors so that they intersect each other. Use the intersection point as the centre to draw a circle that touches each side.

Cumulative Checkup

1. Express as the product of prime factors.

    a. 56   **b.** 48   **c.** 112   **d.** 88

2. Find the cost.

    a. 6 dozen eggs at $1.44 per dozen

    b. 2.75 m of fabric at $3.45/m

    c. 6.5 kg of potatoes at $0.45/kg

3. For each purchase in exercise 2, find the change received from a $20 bill.

4. Joyce is laying wall-to-wall carpeting in her living room.

    a. How much carpeting does Joyce need?

    b. If the carpeting she selects sells for $23.50/m², how much does it cost?

    c. Joyce also needs to buy carpet tape to go all around the baseboard of the living room. What length of carpet tape does she need?

    d. If the carpet tape sells for $0.85/m, how much does it cost?

    e. What is the cost for the carpeting and the tape?

5. Sketch the different faces. Then find the surface area.

6. Find the product.

    a. $\frac{1}{5} \times \frac{1}{5}$ **b.** $\frac{3}{7}$ of $\frac{7}{9}$ **c.** $\frac{3}{10}$ of $\frac{4}{9}$

    d. $9 \times \frac{11}{3}$ **e.** $3\frac{2}{3} \times 3\frac{1}{3}$ **f.** $5\frac{3}{5} \times 1\frac{1}{2}$

7. Find the amount. Express the answer to the nearest cent.

    a. $\frac{1}{3}$ of $25.85   **b.** $\frac{1}{4}$ of $782

    c. $\frac{1}{2}$ of $19.95   **d.** $1\frac{1}{2}$ of $5.45

8. Which pairs are reciprocals?

    a. $\frac{7}{9}, \frac{7}{9}$ **b.** $\frac{8}{5}, \frac{5}{8}$ **c.** $2\frac{3}{4}, \frac{4}{3}$

    d. $5\frac{3}{8}, \frac{8}{43}$ **e.** $7\frac{2}{5}, \frac{37}{5}$ **f.** $4, \frac{1}{4}$

9. In his will a man left $\frac{1}{2}$ of his estate to his wife, $\frac{1}{3}$ to his son, and the rest to be divided equally between his 2 nieces. The value of the estate was $48 000. How much did each relative receive?

10. Express as a fraction in lowest terms.

    a. 0.05   **b.** 0.75   **c.** 3.625

    d. 7.6   **e.** $0.\overline{7}$ **f.** $0.\overline{27}$

    g. $0.1\overline{35}$ **h.** 0.135   **i.** $3.\overline{8}$

11. To make 2 L of pancake batter, 1.2 L of milk is used. Write the ratio of batter to milk in simplest form. Write three equivalent ratios.

12. Write two equivalent ratios for the ratio.

    a. 4:9   **b.** $\frac{1.8}{6}$ **c.** 4 to 16 to 20

    d. $\frac{15}{36}$ **e.** 15 to 12   **f.** 13:26:39

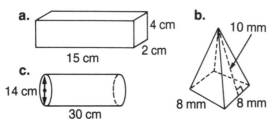

13. Copy. Complete by estimating.

a. $\frac{7}{8} \doteq \frac{\square}{30}$ b. $\frac{2}{9} \doteq \frac{\square}{88}$ c. $\frac{5}{3} \doteq \frac{51}{\square}$

d. $\frac{11}{6} \doteq \frac{57}{\square}$ e. $\frac{11}{12} \doteq \frac{102}{\square}$ f. $\frac{3}{19} \doteq \frac{\square}{80}$

14. A stack of 1000 sheets of paper is 9 cm thick. What is this thickness?

   a. 500 sheets   **b.** 750 sheets

   c. 280 sheets   **d.** 10 sheets

15. a. Find the heartbeat rate in beats per minute for each animal.

   b. Rank the animals from fastest to slowest in heartbeat rate.

Animal	Heartbeat rate
rabbit	5 beats/2 s
sheep	25 beats/20 s
horse	10 beats/15 s

16. Express as a percent.

   a. 37:100   **b.** 151:100   **c.** 6 to 100

   d. $\frac{41}{100}$ **e.** $\frac{36}{100}$ **f.** $\frac{142}{100}$ **g.** 0.71

   h. 0.07 **i.** 7.0   **j.** 0.007 **k.** 1.17

17. Express the fraction as a percent.

   a. $\frac{1}{2}$ **b.** $\frac{3}{4}$ **c.** $\frac{3}{5}$ **d.** $\frac{7}{10}$

18. Express the fraction as a decimal, then as a percent.

   a. $\frac{3}{8}$ **b.** $\frac{1}{3}$ **c.** $\frac{4}{9}$ **d.** $\frac{9}{8}$

19. Express the fraction in lowest terms. Then express the fraction as a percent.

   a. $\frac{3}{12}$ **b.** $\frac{4}{12}$ **c.** $\frac{12}{24}$ **d.** $\frac{16}{24}$

20. Copy and complete.

	Fraction	Decimal	Percent
a.		$0.2\overset{\cdot\cdot}{4}$	
b.			62.5%
c.	$1\frac{3}{4}$		
d.	$\frac{11}{16}$		

21. Use a fraction to estimate.

   a. 25% of 81   **b.** 30% of 38

   c. 62.5% of 163   **d.** $33.\overline{3}$% of 93

22. Calculate each part in exercise 21.

23. A can of mixed nuts is 40% peanuts.

   a. If the can has a mass of 350 g, what is the mass of the peanuts?

   b. If the can were 60% peanuts, what would the mass of the peanuts be?

   c. Which mixture, 40% peanuts or 60% peanuts, do you think would cost more? Why?

24. Estimate. Then calculate.

   a. 32% of 41   **b.** 7% of 4100

   c. 58% of 300   **d.** 310% of 52

   e. 47% of 86   **f.** 92% of 108

25. Decide if the missing number is larger or smaller than the given number.

   a. 25% of a number is 11.

   b. 47 is 50% of a number.

   c. 250% of a number is 30.

   d. A number is 19% of 50.

26. Find each missing number in exercise 25. Check the result.

9/Integers

Meteorologists use integers when recording temperatures, determining temperature changes, and calculating wind-chill temperatures.

Get Set

1. What is the temperature in degrees Celsius?

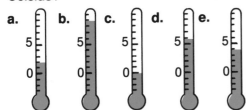

a.   b.   c.   d.   e.

2. How many units is the walk?

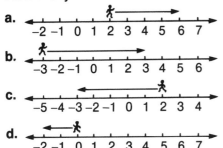

a.

b.

c.

d.

3. Copy and complete.

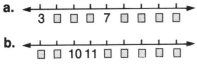

a.   3 ☐ ☐ ☐ 7 ☐ ☐ ☐ ☐

b.   ☐ ☐ 10 11 ☐ ☐ ☐ ☐ ☐

c.   ☐ ☐ ☐ ☐ 19 20 ☐ ☐ ☐

4. Copy and complete.

	Start	End	Up or down	Change
a.	3°C	16°C		
b.	26°C		down	12°C
c.	19°C	2°C		
d.	40°C		up	3°C
e.	17°C		down	17°C

5. Which words may represent a positive quantity?
   loss, rise, above, decrease, below, withdraw, profit, earnings

6. Arrange from least to greatest.

   a. 15, 10, 22, 5, 2

   b. 100, 16, 83, 87, 19, 29

   c. 1.2, 1.8, 1.5, 1.1, 1.6

7. Write the ordered pair for the letter.

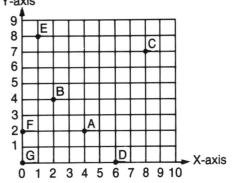

8. Calculate mentally. Write the result.

   a. 17 + 15   b. 35 − 19

   c. 22 + 18 + 12   d. 28 − 12 − 5

   e. 12 × 7   f. 15 × 11

   g. 35 ÷ 5   h. 44 ÷ 11

9. Evaluate.

   a. 2 × 5 + 12   b. 16 ÷ 4 − 2

   c. 18 + 15 ÷ 5   d. 17 − 4 × 4

   e. 20 ÷ (3 + 2) × 6 − 7

10. Write in scientific notation.

   a. 1986   b. 98 106   c. 20 743

   d. 83.1   e. 941.35   f. 1834.04

11. Find the average snowfall.

Month	Jan.	Feb.	Mar.	Apr.
Snowfall (cm)	25	12	13	2

Using Integers

How do storm clouds produce lightning?

The + and − signs in the diagram represent positive and negative electrical charges. Lightning occurs when there is a large buildup of both charges.

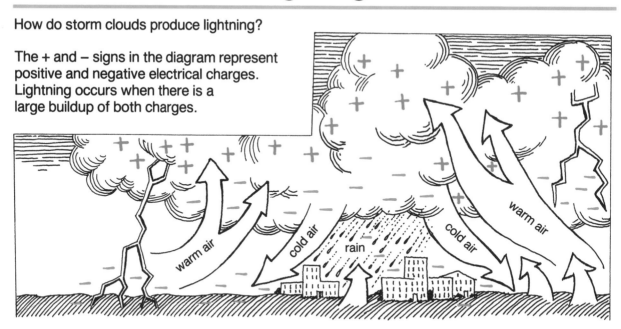

In mathematics, the + and − signs represent the operations of addition and subtraction. They also represent positive and negative numbers. These numbers are called **integers**.

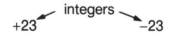

integers
+23   −23

+23 is read positive twenty-three.
+23 is a positive integer.
Positive integers can be written without the + sign.
$$+23 = 23$$

−23 is read negative twenty-three.
−23 is a negative integer.
Negative integers are always written with the − sign.
−23

0 is an integer that is neither positive nor negative.

WORKING TOGETHER

1. What integer is suggested?
   a. 3°C above freezing
   b. 5 m below ground level
   c. ground level
   d. 70 km above sea level
   e. 4°C below freezing
   f. 1 level above ground
   g. 2 floors below ground level

2. Which are positive?
   +3   −11   0   −7   +18   12

3. Which are negative?
   −8   −13   +12   10   −1   0

1. Express the temperature as an integer.

   a. The temperature in Alberta once reached 61°C below freezing.

   b. The highest temperature recorded in Manitoba was 44°C above freezing.

   c. Strong winds and a temperature of 35°C below cause flesh to freeze.

2. Use above freezing or below freezing to describe the temperature.

   a. +12°C **b.** −5°C **c.** −17°C **d.** +22°C

   e. +30°C **f.** −2°C **g.** 14°C **h.** 25°C

3. What integer is suggested?

   a. 560 m above sea level

   b. 6 min before takeoff

   c. a loss of 4 points **d.** a gain of 7 dollars

   e. 212 m below sea level

   f. a raise of 6%

4. In golf a score of −5 means 5 strokes below par. Tell what the score means.

   a. −7 **b.** −1 **c.** +4 **d.** +9

   e. 0 **f.** −3 **g.** +8 **h.** −2

5. In a computer game, Ahmed scored 57 points while Aaron lost 22 points. Represent the scores with integers.

6. If + $7 means a profit of 7 dollars, what does the amount represent?

   a. + $4 **b.** − $11 **c.** − $1 **d.** $16

7. Express the temperature as an integer.

8. The graph shows the monthly profits and losses for a Junior Achievement Club.

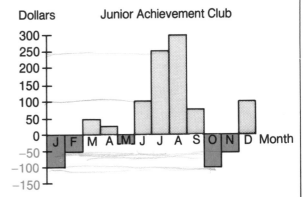

   a. In which months did the club have a profit? a loss?

   b. Express each month's profit or loss as an integer.

   c. On January 1 the club had $400. How much did it end the year with?

---

1. Arrange from greatest to least.

   a. 14, 3, 75, 16, 19 **b.** 9, 12, 21, 17, 43

   c. 71, 19, 97, 79, 10

2. Evaluate.

   a. 62 + 26 **b.** 83 − 38 **c.** 43 + 34

   d. 71 − 17 **e.** 35 + 53 **f.** 42 − 24

Comparing and Ordering

The diagram shows the temperatures
at four cities on the first day of winter.
Compare the temperatures using the diagram.

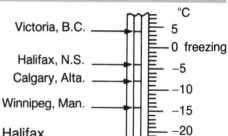

The temperature at Victoria is higher than the temperature at Halifax.
 +4°C is greater than −4°C.   +4°C > −4°C

The temperature at Calgary is lower than the temperature at Halifax.
 −8°C is less than −4°C.   −8°C < −4°C

A **number line** shows the position of positive integers, negative integers, and zero.

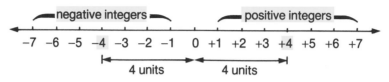

−4 and +4 are the same distance from 0 in opposite directions.
−4 and +4 are **opposite integers**.

Integers can be compared using a number line.

For two integers on a number line, the integer on the right is the greater.

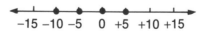

+5 is to the right of −10.   +5 > −10
 0 is to the right of −5.   0 > −5
−10 is to the left of −5.   −10 < −5

WORKING TOGETHER

1. Copy and complete.

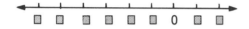

2. Write the corresponding letter or integer.

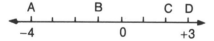

a. +2   **b.** −1   **c.** A   **d.** D

3. What is the opposite integer?
  a. −7   **b.** −3   **c.** +9   **d.** +11

4. Copy and use > or < to make a true
statement.
  a. +6 ◯ +3   **b.** −1 ◯ +1   **c.** −4 ◯ +2

1. Copy and complete.

a.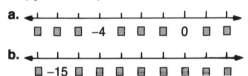

b.

2. Draw and label a number line.

a. from +1 to +10   **b.** from −3 to +4

c. from −15 to −6   **d.** from −7 to +1

3. Copy and complete.

letter	C	J			B				I		G
integer			−1		0	−5		−2			
opposite integer											

4. What is the integer?

a. two greater than zero

b. five less than zero

c. three greater than negative three

d. four less than positive one

5. Copy and use > or < to make a true statement.

a. +1 ◎ +4   **b.** 0 ◎ +8   **c.** −2 ◎ 0

d. +7 ◎ −2   **e.** −2 ◎ +2   **f.** +5 ◎ −1

6. Arrange from least to greatest.

a. −2, +6, −3, −8, +3, +1, −4, −1

b. +7, 0, −5, −9, +10, +5, −11, −6

c. −1, +13, +11, +8, −6, 0, −15, −3

7. Arrange from highest to lowest.

Element	Boiling point (°C)
aluminum	2450
gold	2970
nitrogen	−196
oxygen	−183
platinum	4530
silver	2210

8. Samantha recorded the outside temperature for five days.

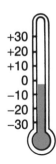

	Temperature (°C)	
Time / Day	12:00	18:00
Mon.	−5	−10
Tues.	−9	−13
Wed.	−7	−6
Thurs.	+1	0
Fri.	−3	−8

a. Which was the coldest day? warmest?

b. On which day was the temperature at 12:00 less than that at 18:00?

Try This

1. **a.** Copy this diagram.

b. Assign letters by following these clues.

A_1 to N is +2	E_2 to Y is −1	T to R is +1
N to L is +4	Y to E_1 is −3	R to D_2 is +11
L to D_1 is −2	E_1 to I is −4	D_2 to A_2 is −3
D_1 to E_2 is +5	I to T is −3	

What is the message?

277

Graphing Ordered Pairs of Integers

Drilling companies can use a grid system to show the locations of their oil wells.

The system is divided into four **quadrants** by two perpendicular number lines called **axes**.

The horizontal number line is the **X-axis**.
The vertical number line is the **Y-axis**.
The axes intersect at a point called the **origin**.

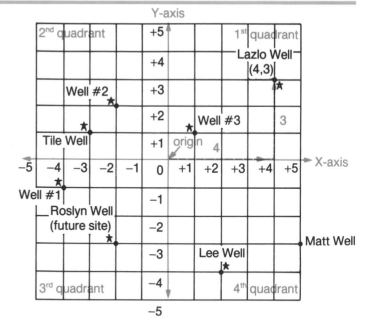

The location of the Lazlo Well is given by the **coordinates** (4,3).

$$(4, \ 3)$$
x-coordinate ⟋ ⟍ y-coordinate

The x-coordinate is always written first, the y-coordinate second.
Therefore, (4,3) is an **ordered pair** of numbers.

The Roslyn Well is to be located at the point with coordinates (−2,−3).
To graph the position, follow these steps:

- Start at the origin.
- Move left 2 units along the X-axis.
- Move down 3 units parallel to the Y-axis.
- Mark a dot and label it.

WORKING TOGETHER

1. Which well has these coordinates?
   a. (−2,2)   b. (5,−3)   c. (−4,−1)

2. Express the location of the well as an ordered pair.
   a. Well #3   b. Lee Well   c. Tile Well

3. Name a well from each quadrant. State the coordinates of the location of the well.

4. a. Which well is 3 units above the X-axis?
   b. Which well is 5 units right of the Y-axis?

1. What ordered pair is named by each letter?

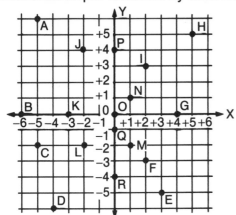

2. Copy and complete.

   a. The *y*-coordinate of all points on the X-axis is ▨.

   b. The *x*-coordinate of all points on the Y-axis is ▨.

3. Locate and name the letter in exercise 1.

   a. 3 units above the X-axis

   b. 6 units left of the origin

   c. 5 units below the X-axis

   d. 5 units right of the Y-axis

   e. 4 units right of the origin

   f. 2 units left of the Y-axis in the second quadrant

   g. 2 units below the X-axis in the fourth quadrant

   h. 5 units left of the Y-axis in the third quadrant

   i. 1 unit right of the Y-axis in the first quadrant

4. Mark coordinate axes on grid paper.

   a. Graph the points with coordinates (1,3), (−3,1), (−1,−3), (3,−1).

   b. Connect the points in order.

   c. Connect the last point to the first.

   d. Classify the resulting polygon.

5. The coordinates of three vertices of a square are (−3,−1), (2,−3), (4,2). Find the coordinates of the fourth vertex.

6. Determine the perimeter of a rectangle whose vertices have coordinates (−1,−1), (−1,4), (2,−1), (2,4).

7. Determine the area of a triangle whose vertices have coordinates (0,8), (6,0), (6,8).

8. Mark coordinate axes on grid paper.

   a. Graph the points with coordinates (−6,−2), (−6,3), (−4,1), (−2,3), (−2,−2).

   b. Connect the points in order.

   c. What letter results?

9. Mark coordinate axes on grid paper.

   a. Graph the points with coordinates (−1,4), (−2,5), (−5,2), (0,−3), (3,0), (2,1), (0,−1), (−1,0), (1,2), (0,3), (−2,1), (−3,2).

   b. Connect the points in order.

   c. Connect the last point to the first.

   d. What is the result?

Try This

1. The coordinates of two vertices of a square are (0,0) and (0,8). What are the coordinates of the other two vertices?

   There is more than one solution. How many solutions can you find?

Adding

At the start of an experiment, the temperature of a liquid is +4°C.
In one minute, the temperature changes by +3°C.
What is the new temperature?

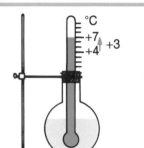

A number line can be used to show the sum.

$$(+4) + (+3)$$

Start at +4 and move 3 units to the right.

The integer at the end of the arrow is the sum.

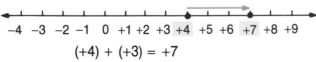

$$-4 \quad -3 \quad -2 \quad -1 \quad 0 \quad +1 \quad +2 \quad +3 \quad +4 \quad +5 \quad +6 \quad +7 \quad +8 \quad +9$$

$$(+4) + (+3) = +7$$

The new temperature is +7°C.

Add. (−2) + (−4)   Start at −2 and move 4 units to the left.

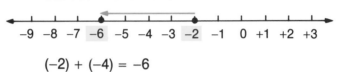

$$(-2) + (-4) = -6$$

Add. (+5) + (−3)   Start at +5 and move 3 units to the left.

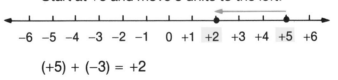

$$(+5) + (-3) = +2$$

Add. (−5) + (+4)   Start at −5 and move 4 units to the right.

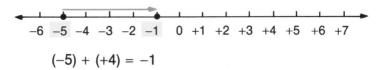

$$(-5) + (+4) = -1$$

WORKING TOGETHER

1. Write the addition sentence.

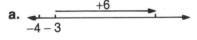

a.

    +6
−4 −3

b.

    −4
+2 +3

2. Draw a number line to show the sum.
Complete the addition sentence.

a. (−1) + (−4) = ☐   **b.** (+3) + (−5) = ☐

c. (−3) + (+1) = ☐   **d.** (+3) + (−3) = ☐

APPLICATIONS AND EXERCISES

1. Use the number line to find the integer at the end of the move.

   a. Start at +1 and move 4 units right.

   b. Start at 0 and move 2 units left.

   c. Start at −1 and move 5 units right.

   d. Start at +3 and move 4 units left.

   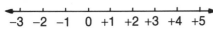

2. Draw a number line to show the sum. Write the addition sentence.

   a. (+5) + (+1)   **b.** (−1) + (+8)

   c. (−5) + 0   **d.** (−7) + (+4)

   e. (−2) + (−2)   **f.** (−6) + (−5)

3. Add using a number line.

   a. (+6) + (−4)   **b.** (−2) + 0

   c. (−3) + (−7)   **d.** (−8) + (+5)

   e. (−9) + (+9)   **f.** (−6) + (+12)

4. Find the sum.

   a. (+7) + (−1)   **b.** (+3) + (−3)

   c. (−3) + (+8)   **d.** (−5) + (+10)

   e. (−9) + (−9)   **f.** (+2) + (−6)

   g. (−7) + (−3)   **h.** (−8) + 0

5. Find the sum. What is the sum of an integer and its opposite?

   a. (+6) + (−6)   **b.** (−7) + (+7)

   c. (−2) + (+2)   **d.** (+12) + (−12)

   e. (+19) + (−19) **f.** (−17) + (+17)

6. Find the sum for each pair.

   a. (−6) + (+5)   **b.** (−4) + (−7)
        (+5) + (−6)   (−7) + (−4)

   Compare the answers in each pair. Does the order of the integers affect the answer?

7. Find the sum for each pair.

   a. (+3) + (−8) + (+6); (+3) + (+6) + (−8)

   b. (−5) + (+2) + (−4); (−5) + (−4) + (+2)

   c. (−6) + (+6) + (−11); (−6) + (−11) + (+6)

   Which of each pair did you find easier to evaluate? Why?

8. Evaluate.

   a. (+7) + (−5) + (+6)

   b. (−9) + (+2) + (−3)

   c. (+1) + (−6) + (+4) + (−7)

   d. (−3) + (+5) + (−1) + (+8)

   e. (+12) + (−9) + (+11) + (−20)

   f. (−13) + (+25) + (−5) + (−17)

9. The penalty points for riders in a show jumping competition are shown.

Rider	Penalty points
Dale	−3,−3,−4,−8
Toni	−3,−4,−4,−5
Tracey	−3,−3,−3,−8

   a. Find the total penalty points for each.

   b. A penalty point total closest to 0 wins. Who placed first? second? third?

Try This

1. Copy the diagram. Place the integers from −4 to +4 in the circles so that the sum along each side of the diagram is 0. How many ways can you do this?

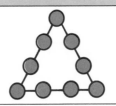

281

Subtracting

I know that 5 − 3 = 2 and (+5) − (+3) = 2.

But I remember that (+5) + (−3) = 2.

That means that (+5) − (+3) = (+5) + (−3).

To subtract an integer, add its opposite.

Find the difference.

(+4) − (−1)

opposites

(+4) − (−1) = (+4) + (+1)
= +5

(+2) − (+9)

(+2) − (+9) = (+2) + (−9)
= −7

(−7) − (+2)

opposites

(−7) − (+2) = (−7) + (−2)
= −9

(−3) − (−5)

(−3) − (−5) = (−3) + (+5)
= +2

WORKING TOGETHER

1. Express with the opposite operation and with the opposite integer.

   a. −(+6) **b.** −(+5) **c.** −(−2)
   d. −(−8) **e.** −(4) **f.** −(9)

2. Add.

   a. (+3) + (+4) **b.** (+3) + (−4)
   c. (+3) + (+2) **d.** (+3) + (−2)

3. Express as an addition sentence.

   a. (+4) − (+7) **b.** (−5) − (+2)
   c. (+3) − (−8) **d.** (+7) − (−1)
   e. (−6) − (−3) **f.** (−8) − (−9)

4. Express as an addition sentence. Evaluate.

   a. (+3) − (+1) **b.** (+4) − (−3)
   c. (−4) − (−1) **d.** (+1) − (−4)

APPLICATIONS AND EXERCISES

1. Copy and complete.

  a. (+5) − (+2) = (+5) + ☐

  b. (−3) − (+6) = (−3) + ☐

  c. (−6) − (+5) = (−6) + ☐

  d. (−7) − (−1) = (−7) + ☐

  e. (+3) − (+8) = (+3) + ☐

  f. (+7) − (−9) = (+7) + ☐

2. Express as an addition sentence.

  a. (−1) − (−3)   **b.** (−4) − (+3)

  c. (+4) − (−2)   **d.** (+4) − (+1)

  e. (+3) − (+5)   **f.** (−5) − (−3)

  g. (−6) − (+1)   **h.** 0 − (−3)

3. Evaluate.

  a. (+5) − (+4)   **b.** (+6) − (−8)

  c. (−7) − (−1)   **d.** (+4) − (−7)

  e. (−3) − (+8)   **f.** (+5) − (−7)

  g. 0 − (+2)   **h.** (−20) − (−11)

  i. (+6) − (−6)   **j.** (−8) − (+8)

4. In one hour, a chinook in Dawson Creek, B.C., raised the temperature from −21°C to +2°C. What was the change in temperature?

5. Find the difference.

  a. (−2) − (+3)   **b.** (−5) − (−3)

    (+3) − (−2)   (−3) − (−5)

Compare the answers in each pair. Does the order affect the answer?

6. Find the result.

  a. (−5) − (−1) − (3) **b.** (−4) − (−6) − (−1)

  c. (−5) − (8) − (6) **d.** (10) − (3) − (−7)

  e. (−2) − (−8) − (4) **f.** (−3) − (−3) − (−7)

  g. (4) − (−1) − (−5) **h.** (−3) − (−4) − (5)

7. For each month, express as an integer the change in temperature a person can expect on a flight from Winnipeg to Miami.

City	Average temperature (°C)			
	Jan.	April	July	Oct.
Miami	+22	+27	+31	+29
Winnipeg	−18	+3	+20	+7

8. Copy and complete the Magic Square.

a.

	−5	0
	−1	
	+3	

b.

		2
−1	1	
0		

Sometimes in a division question, finding the remainder is more important than finding the entire quotient.

345 cans of juice are packed 24 to a case. How many cans are left over?

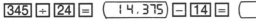 9 cans are left over.

1. Find the remainder. Make up a problem for the situation.

  a. 765 ÷ 32   **b.** 539 ÷ 14   **c.** 1653 ÷ 24   **d.** 3544 ÷ 64

  e. 9085 ÷ 46   **f.** 4500 ÷ 48   **g.** 3400 ÷ 125   **h.** 5187 ÷ 56

1. What integer is suggested?
   a. 5°C below freezing
   b. 600 m above sea level
   c. 3 floors below ground level
   d. a loss of $120   e. a $200 profit

2. What is the opposite integer?
   a. −7   b. +3   c. 2   d. −12   e. 25

3. Copy and use > or < to make a true statement.
   a. −6 ◯ −4   b. −3 ◯ +3   c. 0 ◯ −5
   d. 8 ◯ −1   e. −2 ◯ −7   f. 10 ◯ 13

4. Arrange from least to greatest.
   a. −7, 5, +3, −2, 1, 4, −5
   b. +4, 0, −3, −2, 8, −8, −1
   c. −9, −6, 4, −10, 7, 0, +3, −5

5. Write an ordered pair to represent each letter from A to N.

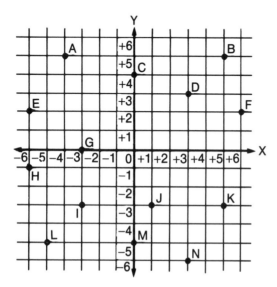

6. Mark coordinate axes on grid paper.
   a. Graph the points with coordinates (−2,3), (−5,−1), (4,−1), (1,3).
   b. Connect the points in order.
   c. Connect the last point to the first.
   d. Classify the polygon.

7. Write the addition sentence.
   a.
   b.
   c.

8. Find the sum.
   a. (−1) + (+2)   b. (+5) + (−4)
   c. (−3) + (+3)   d. (−8) + (−1)
   e. (+9) + (−4)   f. (−5) + (+6)
   g. (−1) + (−6)   h. (+10) + (−3)

9. Express as an addition sentence.
   a. (+6) − (+3)   b. (+8) − (+15)
   c. (−3) − (+13)   d. (+9) − (−4)
   e. (−6) − (−5)   f. (−2) − (−7)

10. Evaluate.
    a. (+8) − (−4)   b. (−5) + (−3)
    c. (−2) − (−7)   d. 0 − (−15) + (−7)
    e. (+13) + (−8)   f. (−3) − (−3)
    g. (+10) − (−15)   h. (−9) + (+9) − (−1)

11. The temperature at 09:00 was −2°C. At 12:00 the temperature had risen by 7°C. What was the temperature at 12:00?

12. On a winter night the temperature dropped from −3°C to −12°C. What was the change in temperature?

The Sign Change Key

Some calculators have a $\boxed{+/-}$ key for changing the sign of a number. When a number is displayed, pressing $\boxed{+/-}$ changes the display to the opposite number.

| $\boxed{36.}$ | $\boxed{+/-}$ | $\boxed{-36.}$ |
| $\boxed{-49.}$ | $\boxed{+/-}$ | $\boxed{49.}$ |

Integers can be added and subtracted using $\boxed{+/-}$.

$+13 + (-25)$ $\boxed{13}\boxed{+}\boxed{25}\boxed{+/-}\boxed{=}$ $\boxed{-72.}$
$-27 + (-38)$ $\boxed{27}\boxed{+/-}\boxed{+}\boxed{38}\boxed{+/-}\boxed{=}$ $\boxed{-65.}$
$-19 - (+22)$ $\boxed{19}\boxed{+/-}\boxed{-}\boxed{22}\boxed{=}$ $\boxed{-41.}$
$-4 - (-9)$ $\boxed{4}\boxed{+/-}\boxed{-}\boxed{9}\boxed{+/-}\boxed{=}$ $\boxed{5.}$

1. Calculate.
   a. $+26 - (+31)$ b. $-18 + (-17)$ c. $+44 - (-12)$ d. $-42 - (-54)$
   e. $-54 - (+39)$ f. $-13 + (-13)$ g. $+72 + (-68)$ h. $-91 - (-91)$
   i. $-91 + (+85)$ j. $-33 + (+29)$ k. $83 - (-17)$ l. $-16 - (-35)$
   m. $-51 - (+47) - (-19)$ n. $-17 - (-26) + (-15)$ o. $+28 - (+24) + (-21)$
   p. $-16 + (-5) - (-8)$ q. $+42 - (-18) - (+27)$ r. $-13 - (-14) - (+15)$

The $\boxed{+/-}$ key sometimes is used in place of memory.

$42 - 13 \times 7$ $\boxed{13}\boxed{\times}\boxed{7}\boxed{M+}\boxed{42}\boxed{-}\boxed{MR}\boxed{=}$ $\boxed{-49.}$
   or $\boxed{13}\boxed{\times}\boxed{7}\boxed{=}\boxed{+/-}\boxed{+}\boxed{42}\boxed{=}$ $\boxed{-49.}$

2. Calculate. Do not use memory.
   a. $53 - (17 + 24)$ b. $-34 - 72 \div 9$ c. $26 - (28 - 15)$
   d. $86 - 3 \times 9$ e. $19 - (14 - 23)$ f. $2 - 144 \div 12$
   g. $-17 - (19 - 13)$ h. $105 - 11 \times 3$ i. $-85 - (23 + 14)$
   j. $-4 - 108 \div 9$ k. $-3 - [16 - (7 - 9)]$ l. $12 - [18 - (29 - 1)]$

3. An airplane was at an altitude of +1872 m. It is now at +789 m. What was the change in altitude?

4. The altitude of an airplane is +2134 m. The altitude of a submarine is −186 m. How far above the submarine is the airplane?

285

Multiplying

During an equestrian competition, Tammy makes several jumping faults. The points that she is penalized are shown in the table.

Day	Penalty points
1	–4
2	–4
3	–4

Her penalty point total can be determined by multiplying. $+3 \times (-4)$

To determine the product of a positive integer and a negative integer, study the pattern.

$+3 \times (+3) = +9$
$+3 \times (+2) = +6$
$+3 \times (+1) = +3$
$+3 \times (0) = 0$
$+3 \times (-1) = \blacksquare$
$+3 \times (-2) = \blacksquare$
$+3 \times (-3) = \blacksquare$
$+3 \times (-4) = \blacksquare$

The pattern shows that the products are decreasing by 3.
Extending the pattern,
$+3 \times (-1) = -3$
$+3 \times (-2) = -6$
$+3 \times (-3) = -9$
$+3 \times (-4) = -12$
Tammy's penalty point total is –12.

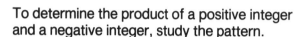

The product of a positive integer and a negative integer is a negative integer.

This result is used to determine the product of two negative integers.

$-3 \times (+3) = -9$
$-3 \times (+2) = -6$
$-3 \times (+1) = -3$
$-3 \times (0) = 0$
$-3 \times (-1) = \blacksquare$
$-3 \times (-2) = \blacksquare$
$-3 \times (-3) = \blacksquare$
$-3 \times (-4) = \blacksquare$

The pattern shows that the products are increasing by 3.

Extending the pattern,
$-3 \times (-1) = +3$
$-3 \times (-2) = +6$
$-3 \times (-3) = +9$
$-3 \times (-4) = +12$

The product of two negative integers is a positive integer.

WORKING TOGETHER

1. Copy and complete.

×	+3	+2	+1	0	–1	–2	–3
+2							
+5							

2. Copy and complete.

×	+3	+2	+1	0	–1	–2	–3
–2							
–5							

1. Express the sum as a product.

   a. $(-2) + (-2) + (-2) + (-2)$

   b. $(-6) + (-6) + (-6)$

   c. $(+5) + (+5) + (+5) + (+5)$

   d. $(-3) + (-3) + (-3) + (-3) + (-3)$

2. Copy and complete.

   a. $+7 \times (+3) = \square$ **b.** $-6 \times (+3) = \square$
        $+7 \times (+2) = \square$ $-6 \times (+2) = \square$
        $+7 \times (+1) = \square$ $-6 \times (+1) = \square$
        $+7 \times (0)\ \ = \square$ $-6 \times (0)\ \ = \square$
        $+7 \times (-1) = \square$ $-6 \times (-1) = \square$
        $+7 \times (-2) = \square$ $-6 \times (-2) = \square$
        $+7 \times (-3) = \square$ $-6 \times (-3) = \square$

3. Decide whether the product is positive or negative. Then find the product.

   a. $-2 \times (+6)$ **b.** 3×4 **c.** $+4 \times (-2)$

   d. $-7 \times (-1)$ **e.** $+1 \times (-8)$ **f.** $-3 \times (+7)$

   g. $-2 \times (-2)$ **h.** $-4 \times (+3)$ **i.** 6×4

4. Find the product.

   a. $-1 \times (+20)$ **b.** $-8 \times (-3)$ **c.** $0 \times (-7)$

   d. $-8 \times (+8)$ **e.** $-3 \times (+4)$ **f.** 5×8

   g. $3 \times (-11)$ **h.** -4×4 **i.** -6×0

5. Find the product for each pair.

   a. $-6 \times (+9)$ **b.** $+8 \times (-7)$
       $+9 \times (-6)$ $-7 \times (+8)$

   Compare the answers in each pair. Does the order affect the answer?

6. Evaluate.

   a. $-1 \times (-2) \times (-3)$ **b.** $4 \times (-2) \times (+3)$

   c. $3 \times (-1) \times (-2)$ **d.** $-5 \times (-2) \times (-1)$

   e. $-8 \times (-4) \times 0$ **f.** $6 \times (-3) \times 2$

7. Multiply only if the product is positive.

   a. $-3 \times (+12)$ **b.** $5 \times (-7)$

   c. $-11 \times (-5)$ **d.** $7 \times (+9)$

   e. $2 \times (-14)$ **f.** $-3 \times (-4) \times (+4)$

8. Multiply only if the product is negative.

   a. $-5 \times (-11)$ **b.** $6 \times (-13)$

   c. -6×5 **d.** -9×0

   e. $5 \times (-14)$ **f.** $-7 \times 2 \times 10$

9. Express as a product.

   a. $(-7)^2$ **b.** $(-7)^3$ **c.** $(-7)^4$ **d.** $(-7)^5$

   Which products are positive? negative?

10. Copy and complete.

   a. The product of an even number of negative integers is a $\blacksquare$ integer.

   b. The product of an odd number of negative integers is a $\blacksquare$ integer.

11. a. Multiply the sum of -3 and -7 by $+3$.

   b. Multiply the sum of 9 and -14 by -6.

   c. Subtract 2 from 4 and multiply the difference by -5.

   d. Subtract -4 from 7 and multiply the difference by 2.

Try This

1. Arrange four 1's and five -1's in the nine squares so that the product of the three integers in each row, column, and diagonal is -1.

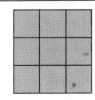

Dividing

Pulling back on the control stick causes the plane to climb. The climbing motion is undone by pushing forward on the stick.

Pushing forward on the control stick causes the plane to dive. The diving motion is undone by pulling back on the stick.

Multiplication and division undo each other.

From whole numbers recall.

$$3 \times 2 = 6 \quad \Rightarrow \quad \frac{6}{2} = 3$$

This applies to integers as well.

$$+3 \times (+2) = +6 \quad \Rightarrow \quad \frac{+6}{+2} = +3$$

$$+3 \times (-2) = -6 \quad \Rightarrow \quad \frac{-6}{-2} = +3$$

The quotient of two positive integers or two negative integers is a positive integer.

$$-3 \times (-2) = +6 \quad \Rightarrow \quad \frac{+6}{-2} = -3$$

$$-3 \times (+2) = -6 \quad \Rightarrow \quad \frac{-6}{+2} = -3$$

The quotient of a positive integer and a negative integer is a negative integer.

WORKING TOGETHER

1. Copy and complete.

   a. $+4 \times (+2) = \square \Rightarrow \square \div (+2) = +4$

   b. $-5 \times (-2) = \square \Rightarrow \square \div (-2) = -5$

   c. $+4 \times (-5) = \square \Rightarrow \square \div (-5) = +4$

   d. $-8 \times (+3) = \square \Rightarrow \square \div (+3) = -8$

2. Copy and complete.

   a. $\frac{+10}{+5} = \square$ **b.** $\frac{-15}{+3} = \square$

   c. $\frac{+16}{-4} = \square$ **d.** $\frac{-20}{-10} = \square$

1. Copy and complete. Check by multiplying.

   a. $\frac{+14}{+2} = \square 7$ **b.** $\frac{+24}{-6} = \square 4$

   c. $\frac{-50}{+5} = \square 10$ **d.** $\frac{-56}{-8} = \square 7$

   e. $\frac{+84}{-7} = \square 12$ **f.** $\frac{-96}{+6} = \square 16$

2. Decide whether the quotient is positive or negative. Then find the quotient.

   a. $\frac{+8}{-2}$ **b.** $\frac{+12}{-6}$ **c.** $\frac{+20}{-4}$ **d.** $\frac{-40}{+5}$

   e. $\frac{-16}{+2}$ **f.** $\frac{+28}{-7}$ **g.** $\frac{-24}{-3}$ **h.** $\frac{+18}{-6}$

3. Find the quotient.

   a. $\frac{-8}{-4}$ **b.** $\frac{-7}{+7}$ **c.** $\frac{+10}{-5}$ **d.** $\frac{-30}{-6}$

   e. $\frac{-32}{+8}$ **f.** $\frac{+25}{+5}$ **g.** $\frac{+5}{-5}$ **h.** $\frac{-12}{-12}$

   i. $-39 \div (-13)$ **j.** $-10 \div (-10)$

4. Divide only if the quotient is positive.

   a. $70 \div (-10)$ **b.** $26 \div 2$

   c. $20 \div (+10)$ **d.** $-18 \div (-9)$

   e. $-32 \div (+16)$ **f.** $-21 \div (-7)$

   g. $-12 \div (-12)$ **h.** $-44 \div 4$

5. Divide only if the quotient is negative.

   a. $17 \div 17$ **b.** $-45 \div 5$

   c. $35 \div (-5)$ **d.** $-26 \div 2$

   e. $-13 \div (-13)$ **f.** $-33 \div 11$

   g. $-21 \div 3$ **h.** $28 \div (-4)$

6. A submarine descends at the rate of 50 m/min. How many minutes will it take to descend from sea level to −1500 m?

7. A watch loses 2 min/h. If the watch is set to the correct time at 1 p.m., how many minutes slow will it be at 9 p.m.?

8. The temperature inside a freezer falls at the rate of 2°C/h. If the temperature is −4°C, how many hours will it take to reach −12°C?

9. Copy and complete.

   a.

$0 \times 8 = \square$
$0 \times (-27) = \square$
$0 \times (+9) = \square$
$0 \times (-41) = \square$

   b.

$0 \div 8 = \square$
$0 \div (-27) = \square$
$0 \div (+9) = \square$
$0 \div (-41) = \square$

10. Copy and complete the table by finding a pattern in each row and in each column.

   a.

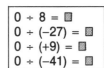

   b.

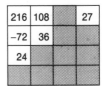

11. a. Divide the sum of 12 and 2 by −7.

   a. Multiply the sum of −7 and 4 by −6.

   c. Subtract 5 from 9 and multiply the difference by −4.

   d. Subtract 8 from −10 and divide the difference by 9.

KEEPING SHARP

1. Estimate.

   a. $\begin{array}{r} 15.9 \\ \times\, 2.3 \end{array}$ **b.** $\begin{array}{r} 60.7 \\ \times\, 0.38 \end{array}$ **c.** $\begin{array}{r} 214 \\ \times\, 8.7 \end{array}$ **d.** $\begin{array}{r} 0.095 \\ \times\, 0.72 \end{array}$ **e.** $3.2\,)\,\overline{21.76}$ **f.** $0.64\,)\,\overline{124.8}$

Order of Operations

On a multiple choice quiz, 2 points were
given for each correct answer and −1 point
for each incorrect answer.
Sasha had 10 correct answers and 5
incorrect answers. What was her score?

Score: 10 × 2 + 5 × (−1)
    = 20 + (−5)
    = 15
Sasha's score was 15.

The rules for the order of operations that apply to
whole numbers also apply to integers.

Rules for the Order of Operations
1. Perform operations inside parentheses.
2. Evaluate powers.
3. Multiply and divide from left to right.
4. Add and subtract from left to right.

Evaluate. $[−5 + (+10)] + 20 ÷ (−4) × (−3)$

$[−5 + 10] + 20 ÷ (−4) × (−3)$ *parentheses*

$= 5 + 20 ÷ (−4) × (−3)$ *divide*

$= 5 + (−5) × (−3)$ *multiply*

$= 5 + 15$ *add*

$= 20$

Evaluate. $−2 + (−3)^2 − 6$

$−2 + (−3)^2 − 6$ *powers*

$= −2 + (−3) × (−3) − 6$

$= −2 + 9 − 6$ *add*

$= 7 − 6$ *subtract*

$= 1$

WORKING TOGETHER

1. For $−30 ÷ (−5) − 4$,
   a. which operation is performed first?
   b. which operation is performed next?
   Evaluate the expression.

2. Express as a product. Then multiply.
   a. 4^2 **b.** 5^2 **c.** 6^2
   d. $(−8)^2$ **e.** $(−7)^2$ **f.** $(−10)^3$

3. For $−3 × 5 + (−2)^2$,
   a. which operation is performed first?
   b. which operation is performed next?
   Evaluate the expression.

4. Find the average temperature.
   a. $−7°C, −9°C$
   b. $−6°C, −4°C, −8°C$

APPLICATIONS AND EXERCISES

1. Evaluate.

   a. $42 ÷ (−6) + (−3)$ **b.** $41 + (−12) ÷ (−2)$

   c. $−8 × (−5) ÷ 10$ **d.** $(15 − 5) × (−8)$

   e. $(−2)^2 + 9$ **f.** $36 × (−4) − (−7)$

   g. $(−3) + (−5)^2$ **h.** $(−8 − 11) ÷ (−1)$

2. Evaluate.

   a. $5 × (6 + 4)$ **b.** $8 × (7 − 3)$

   c. $−2 × (9 + 5)$ **d.** $−4 × (11 − 6)$

   e. $−2 × [5 + (−3)]$ **f.** $−3 × [−4 + (−2)]$

   g. $6 × [(−1) − (−6)]$ **h.** $5 × (−7 − 3)$

3. Evaluate.

   a. $12 − (−4) + (−2) + 5$

   b. $5 ÷ (−5) − 3 × (−3)$

   c. $−10 × (−4) ÷ (−2) − (−3)$

4. On a multiple choice quiz, 2 points were given for each correct answer and −1 point for each incorrect answer. Whose score is represented by $7(2) + 2(−1)$? Calculate the score for this student.

Student	Correct	Incorrect
Nora	8	2
Ming	7	2
Anna	9	0
Troy	9	1
Grant	7	1

5. **a.** Write an expression to represent the score for each of the other students in exercise 4.

   b. Calculate the scores.

   c. Arrange them from highest to lowest.

6. Evaluate.

   a. $16 + (−3)^2$ **b.** $20 + (−2)^2$

   c. $6^2 − 6$ **d.** $7^2 + 5^2$ **e.** $(7 + 5)^2$

   f. $(−2)^2 + (−3)^2$ **g.** $[−2 + (−3)]^2$

7. On a multiple choice quiz, 3 points were given for each correct answer, −2 points for each incorrect answer, and −1 point for each question left unanswered. Out of 20 questions, Jim answered 13 correctly and 4 incorrectly. What was his score?

8.
Location	Temperature (°C)
Calgary, Alta.	−4
Churchill, Man.	−20
Regina, Sask.	−8
Winnipeg, Man.	−6

   a. How much colder is Churchill than Winnipeg?

   b. What is the average temperature for the four locations?

   c. In which locations is the temperature above the average?

---

1. Explain how the bar graph program works.
2. Modify the program to include labels and a title for the graph.
3. Adjust the program to print other bar graphs.

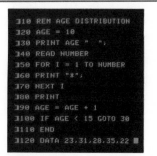

```
10 REM AGE DISTRIBUTION
20 AGE = 10
30 PRINT AGE " ";
40 READ NUMBER
50 FOR I = 1 TO NUMBER
60 PRINT "*";
70 NEXT I
80 PRINT
90 AGE = AGE + 1
100 IF AGE < 15 GOTO 30
110 END
120 DATA 23,31,28,35,22
```

Scientific Notation

Dana uses her calculator to evaluate 10^4, 10^3, 10^2, and 10^1. She sees a pattern and uses it to give meaning to new powers of 10.

$10^4 = 10000$
$10^3 = 1000$
$10^2 = 100$
$10^1 = 10$
$10^0 = $ ▨
$10^{-1} = $ ▨
$10^{-2} = $ ▨
$10^{-3} = $ ▨
$10^{-4} = $ ▨

The exponents are decreasing by 1.

The pattern shows that each result can be found by dividing the previous result by 10.
Extending the pattern,

$10^0 = 10 \div 10$ or **1**
$10^{-1} = 1 \div 10$ or **0.1**
$10^{-2} = 0.1 \div 10$ or **0.01**
$10^{-3} = 0.01 \div 10$ or **0.001**
$10^{-4} = 0.001 \div 10$ or **0.0001**

Powers of 10 with negative exponents are used to express small quantities in **scientific notation**.

A microcomputer can carry out an instruction in about 0.000 35 s. Express this time in scientific notation.

$0.000\,35 = 3.5 \times 0.0001$

A number between 1 and 10

A power of 10

$= 3.5 \times 10^{-4}$

In scientific notation, 0.000 35 s is written 3.5×10^{-4} s.

WORKING TOGETHER

1. Express as a decimal.
   a. 10^{-5} **b.** 10^{-6} **c.** 10^{-9} **d.** 10^{-8}

2. Copy and complete.
   a. $0.59 = \square \times 10^{-1}$
   b. $0.073 = \square \times 10^{-2}$
   c. $0.0086 = \square \times 10^{-3}$

3. Copy and complete.
   a. $8.25 = 8.25 \times 10^{\square}$
   b. $0.627 = 6.27 \times 10^{\square}$
   c. $0.0053 = 5.3 \times 10^{\square}$
   d. $0.000\,81 = 8.1 \times 10^{\square}$

4. Express in standard form.
   a. 5.4×10^{-1} **b.** 5.4×10^{-3}
   c. 5.4×10^{-4} **d.** 5.4×10^{-5}

APPLICATIONS AND EXERCISES

1. Match the decimal with the corresponding expression in scientific notation.

   a. 0.051

   b. 0.0051

   c. 0.000 51

   d. 0.51

   e. 0.000 051

   i. 5.1×10^{-1}

   ii. 5.1×10^{-5}

   iii. 5.1×10^{-3}

   iv. 5.1×10^{-2}

   v. 5.1×10^{-4}

2. Copy and complete.

   a. $0.087 = 8.7 \times 10^{\blacksquare}$

   b. $0.124 = 1.24 \times 10^{\blacksquare}$

   c. $0.0075 = \blacksquare \times 10^{-3}$

   d. $819 = 8.19 \times 10^{\blacksquare}$

   e. $0.000\ 004 = 4 \times 10^{\blacksquare}$

   f. $0.000\ 96 = \blacksquare \times 10^{-4}$

3. Express in scientific notation.

   a. 0.000 57   **b.** 0.061   **c.** 2.89

   d. 0.934   **e.** 478.4   **f.** 89 105

   g. 0.000 0084   **h.** 0.005 801

4. Express the number in scientific notation.

   a. The diameter of a bacterium is about 0.0304 mm.

   b. The diameter of a snowflake is about 0.25 cm.

   c. The thickness of a human cell membrane is about 0.000 000 75 mm.

   d. The length of a virus is about 0.000 002 5 mm.

5. The diameter of a human red blood cell is about 0.0075 mm.

   a. If placed side by side, how many cells would fit along this segment ⊢mmm⊣ ?

   b. Express your answer to part **a** in scientific notation.

6. Express the time as a decimal.

   a. A millisecond is 10^{-3} s.

   b. A microsecond is 10^{-6} s.

   c. A nanosecond is 10^{-9} s.

7. Express the number in standard form.

   a. 7.3×10^{-2} **b.** 6.4×10^{-1}

   c. 2.51×10^{-4} **d.** 3.14×10^{3}

   e. 7.32×10^{5} **f.** 6.07×10^{-7}

   g. 1.006×10^{-3} **h.** 4.03×10^{-5}

8. Express the number in standard form.

   a. Your eye can distinguish nearly 8×10^{6} differences in colors.

   b. Your body produces about 1×10^{9} red blood cells every day.

   c. Your fingers can detect a movement of about 2×10^{-5} mm.

9. A computer can add two numbers in 0.000 004 42 s.

   a. Express this time in scientific notation.

   b. How long would the computer take to perform 10^{6} two-number additions?

---

1. Begin each time with the arrangement shown.

   a. Remove four toothpicks to make two squares.

   b. Remove four toothpicks to make one square.

   c. Remove two toothpicks to make two squares.

Try This

293

Rational Numbers

The greatest one-day use of electricity in Ontario occurred on 1982 01 17. On that day the temperature was −25°C in Southern Ontario and −44°C in Northern Ontario. What was the average of the temperatures?

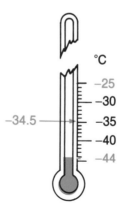

Average temperature = $\frac{-25 + (-44)}{2}$

$= \frac{-69}{2}$

$= -34.5$

The average of the temperatures was −34.5°C.

The negative number, −34.5, is not an integer. It is a **rational number**. Any number that can be expressed as the quotient of two integers is a rational number.

Some rational numbers are $\qquad$ $-1\frac{1}{2}, -1, -\frac{3}{4}, -0.25, \ 0.25, \frac{3}{4},$ and 2.

Each can be expressed as the quotient of two integers. $\qquad$ $-\frac{3}{2}, -\frac{1}{1}, -\frac{3}{4}, \quad -\frac{1}{4}, \quad \frac{1}{4}, \frac{3}{4},$ and $\frac{2}{1}$

Rational numbers can be shown on a number line.

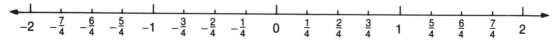

A number line can be used to compare rational numbers.

$\frac{1}{4}$ is to the right of $-\frac{3}{4}$. $\quad \frac{1}{4} > -\frac{3}{4}$ $\qquad\qquad$ $-\frac{6}{4}$ is to the left of $-\frac{1}{4}$. $\quad -\frac{6}{4} < -\frac{1}{4}$

WORKING TOGETHER

1. Is the number a rational number?

   $5, -\frac{7}{2}, 0.3, \pi, 0, 0.\overline{5}, 1.37$

2. Express as a quotient of two integers.

   a. 0.7 $\quad$ **b.** −5 $\quad$ **c.** $2\frac{3}{4}$ $\quad$ **d.** $-0.\overline{2}$

3. Copy and complete.

   a.

   b.
   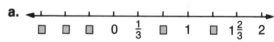

294

APPLICATIONS AND EXERCISES

1. Copy and complete.

   a.
   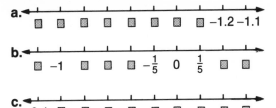

   b.

   c.

2. Use the number lines from exercise 1 to determine the greater number.

   a. $\frac{2}{5}$ or $-\frac{4}{5}$ **b.** $-\frac{3}{5}$ or $-1\frac{1}{5}$

   c. -0.4 or 0 **d.** -2 or -1.2

3. Which rational numbers are indicated by the letters?

4. Copy and use $>$ or $<$ to make a true statement.

   a. $-\frac{4}{5} \bigcirc \frac{1}{5}$ **b.** $-\frac{1}{3} \bigcirc -\frac{2}{3}$ **c.** $0.1 \bigcirc -0.8$

   d. $0 \bigcirc 1\frac{1}{2}$ **e.** $-\frac{3}{4} \bigcirc -1\frac{3}{4}$ **f.** $-2.5 \bigcirc -1.7$

   g. $-5.8 \bigcirc -8.5$ **h.** $-0.78 \bigcirc -0.7$

5. Arrange from greatest to least.

   a. $-\frac{1}{4}, \frac{3}{4}, 0$ **b.** $1.5, -0.5, -0.2$

6. Arrange the January record cold temperatures from warmest to coldest.

City	Temperature (°C)
Edmonton	−49.4
Halifax	−27.2
Montréal	−35.2
St. John's	−21.1
Toronto	−32.8
Winnipeg	−44.4

7. Express as a quotient of two integers.

   a. 0.13 **b.** $-0.\overline{7}$ **c.** $-1\frac{7}{8}$ **d.** 2.09

8. Which rational number is greater?

   a. $\frac{9}{10}, 0.8$ **b.** $-1\frac{1}{4}, -1\frac{3}{4}$ **c.** $-0.\overline{3}, -\frac{2}{3}$

   d. $2\frac{3}{5}, 2.3$ **e.** $-0.25, -\frac{1}{3}$ **f.** $-2.6, -2\frac{1}{2}$

9. Arrange from least to greatest.

   a. $-0.1, \frac{1}{2}, -\frac{3}{10}$ **b.** $-\frac{3}{8}, -1.25, -0.8$

10. Arrange the record cold temperatures from coldest to warmest.

Province	Temperature (°C)
Alberta	−61.1
Manitoba	−52.8
Nova Scotia	−41.1
Ontario	−58.3
P.E.I.	−37.2
Québec	−54.4

1. Mary brought some apples and gave them to Phil, David, and Kathy. She gave half of her apples and half an apple to Phil. David received half the remaining apples and half an apple. Kathy was given the last apple. If no apples were cut, how many did Mary bring? How many did each boy receive?

Try This

295

1. Is the product positive or negative?

    a. -6×2 **b.** $-3 \times (-8)$

    c. 5×7 **d.** $7 \times (-4)$

    e. -4×9 **f.** $-10 \times (-10)$

2. Find the products in exercise 1.

3. Evaluate.

    a. $3 \times (-1) \times (-5)$ **b.** $-4 \times (-2) \times (-5)$

    c. $-6 \times 4 \times 0$ **d.** $-1 \times 8 \times (-4)$

    e. $12 \times (-2) \times 3$ **f.** $-10 \times (-3) \times (-1)$

4. In each of three video games, Roger had a score of -11. What was his total for all three games?

5. Is the quotient positive or negative?

    a. $\frac{-12}{3}$ **b.** $\frac{25}{-5}$ **c.** $\frac{28}{4}$ **d.** $\frac{-32}{-4}$

    e. $\frac{21}{-7}$ **f.** $\frac{60}{-3}$ **g.** $\frac{50}{-25}$ **h.** $\frac{-36}{9}$

6. Find the quotients in exercise 5.

7. The temperature fell from $-2°C$ to $-14°C$ in 3 h. How many degrees did it fall per hour?

8. Find the result.

    a. -3×7 **b.** $12 \div (-2)$

    c. $-32 \div (-4)$ **d.** 15×2

    e. -6×6 **f.** $-14 \div 2$

    g. $0 \times (-8)$ **h.** $-24 \div (-3)$

    i. $5 \times (-8)$ **j.** $11 \times (-11)$

    k. $-35 \div 5$ **l.** $22 \div (-11)$

    m. $0 \div (-4)$ **n.** $14 \times (-3)$

    o. $-20 \div 2$ **p.** $-9 \times (-12)$

9. Evaluate.

    a. $3 \times (-12) \div (-4)$ **b.** $-3 \times (-2) \div (-3)$

    c. $-14 \div 2 + 18$ **d.** $6 - (-3) \times (-5)$

    e. $(-5)^2 + (-4)^2$ **f.** $(-6)^2 \div (-9)$

    g. $0 \div (-2) + (-27) \div (-3)$

    h. $-3 \times (-7 + 5) + (-12) \div (-12)$

    i. $(-12 \times 2) \div (-4 \times 2) - (-5)$

10. The penalty points of an equestrian team are shown in the table. Find the average penalty points for the team.

Rider	Penalty points
Lisa	-4
Mano	-6
Franz	-4
Holly	-6

11. Express in scientific notation.

    a. 5178   **b.** 0.0007   **c.** 0.0615

    d. 0.000 061   **e.** 4 175 000

12. Express in standard form.

    a. 1.8×10^5 **b.** 2.3×10^{-2}

    c. 7.83×10^{-5} **d.** 9.04×10^3

    e. 1.006×10^{-1} **f.** 8.8×10^0

13. Which rational numbers are indicated by the letters?

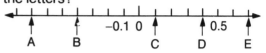

14. Copy and use $>$ or $<$ to make a true statement.

    a. $-1\frac{2}{3} \bigcirc -\frac{4}{3}$ **b.** $-\frac{1}{5} \bigcirc 0$ **c.** $-\frac{7}{8} \bigcirc 1$

15. Arrange from greatest to least.

    a. $5.2, -4.5, -2.1$ **b.** $-2\frac{1}{4}, -3\frac{1}{4}, -\frac{3}{4}$

Grisly Grids

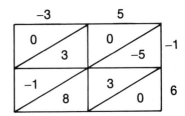

I.

-5 ... 5 / -1 ... 3

-7 ... 4 / 2 ... -6

upper region ... lower region

II.

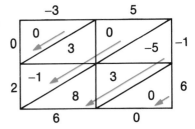

-3 ... 5

0 / 3 ... 0 / -5 ... -1

-1 / 8 ... 3 / 0 ... 6

III.

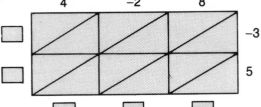

-3 ... 5

0 ... 0 / 3 ... 0 / -5 ... -1

2 ... -1 / 8 ... 3 / 0 ... 6

6 ... 0

Special grids can be used to organize information about numbers. In these grids, the tens digit is recorded in the upper region, and the ones digit is recorded in the lower region.

The marginal entries at the top and right of the grid are factors.

I. $(-5)(3) = -15$ ⠀⠀ $(-7)(-6) = 42$

II. $(-3)(-1) = 3$ ⠀⠀ $(5)(-1) = -5$
$(-3)(6) = -18$ ⠀⠀ $(5)(6) = 30$

The marginal entries at the left and bottom are sums. Sums are found by adding down diagonally.

III.
$$0 = 0$$
$$0 + 3 - 1 = 2$$
$$-5 + 3 + 8 = 6$$
$$0 = 0$$

---

1. Copy and complete. Work backward and guess and test.

a.

4 ⠀ -2 ⠀ 8 ⠀ -3 ⠀ 5

b.

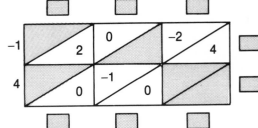

0 / 2 ... 0 / -2 ... 4

-1 / 0 ... -1 / 0

c.

-3 / 0 ... 1 / 2 ... 4 / 2 ... -1 / 8

2 / 0 ... 0 / -8 ... -2 / 8 ... 1 / 2

BASIC Programming III

You have learned how to round numbers to a given place value. How can you tell the computer to do this?

1. Predict the output of the BASIC command.

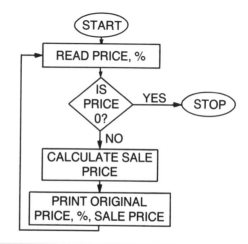

a. PRINT INT (3.1416)

b. PRINT 15/2

c. PRINT INT(15/2)

d. PRINT INT(0.943 * 10)

e. PRINT INT(0.943 * 100)

f. PRINT INT(3.7 + 4.5)

g. PRINT INT(3.7) + INT(4.5)

h. PRINT INT(23/7 * 7)

i. PRINT INT(23/7) * 7

j. PRINT INT(−3.28)

> INT tells the computer to drop the decimal part of a positive number.

In BASIC the **integer function**, INT( ), does not round a number.
It outputs the greatest integer less than or equal to the given number.
This function can help you tell the computer to round a number.

PRINT INT(N * 100 + 0.5)/100 tells the computer to round a number, N, to two decimal places.

2. Predict the output. Then try it on a computer.

a. PRINT INT(4.132 * 100 + 0.5)/100

b. PRINT INT(4.1386 * 100 + 0.5)/100

c. PRINT INT(123.4786 * 100 + 0.5)/100

d. PRINT INT(123.4786 * 10 + 0.5)/10

e. PRINT INT(123.4786 * 1000 + 0.5)/1000

3. A clothing store is having a sale, cutting the price of merchandise by up to 50%. Design a program that inputs the original price and the percent of discount, and outputs the sale price rounded to 2 decimal places. For example:

Original Price ($)	Percent Off (%)	Sale Price ($)
100.00	15	85.00
16.95	30	11.87

In your program for exercise 3, you may have used INPUT statements or READ/DATA statements to give the original prices and percents to the computer. If you used READ/DATA statements, the computer might have printed an OUT OF DATA ERROR message after it read the last number. To avoid this, you can use an IF/THEN statement and a specific number in the DATA statement to tell the computer to stop.

```
 75  IF PRICE = 0 THEN END
400  DATA 100, 15, 16.95, 30, 62.98, 25,..., 0, 20
```

4. Banks and trust companies have many different kinds of savings accounts that pay interest at different rates. Design a program so that a user can input the principal and the simple interest rate, and have the program output the annual interest correct to the nearest cent.

5. Design a program to print the decimal value of fractions $\frac{1}{2}, \frac{1}{3}, \frac{1}{4}, \ldots, \frac{1}{20}$ correct to three decimal places.

The INT function can also be used to determine if one number is a factor of another.

```
10    REM DETERMINING FACTORS
20    READ A, B
30    LET C = INT(B/A) * A
40    IF B = C GOTO 70
50    PRINT A "IS NOT A FACTOR OF " B
60    GOTO 20
70    PRINT A "IS A FACTOR OF " B
80    END
90    DATA 3, 5, 6, 30, 42, 7
```

6. Draw a flow chart for the program.

7. a. When will the computer end the program?

   b. How might you change this?

8. Modify the program to accept input from the keyboard.

9. a. What will the computer do if A = B?

   b. What will happen if B = 0?

   c. What will happen if A = 0?

The flow chart at right shows a way to determine whether any number is a prime number.

10. a. Write a BASIC program for the task.

    b. Test the program with some numbers. Choose some prime and some composite.

    c. Can the number N be less than 2? What will happen if N = 1?

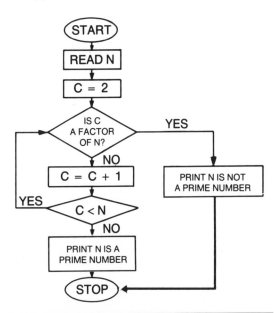

299

Is the Answer Reasonable?

It takes Jan 3 h to wax the family car. Don takes 2 h to do the same job. How long would it take both of them if they worked together?

Think. The answer should be less than 3 h.

Assume that Jan and Don can work at their usual pace without getting in each other's way.

Plan and do. Don used the following reasoning.

Jan: 3 h to wax the car → 1 h to wax $\frac{1}{3}$ of the car

Don: 2 h to wax the car → 1 h to wax $\frac{1}{2}$ of the car

Together in 1 h, they can wax $\frac{1}{3} + \frac{1}{2}$ or $\frac{5}{6}$ of the car.

It would take them 60 min ÷ 5 or 12 min to wax $\frac{1}{6}$ of the car.

It would take 1 h 12 min for Jan and Don to wax the car.

Look back. Is Don's answer reasonable? Explain.

Jan investigated further. She made the chart below.

	Time (h)	Reciprocal	Sum	Reciprocal
Jan	3	$\frac{1}{3}$	$\frac{1}{3} + \frac{1}{2} = \frac{5}{6}$	$\frac{6}{5}$
Don	2	$\frac{1}{2}$		

1 h 12 min $= 1\frac{1}{5}$ h

What rule seems to fit the information in the chart?

WORKING TOGETHER

1. It takes Trish 3 h to paint a room and Ugo 4 h to paint the same room. How long would it take them working together?

   a. Use the same type of reasoning as Don did.

   b. Check your answer using the pattern from Jan's chart.

PROBLEMS

Which answer is most reasonable? Explain.

1. What is the height of the tree?

   a. 180 cm

   b. 300 cm

   c. 2 m

   d. 5 m

2. You spin the arrow of a spinner ten times. What is the sum of the outcomes?

   a. 2   b. 9

   c. 34   d. 96

Explain why the given conclusion is unreasonable. How might the error have been made? What should the result be?

3. Heather is 4 years old. Her sister is three times as old as she is. In six years Heather will be 10, so her sister will be 30.

4. A class of 20 students averaged 70% on a test. Another class of 30 students averaged 60% on the same test. The class average for all the students should be 65%.

5. A pizza with a diameter of 20 cm costs $5.50. The same type of pizza but with a diameter of 40 cm should cost $11.00.

6. One moving company charges $110 per load. Another moving company has trucks that are twice as long, twice as wide, and twice as high; therefore it should charge $220 per load.

Draw diagrams on grid paper and choose numbers to help you solve the problem. Does the answer change when you choose different numbers?

7. If the length of the side of a square is increased by 25%, by what percent does the area increase?

8. If the length and the width of a rectangle are each increased by 50%, by what percent does the area increase?

Solve. Is your answer reasonable?

9. Which is heavier, a tonne of feathers or a tonne of bricks?

10. An empty box has a mass of 1.26 kg. What can you put into the box so that its mass is 800 g?

11. Of 1000 eggs, 284 are large, 516 are medium, and 150 are small. The rest are extra large.

    a. If a carton holds one dozen, how many cartons of each size are needed?

    b. How many filled cartons of each size can be shipped?

12. One water hose takes 8 h to fill a swimming pool. Another water hose takes 7 h to fill the same pool. How long would it take to fill the pool if both hoses were used at the same time?

301

Problem Solving Review

Which answer is most reasonable? Explain.

1. It takes Nigel 15 min to walk from his home to school. What is the distance to the school?

   a. 1.5 km **b.** 15 km **c.** 15 m **d.** 150 m

2. How far would you walk if you walked in and out of this maze?

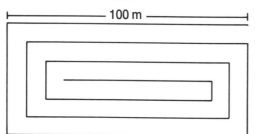

   a. 600 m **b.** 1200 m **c.** 12 km **d.** 900 m

3. To what angle does a pencil sharpener sharpen a pencil?

   a. 90° **b.** 180°

   c. 45° **d.** 26°

Solve.

4. How many rolls of quarters can be made with 150 quarters?

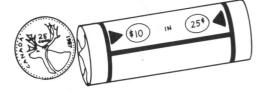

5. A class of 25 students averaged 66% on a test. Another class of 35 students averaged 56% on the same test. What was the average for the 60 students altogether?

6. A hockey player is offered a bonus, in addition to his regular salary. He can choose either Bonus A or Bonus B. Bonus A is $200 per goal. Bonus B is 2¢ for the first goal, 4¢ for the second, 8¢ for the third, and so on.

   a. If the player can score 25 goals during the season, which bonus plan should he accept?

   b. How much more is the better plan worth to him?

7. What is the last digit of the product for 7^{20}?

8. If the diameter and the height of a cylindrical can are doubled, by how much does the volume increase?

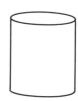

9. Classes are scheduled on a four-day cycle: Day 1, Day 2, Day 3, and Day 4.

   a. What day of the cycle is the twenty-first day of classes?

   b. If there are 187 days of classes in the school year, what day of the cycle is the last day of school?

10. The host and hostess of a party shook hands with each of their guests. If there were 10 couples at the party, how many handshakes were there?

11. How many points of intersection can there be for 6 line segments?

Chapter Checkup

1. What integer is suggested?

  a. 60 m below sea level

  b. 12 floors above ground level

  c. 7°C below freezing

  d. $35 under the estimate

2.

  a. Which integer corresponds to B?

  b. Which letter corresponds to 2?

  c. Which integer is the opposite of the integer at A?

3. Copy and use > or < to make a true statement.

  a. 4 ◯ −3   **b.** −5 ◯ 2

  c. 0 ◯ −2   **d.** 7 ◯ 3

  e. 5 ◯ −6   **f.** −4 ◯ −3

4. What ordered pair is named by each letter from J to U?

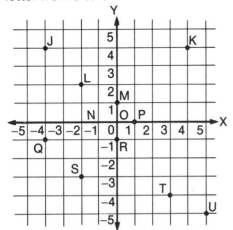

5. Determine the perimeter of a rectangle whose vertices have coordinates (−4,3), (−4,−1), (1,−1), (1,3).

6. Evaluate.

  a. −6 + (−8)   **b.** 8 + (−8)

  c. −2 − 11   **d.** 8 − (−2)

  e. 3 + (−6)   **f.** (−2) − (−20)

  g. −17 + 5 + (−6) **h.** 3 − (−14) − 13

7. Evaluate.

  a. −8 × (−4)   **b.** −3 × 8

  c. −45 ÷ (−9)   **d.** −15 ÷ 3

  e. −3 × (−6) × (−2) **f.** 9 × 7 × (−1)

  g. 3^3 **h.** $(-4)^3$ **i.** $\frac{45}{-3}$ **j.** $\frac{-70}{7}$

8. Evaluate.

  a. −20 ÷ (−5) − (−3) × 4

  b. $(-3)^2$ − 7 + (−6 − 4)

  c. 3 + (−27) ÷ (−3) + 0 ÷ (−2)

  d. −18 − (−12) ÷ 2 + $(-1)^3$

  e. −8 × (−9) − (−5) × 8 − (−4)

  f. −3 × [−2 − (−7)] + $(-4)^2$ ÷ 8

9. Express in scientific notation.

  a. 0.000 000 48   **b.** 0.000 003

  c. 0.106   **d.** 95.71

10. Express the number in standard form.

  a. The mass of a body cell is about 2.0×10^{-9} g.

  b. The volume of a drop of water is about 4×10^{-4} L.

11. Express the rational number as the quotient of two integers.

  a. 0.9   **b.** −3   **c.** $4\frac{1}{2}$ **d.** $-2.\overline{1}$

12. Arrange from least to greatest.

  a. $\frac{3}{8}, -1\frac{1}{8}, -\frac{7}{8}$ **b.** −0.1, −1, −0.01

Cumulative Checkup

1. Express the number in standard form.
   a. Jupiter is 1.41×10^5 km in diameter.
   b. Mercury, the closest planet to the Sun, is 6.94×10^7 km from it.
   c. Pluto, the farthest from the Sun, is 7.28×10^9 km away.

2. Estimate.
   a. 875×0.095　　b. 75.6×0.008
   c. $6495 \div 0.089$　　d. $2.16 \div 0.0009$
   e. $38\ 106 \times 19.4$　　f. $794.2 \div 4.89$

3. Calculate the area of the shaded region to the nearest tenth.

   a.
   1.8 cm　　1.2 cm

   b.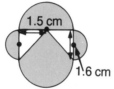
   1.5 cm
   1.6 cm

4. Find the volume.

   a.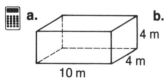
   4 m
   4 m
   10 m

   b.
   9 cm
   11 cm
   8 cm

   c.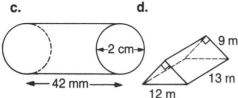
   ←2 cm→
   ←42 mm→

   d.
   9 m
   13 m
   12 m

5. What is the capacity of each shape in exercise 4?

6. What fraction of the figure is shaded?
   a. 　　b.　　c.

7. Express in lowest terms.
   a. $\frac{9}{27}$　b. $\frac{15}{35}$　c. $\frac{12}{32}$　d. $\frac{8}{52}$
   e. $\frac{72}{28}$　f. $\frac{88}{24}$　g. $\frac{125}{100}$　h. $\frac{70}{25}$

8. Find the result.
   a. $\frac{5}{9} \div \frac{2}{3}$　　b. $\frac{5}{9} + \frac{2}{3}$
   c. $\frac{5}{9} - \frac{1}{3}$　　d. $\frac{5}{9} \times \frac{2}{3}$
   e. $5\frac{1}{4} - 3\frac{7}{10}$　　f. $7\frac{1}{8} + 6\frac{3}{4}$
   g. $4\frac{1}{3} \times 2\frac{3}{5}$　　h. $12 \div 5\frac{1}{7}$

9. On a trip a man drove for $3\frac{1}{2}$ h. His wife drove for $2\frac{3}{4}$ h, and then their son drove for $2\frac{1}{2}$ h. How many hours did the family travel?

10. Paul's father gives him a ride $\frac{3}{4}$ of the way to school. Paul walks the rest of the way. If they live 3 km from the school, how far does he walk?

11. Express using bar notation.
    a. $0.777\ldots$　　b. $0.143\ 143\ldots$
    c. $12.357\ 57\ldots$　　d. $9.751\ 251\ 251\ldots$

12. Express as a decimal using bar notation.
    a. $\frac{5}{9}$　b. $\frac{4}{11}$　c. $\frac{7}{6}$　d. $\frac{25}{12}$

13. Express as a unit rate.
    a. 8 h to travel 752 km
    b. 7.5 h of work for $44.63
    c. 14 cars to carry 84 people

14. Find the unit price to the nearest cent.

    a. 4 boxes of juice for $2.12

    b. 8 markers for $9.95

    c. 11 evergreens for $315

15. John is drawing a map of his neighborhood. He uses a scale of 1 cm to 200 m. What length on his map would represent the distance on the ground?

    a. 100 m   **b.** 1 km   **c.** 1.4 km

    d. 0.6 km   **e.** 20 m   **f.** 1.5 km

16. Use this map of the Prairie Provinces to find the actual distance.

    a. between Regina and Winnipeg

    b. between Calgary and Regina

    c. between Edmonton and Saskatoon

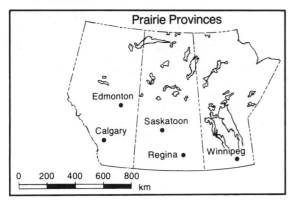

17. Estimate. Then calculate.

    a. 50% of 840   **b.** 75% of 780

    c. 33.3̄% of 589   **d.** 55.5̄% of 177

    e. 74% of 31   **f.** 89% of 316

18. A company that ships glass bottles allows for a 6% breakage rate. In a shipment of 4000 bottles, how many can be expected to arrive broken?

19. A store advertises a sofa on sale at 20% off the regular price of $875. The store also advertises that buying before the end of the month saves the buyer from paying 7% sales tax.

    a. What is the discount?

    b. What is the sale price?

    c. What is the sales tax on the sale price?

    d. What is the saving on the sofa if it is bought before the end of the month?

20. Paul buys a pair of jeans and pays $1.75 for the 7% sales tax. What is the price of the jeans?

21. Estimate the size of the angle. Classify the angle.

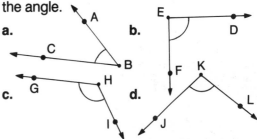

22. Copy each angle in exercise 21. Extend the arms of each angle, then measure the angle.

23. Calculate the unknown angle measure.

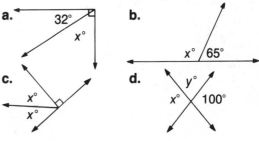

10/Organizing and Representing Data

Data are collected, organized, graphed, and analysed by organizations like Statistics Canada. This information is published regularly to keep the Canadian public up to date.

Get Set

1. What letter names the ordered pair?

   a. (1,4) **b.** (5,0)

   c. (4,5) **d.** (3,2)

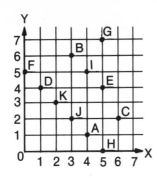

2. What is the ordered pair?

   a. C **b.** G

   c. K **d.** B

Use the following graphs to answer exercises 3 to 6.

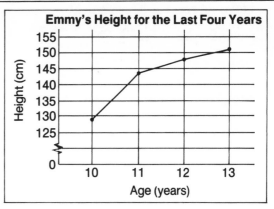

Emmy's Height for the Last Four Years

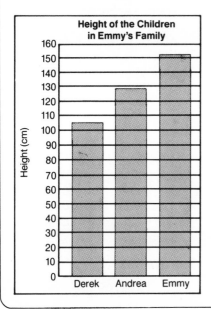

Students in Emmy's Class for the Last Four Years

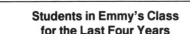

One ☺ represents 2 students.

Height of the Children in Emmy's Family

3. What type is each graph?

4. **a.** How many students were in Emmy's Grade 5 class?

   b. How many more students were in Emmy's Grade 7 class?

   c. Which other type of graph would also be suitable to display this data?

5. **a.** Is the bar graph vertical or horizontal? Why were the bars drawn this way?

   b. How tall is Emmy's brother, Derek?

6. **a.** How tall was Emmy when she was 10?

   b. Why is a broken-line graph suitable for this data?

   c. Why is a broken-line graph not suitable for graphing the three children's heights?

7. Express as a decimal, then as a percent.

   a. $\frac{450}{900}$ **b.** $\frac{400}{2000}$ **c.** $\frac{75}{120}$ **d.** $\frac{2000}{8000}$

8. Calculate.

   a. 15% of 360 **b.** 22.5% of 360

9. Use a protractor to draw the angle.

   a. 40° **b.** 62° **c.** 115° **d.** 137°

Relations

Erik's favorite sport is tennis and Mary Beth's is swimming. Volleyball and basketball are Carmen's favorite sports. Baseball is Beverly's and Josh's favorite sport.

This information can be represented in different ways.

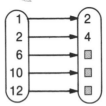

- **an arrow diagram**

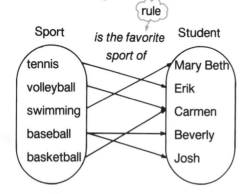

- **a table**

Sport	Student
tennis	Erik
volleyball	Carmen
swimming	Mary Beth
baseball	Beverly
baseball	Josh
basketball	Carmen

- **ordered pairs** (tennis, Erik) (volleyball, Carmen) (swimming, Mary Beth)
  (baseball, Beverly) (baseball, Josh) (basketball, Carmen)

Ordered pairs, a table of values, or an arrow diagram shows a **relation**.

WORKING TOGETHER

1.

Adult   *is the parent of*   Young

(seal   (fawn
  dog   cub
  fox   pup)
  bear
  deer)

a. What rule describes the relation between the sets?

b. Copy and complete the arrow diagram.

c. Make a table of values.

d. List the ordered pairs.

2.

1 → 2
2 → 4
6 → ▨
10 → ▨
12 → ▨

a. What rule describes the relation between the sets?

b. Copy and complete the arrow diagram.

c. Make a table of values.

d. List the ordered pairs.

1. Write a rule to describe the relation between the sets. Make a table of values. Then list the ordered pairs.

a.

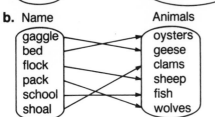

Mass → Object

7 t	elephant
20 mg	desk telephone
5 g	slice of bread
2 kg	nickel
25 g	postage stamp

b. Name → Animals

gaggle	oysters
bed	geese
flock	clams
pack	sheep
school	fish
shoal	wolves

2. Copy and complete the diagram. Then write a rule that describes the relation between the sets.

a.

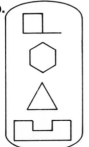

C	radius
d	base
r	circumference
b	height
h	diameter

b.

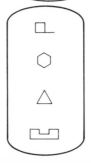

3. Write a rule that describes the relation. Then list two other ordered pairs.

a. (white, black), (fast, slow), (happy, sad), (hot, cold)

b. (a,b), (m,n), (x,y), (d,e)

c. (door, rectangle), (dinner plate, circle), (floor tile, square), (stop sign, octagon)

d. (3,6), (4,7), (10,13)

4. Write a rule that describes the relation. Then list the ordered pairs.

a.

10	17
15	22
17	24
25	32

b.

| 0 → 3 |
| 1 → 4 |
| 2 → 5 |
| 3 → 6 |
| 4 → 7 |

c.

| 0 → 0 |
| 5 → 1 |
| 25 → 5 |
| 1.5 → 0.3 |

d.

Pens	Cost ($)
1	0.70
4	2.80
6	4.20
11	7.70

5. Copy and complete the table for the rule. Then list the ordered pairs.

a. Add 10.

b. Divide by 2.

c. Divide by 3; then subtract 1.

d. Multiply by 2; then subtract 10.

6	
12	
18	
24	

KEEPING SHARP

1. a. On grid paper draw a 15 x 15 grid. Then plot the points.

A (1,10)	B (1,6)	C (1,8)	D (3,8)	E (3,10)	F (3,6)	G (6,10)	H (4,10)
I (4,8)	J (5,8)	K (4,8)	L (4,6)	M (6,6)	N (7,10)	O (7,6)	P (9,6)
Q (10,10)	R (10,6)	S (12,6)	T (15,6)	U (15,10)	V (13,10)	W (13,6)	X (15,6)

b. Join ABCDEF, GHIJKLM, NOP, QRS, and TUVWX. What is the message?

Graphing Relations

The Connellys drove 560 km from Welland to Ottawa at an average speed of 80 km/h.
A table of values and ordered pairs shows the relation between the time and distance travelled.

Time (h)	Distance (km)	Ordered pair
0	0	(0,0)
1	80	(1,80)
2	160	(2,160)
3	240	(3,240)
4	320	(4,320)
5	400	(5,400)
6	480	(6,480)
7	560	(7,560)

To graph the relation, plot the points given by the ordered pairs. Join the points.

The graph of the relation is a straight line.

Distance is shown on the **vertical axis**.

Time is shown on the **horizontal axis**.

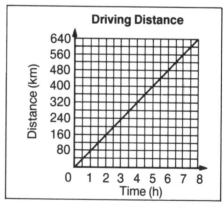

WORKING TOGETHER

1. Use the line graph above to find the distance travelled in this time.

   a. 2 h   **b.** 5 h   **c.** 2.5 h   **d.** 4.5 h

2. Use the line graph above to find the time required to travel this distance.

   a. 240 km   **b.** 480 km   **c.** 200 km

3. What rule describes the relation above between the time and distance travelled?

4. A car travels at 90 km/h.

   a. Make a table of five values to show the relation between the time and the distance travelled.

   b. On grid paper draw and label the coordinate axes. Choose a scale for each axis.

   c. Plot the points. Then join them.

   d. Title the graph.

1.

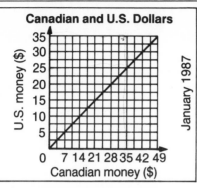

Canadian and U.S. Dollars

January 1987

a. Estimate the equivalent in U.S. money for this amount of Canadian money.
   i. $21   ii. $35   iii. $45.50

b. Estimate the equivalent in Canadian money for this amount of U.S. money.
   i. $10   ii. $35   iii. $22.50

2. Write a rule for the relation. Then list three other ordered pairs and draw a graph.

   a. (0,0), (1,6), (2,12), (3,18)

   b. (0,4), (1,5), (2,6), (3,7)

3. Make a table of six values using the rule. Then draw a graph.

   a. Multiply by 2 and then add 3.

   b. Multiply by 3 and then subtract 1.

4. Make a table of six values using the relation. Then draw a graph.

   a. Phil runs 9 km/h.

   b. Gayle cycles 16 km/h.

   c. The train travels 90 km/h.

5. List five ordered pairs of whole numbers for the relation. Write a rule.

   a. 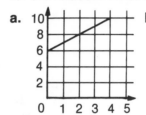   b.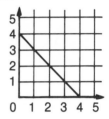

6. The pressure on a scuba diver increases with the depth below sea level.

Depth below sea level (m)	Pressure in kilopascals (kPa)	Ordered pair
0	103	
25	342	
50	581	
75	820	
100	1059	

List the ordered pairs. Then draw a graph.

Try This

1. a. Make a table of five values to show the relation between the length of one side of a square and its perimeter.

   b. What is the rule?

   c. Draw a graph.

   d. Use the graph to find the perimeter of a square with sides of this length.
      i. 7 cm   ii. 5 cm   iii. 8 cm

   e. Use the graph to find the length of a side of a square with this perimeter.
      i. 36 cm   ii. 16 cm   iii. 24 cm

2. a. Make a table of five values to show the relation between the length of one side of a square and its area.

   b. Write the rule. Then draw the graph.

   c. Use the graph to find the area of a square with sides of this length.
      i. 2 cm   ii. 8 cm   iii. 3.5 cm

   d. Use the graph to estimate the length of a side of a square with this area.
      i. 36 cm²   ii. 16 cm²   iii. 30 cm²

Interpreting Graphs

What was the increase in the number of women in the work force from 1960 to 1985?

The **pictograph** displays the information by using a **symbol**.

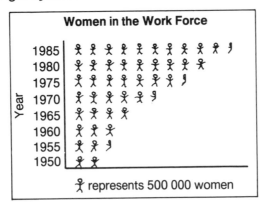

The pictograph shows
1985 → 10.5 × 500 000 = 5 250 000
1960 →   3 × 500 000 = 1 500 000
The increase was   3 750 000.

The **bar graph** displays the information by using a **scale**.

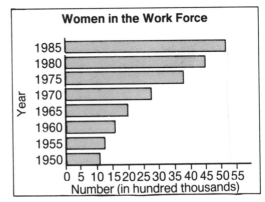

The bar graph shows
1985 → 52.5 × 100 000 = 5 250 000
1960 →   16 × 100 000 = 1 600 000
The increase was   3 650 000.

The **broken line graph** displays the information by using a **scale**.

The broken-line graph shows
1985 → 52.5 × 100 000 = 5 250 000
1960 →   16 × 100 000 = 1 600 000
The increase was   3 650 000.

Why does a pictograph give a different result from the others?

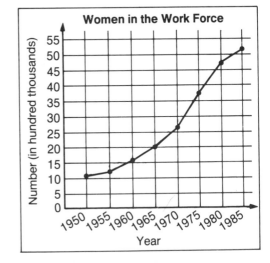

WORKING TOGETHER

1. **a.** Use each of the graphs above to find the number of women in the work force in 1950.

   b. Which graph illustrates the least accurate information?

   c. How does a large increase affect the steepness of each graph?

APPLICATIONS AND EXERCISES

1.

Net Value of Fishery Products

B.C.	● ● ● ● ● ● ● ● ● ● ● ● ● ● ● ●
N.S.	● ● ● ● ● ● ● ● ● ● ●
Nfld.	● ● ● ● ● ● ● ● ● ◠
N.B.	● ● ● ● ◠
P.E.I.	● ● ◠

● represents 15 million dollars

a. What was the net value of fishery products from each province?

b. About how much more was the net value from Nfld. than from P.E.I.? from B.C. than from N.S.?

2.

Canada's Leading Trade Partners in 1985

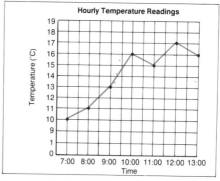

Legend: Exports, Imports

Dollar value of trade (in billions): 5 10 15 20 25 30 35 40 45 50 55 60 65 70 75 80 85 90

Countries: Japan, United Kingdom, United States

a. For which country were Canada's exports more than her imports?

b. About how many times as much did Canada export to Japan as to the United Kingdom?

3.

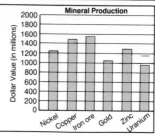

Mineral Production — Dollar Value (in millions): Nickel, Copper, Iron ore, Gold, Zinc, Uranium

a. About how much more valuable is the copper than the gold? the zinc than the uranium?

b. If the scale started with 600, how many times as valuable as the gold would the copper appear to be? How might this idea be misused in advertising?

4.

Hourly Temperature Readings

Temperature (°C) vs Time: 7:00 8:00 9:00 10:00 11:00 12:00 13:00

a. What is the highest temperature?

b. Between which two hours is the change the greatest?

KEEPING SHARP

1. Use the circle graph to calculate the assets of each type of financial institution if the total assets are 73.4 billion dollars.

Total Assets of Financial Institutions in Canada

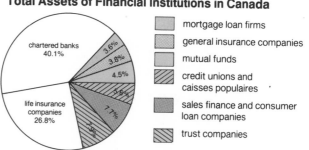

chartered banks 40.1%

life insurance companies 26.8%

3.6%
3.8%
4.5%
3.6%
7.7%
7.9%

- mortgage loan firms
- general insurance companies
- mutual funds
- credit unions and caisses populaires
- sales finance and consumer loan companies
- trust companies

Estimating from Graphs

Every ten years Statistics Canada takes a census and the population of Canada is counted.

The population of Canada for this century is plotted.

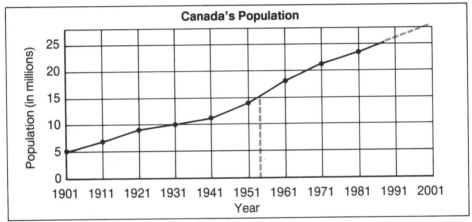

From the broken-line graph it is possible to estimate the population for years when there was no census.
In 1936, the population appears to have been about 10 500 000.

It is also possible to estimate the future population by extending the graph.
In 1991, the population will be about 26 000 000.

As well, for a given population, the year can be estimated.
The population was about 15 000 000 in 1954.

WORKING TOGETHER

1. Estimate the population for the year.

    a. 1921   **b.** 1941   **c.** 1951

    d. 1916   **e.** 1986   **f.** 2001

2. Estimate the year for the population.

    a. 17 000 000   **b.** 5 000 000

    c. 20 000 000   **d.** 24 000 000

1.

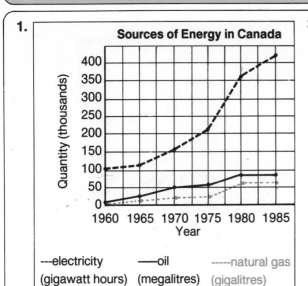

Sources of Energy in Canada

---electricity   —oil   -----natural gas
(gigawatt hours)   (megalitres)   (gigalitres)

Estimate the energy from each source.

a. in 1950   **b.** in 1960   **c.** in 1970

d. in 1980   **e.** in 1940   **f.** in 1990

2. The temperature of Earth increases with the depth below the surface.

Depth (km)	Temperature (°C)
25	500
50	850
75	1150
100	1250
125	1300
150	1450

a. Display the data in a broken-line graph.

b. Estimate the temperature at this depth.

    i. 60 km   **ii.** 110 km   **iii.** 175 km

3. The sales of a popular sports car vary between Canada and the United States.

Year	Canada	U.S.	Year	Canada	U.S.
1974	2487	29 750	1980	4473	36 507
1975	3708	40 607	1981	2002	29 039
1976	4071	41 673	1982	627	22 477
1977	4114	42 571	1983	1030	28 144
1978	4821	42 247	1984	1207	30 424
1979	5382	38 631	1985	1638	31 825

a. Display the data in a double broken-line graph.

b. Estimate the sales in each country.

    i. for 1986   **ii.** for 1990   **iii.** for 1973

4.

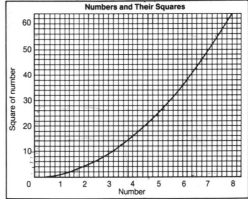

Numbers and Their Squares

a. Estimate the square of the number.

    i. 4.6   **ii.** 5.2   **iii.** 7.4   **iv.** 1.7

b. Estimate the number whose square is this number.

    i. 7   **ii.** 14   **iii.** 40   **iv.** 54

c. Check the estimates in parts **a** and **b**.

Try This

A graph that is not continuous between points is called a **discrete graph**.

1. a. Make a table of values to show the relationship between the number of sides and the number of diagonals of a polygon. Use polygons having three to ten sides.

b. Plot the set of ordered pairs (number of sides, number of diagonals).

c. Why is this a discrete graph?

d. Estimate the number of diagonals.

    i. for 12 sides   **ii.** for 20 sides

Constructing Circle Graphs

Kyle's family has a monthly income of $2000. They make a list of their expenses to plan their budget.

Kyle displays this data in a **circle graph**.

Each budget item is a percent of the total budget.

For housing, $\frac{800}{2000} = 0.4$ or 40%

For food, $\frac{450}{2000} = 0.225$ or 22.5%

Each percent is used to find the size of the angle for the corresponding sector in the circle graph.

 Housing sector   40% of 360° = 0.4 × 360° or 144°

Food sector   22.5% of 360° = 0.225 × 360° or 81°

Kyle draws a large circle and marks one radius. He draws a 144° angle for the housing sector.

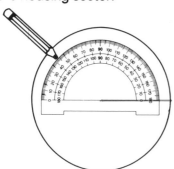

He marks the second radius and labels the sector. Then he measures an 81° angle for the food sector.

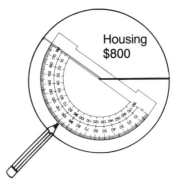

Housing
$800

WORKING TOGETHER

1. **a.** Find the percent of the total for each of the remaining budget items.

   b. Find the measure of each of the corresponding sector angles.

2. **a.** Draw the graph.

   b. Label each sector with its name, amount, and percent.

   c. Title the graph.

📟 APPLICATIONS AND EXERCISES

1. In 180 kg of garbage, the mass of each type of waste was 60 kg paper, 50 kg food, 30 kg glass, 10 kg vegetation, 15 kg cans, 10 kg plastics, and 5 kg other.

   a. Express each type as a percent, to the nearest tenth, of the total mass.

   b. Display the data in a circle graph.

   c. By what percent would the total garbage be reduced if food and vegetation were made into compost?

   d. By what percent would the total garbage be reduced if people made compost and recycled paper, cans, and glass?

2.

Age group	Percent of Canada's population
0-14	21%
15-29	27%
30-44	23%
45-60	14%
61 and over	15%

   a. Display the data in a circle graph.

   b. If the population was 25 000 000, how many people were in each age group?

3.

Regional Population	
Western Canada	7 330 400
Central Canada	15 646 900
Eastern Canada	2 307 400
Northern Canada	73 700

   a. Express the population of each region as a percent, to the nearest tenth, of the total.

   b. Display the data in a circle graph.

   c. Which region had more than half the population?

4.

Costs of Fighting Pollution	
Air	$350 billion
Water	$180 billion
Solid waste	$ 20 billion
Land reclamation	$ 20 billion
Other	$ 30 billion

   a. Express the cost of each type of pollution as a percent, to the nearest tenth, of the total.

   b. Display the data in a circle graph.

More than one FOR-NEXT loop can be used in a program as long as the loops are **nested** (one is completely within the other).

1. Predict the output of the programs.

ø means blank

a.
```
10   FOR A = 1 TO 3
20   PRINT "NESTED"
30   FOR B = 1 TO 4
40   PRINT "øøøøøø LOOPS"
50   NEXT B
60   NEXT A
70   END
```

b.
```
10   REM PRINTING STARS
20   FOR A = 1 TO 3
30   INPUT "HOW MANY STARS? "; S
40   FOR B = 1 TO S
50   PRINT " * ";
60   NEXT B
70   PRINT
80   NEXT A
90   END
```

2. Design a program that prints all the combinations for wearing a brown, black, or blue pair of pants with a red, green, or white sweater.

PRACTICE

1. In an experiment, five different masses were hung from an elastic band. The length that the band stretched was recorded for each mass.

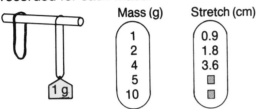

Mass (g)	Stretch (cm)
1	0.9
2	1.8
4	3.6
5	▨
10	▨

   a. What rule describes the relation between the mass and the stretch?

   b. Copy and complete the arrow diagram.

2. Copy and complete the table for the rule. Then list the ordered pairs.

   a. Multiply by 2.

   b. Divide by 3.

   c. Multiply by 3, then subtract 15.

6	
9	
12	
15	

3. Write a rule for the relation. Then list three other ordered pairs and draw a graph.

   a. (1,5), (2,10), (3,15) b. (1,3), (2,4), (3,5)

4. Make a table to show six ordered pairs for the relation. Then draw a line graph.

   a. Jim walks 5 km/h.

   b. The car travels 100 km/h.

5. Misha's class collected and sent about 444 kg of paper, 333 kg of cans, and 333 kg of bottles to the recycling depot.

   a. Express each type of material as a percent of the total.

   b. Display the data in a circle graph.

   c. Misha collected 150 kg. How many kilograms of each type would you expect?

6.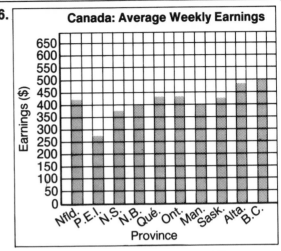

   a. What was the approximate difference in weekly earnings between P.E.I. and Nfld.?

   b. Between which two provinces was the difference in earnings the greatest?

7.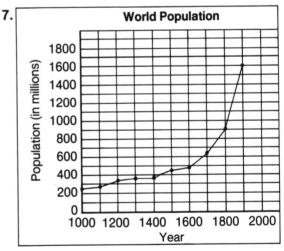

   a. In which century did the world population increase the most?

   b. In which century did the world population decrease? Find out why.

   c. Estimate the population in 1850.

   d. Estimate the population in 2000.

Chances are...

Chances are that you use the expression "chances are" in many conversations. It reflects your built-in sense of experimental probability.

1. Complete the caption for the photograph. "Chances are..."

2. "The possibility of precipitation is 10% today, 20% tonight, and 70% tomorrow." According to this weather forecast, when is it most likely to rain?

3. Is the event likely or unlikely?

   a. the sun setting
   b. a horse counting to 10
   c. a snowstorm in July
   d. a person eating at least once a day
   e. rain falling continuously for 7 d
   f. children age 6 to 12 going to school

4. It has been estimated that every week about 1 000 000 people buy tickets for the Provincial lottery. Wintario sells about 4 000 000 tickets weekly, Lottario sells nearly 3 000 000, and Lotto 649 sells about 12 000 000. A church bazaar might sell 2000 tickets for its raffle, and a fund-raising draw held within your school might sell several hundred.

   a. In which draw would you have the best chance of winning?

   b. Would buying more than one ticket be worthwhile in any of these draws? Explain.

5. In a group of 22 people, there is a 49% chance that two of them share a birthday. In a group of 23 people, there is a 52% chance. Survey 32 students of all ages in your school. Do any share a birthday?

6. In the natural course of events, twins occur about once in 80 births. Triplets occur about once in 80^2 births, quadruplets about once in 80^3 births, and quintuplets about once in 80^4 births.

   a. How many sets of twins are in your school?

   b. Are there any triplets or quadruplets?

Histograms

The coach made a **tally chart** to find the frequency of each number of goals scored per game.

Frequency is the number of times an event occurs.

The distribution of data is displayed in a **histogram**.

Number of games

Number of goals	Tally	Frequency
0				2
1						4
2					3
3							6
4						4
5				2
6			1

Goals Scored per Game

WORKING TOGETHER

1. **a.** What does the vertical axis in a histogram show?

   b. How does the spacing of the bars in a histogram differ from the spacing in a bar graph?

2. Students received these marks on a quiz.

   8, 6, 9, 1, 6, 4, 7, 5, 6, 2, 6, 4, 8, 5, 7, 3,
   8, 5, 6, 3, 7, 4, 8, 5, 6, 8, 10, 9, 7, 10,
   6, 5, 7, 9, 6, 5, 7, 7, 8

   a. Organize the data in a tally chart.

   b. Display the data in a histogram.

1.

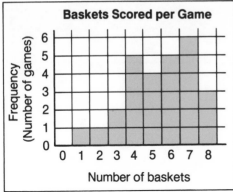

Baskets Scored per Game

a. What was the greatest number of baskets scored in a game?

b. What number of baskets was scored most frequently in a game?

c. How many games were played?

2. The participants in a 15 km walkathon completed these distances.

```
12, 11, 8, 5, 13, 9, 9, 6, 7, 11, 5, 10, 13,
9, 8, 14, 7, 5, 10, 6, 11, 5, 7, 6,
12, 5, 6, 14, 10, 13, 12, 11, 14,
10, 8, 6, 15, 11, 9, 12, 8, 11, 11,
10, 12, 13, 10, 14, 12, 12, 15, 13, 15
```

a. Organize the data in a tally chart.

b. Display the data in a histogram.

c. What distance did most of the people walk?

d. What percent of the participants completed the whole distance?

3.

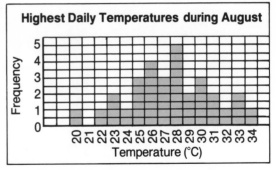

Highest Daily Temperatures during August

a. Which highest temperature occurred most frequently?

b. How many days had a high temperature of more than 30°C?

c. Which highest temperatures occurred least frequently?

d. On how many days during August was the temperature recorded?

4. a. Conduct a survey in your class to complete the tally chart.

Distance from home to school	Tally	Frequency
1.0 km or less		
1.1 km to 2.0 km		
2.1 km to 3.0 km		
3.1 km to 4.0 km		
4.1 km to 5.0 km		
more than 5.0 km		

b. Display the data in a histogram.

Try This

The height of a plant was recorded every ten days after it sprouted.

1. a. Display the data in a broken-line graph.

b. Display the data in a vertical bar graph.

Day	10	20	30	40	50	60	70
Height (cm)	7	23	35	42	46	48	49

c. Which type of graph do you think displays the data better? Why?

d. Why is a pictograph or a circle graph not suitable for displaying the data?

Mean, Median, and Mode

During the first five weeks of her junior bowling league, Deb had these scores.

Date	Game 1	Game 2	Game 3
Jan. 3	152	154	150
Jan. 10	150	158	155
Jan. 17	155	158	107
Jan. 24	154	155	160
Jan. 31	152	150	155

The tally chart helps Deb find an average for her scores in three different ways.

Score	Tally	Frequency
107	I	1
150	III	3
152	II	2
154	II	2
155	IIII	4
158	II	2
160	I	1

The **mode** is the number that occurs most frequently in a list.

mode 155

The **median** is the middle number in an ordered list.
The middle number can be found by counting down the tally.

median 154 (8th number out of 15)

The **mean** is the total of all scores divided by the number of scores.

$$\text{mean} = \frac{\text{total of scores}}{\text{number of scores}}$$

$$= \frac{107 \times 1 + 150 \times 3 + 152 \times 2 + 154 \times 2 + 155 \times 4 + 158 \times 2 + 160 \times 1}{15}$$

$$= \frac{107 + 450 + 304 + 308 + 620 + 316 + 160}{15}$$

$$= \frac{2265}{15}$$

$$= 151$$

WORKING TOGETHER

1. Compare the mean, the median, and the mode of Deb's scores.

   a. Which average best suggests a score Deb is likely to bowl?

   b. Why is the mean not the best indicator of Deb's bowling scores?

2. When there are two numbers in the middle of an ordered list, the median is halfway between. Find the mean, the median, and the mode of Deb's scores.

   a. after 3 weeks   b. after 2 weeks

APPLICATIONS AND EXERCISES

1. Find the mean.

  a. 131, 110, 119, 156

  b. 81, 74, 69, 73, 91, 55, 61

2. Find the median.

  a. 35, 46, 21, 18, 22

  b. 17, 8, 9, 8, 15, 11

  c. 52, 21, 18, 48, 31, 41, 48, 27

3. Find the mode.

  a. 5, 7, 8, 6, 9, 4, 6, 1

  b. 21, 23, 28, 23, 25

  c. 14, 9, 8, 9, 14, 11, 9

4. Find the mean, median, and mode.

  a. 9, 4, 10, 11, 13, 4, 5

  b. 13, 16, 26, 20, 18, 15

  c. 81, 64, 75, 64, 89, 56, 89

5. Deb recorded in a tally chart the hours she spent practising her bowling skills.

Practice time (h)	Tally	Frequency
1	卌 l	6
2	卌 ll	7
3	卌	5
4	lll	3

  a. Find the mode, the mean, and the median of the practice times.

  b. About how many hours did Deb usually practise?

6. In archery, points are awarded according to the ring in which the arrow lands.

  a. Make a tally chart for these scores.

> 7, 5, 9, 9, 3, 1, 9, 7, 5, 3,
> 1, 1, 9, 7, 7, 5, 5, 5, 3, 1,
> 5, 3, 5, 1, 5, 7, 7, 9, 9, 1

  b. Find the mean, the median, and the mode of the scores.

7. The students in Tim's class received these marks for their science projects.

> 83, 61, 48, 73, 76,
> 58, 52, 67, 61, 79,
> 61, 90, 55, 58, 84

  a. Make a tally chart for these marks.

  b. Find the mean, the median, and the mode of the marks.

8. The members of a tug-of-war team have these masses: 62 kg, 65 kg, 52 kg, 70 kg, 61 kg, 51 kg, 49 kg, 55 kg, 56 kg.

Find the mean mass of the team.

9. a. Survey your class to determine the number of hours each person watches television in a typical week. Record the data in a tally chart.

  b. Find the mean, the median, and the mode of the data.

Try This

1. Calculate the mean of 2, 5, 9, 14, 20, 22, then of 202, 205, 209, 214, 220, 222. Compare your results.

2. Find the mean of 802, 805, 809, 810, 820, 822, then of 82, 85, 89, 94, 100, 102.

Sampling

The student council is considering a proposal to remove the soft drink vending machine from the school cafeteria. To reach a decision, the council members decide to ask a **sample** of the 550 students in the school for their opinion. How should they choose their sample?

6 out of 6 students want to keep the vending machine. This sample is **biased** because the students surveyed all use the machine.

2 out of 5 student council members want to keep the vending machine. This sample is biased because the student council is proposing to remove the machine.

43 out of 55 students want to keep the vending machine. This is a **representative sample**, as the school is well represented with every tenth student on the school's roll being surveyed.

The results from the representative sample can be used to estimate the number of students who want to keep the vending machine.

Write a proportion and find the missing team. $\frac{43}{55} = \frac{\square}{550}$

$$\overset{\times 10}{\frac{43}{55} = \frac{430}{550}}_{\times 10}$$

About 430 students would want to keep the vending machine.

WORKING TOGETHER

1. Which is the best sample for estimating how many people own a pet?

   a. people in a pet store

   b. people going into a drugstore

   c. three of your friends

2. In a representative sample of 30 students at a school, 5 have a part-time job. Estimate how many of the 450 students at the school have a part-time job.

1. Which is the better sample for predicting how many people enjoy watching ballet?

a.

b.

2. The average height of the five starting players on Canada's men's national basketball team was calculated. Can this be used as a sample to estimate the average height of the following group of people? Give a reason for your answer.

a. all Canadian men

b. all Canadian basketball players

c. the Canadian men's national basketball team

d. all national men's basketball teams

3.

WARNING: Health and Welfare Canada advises that danger to health increases with amount smoked—avoid inhaling.	Av. /Moyenne "Tar/Goudron" 9 mg Nic. 0.9 mg	AVIS: Santé et Bien-être social Canada considère que le danger pour la santé croît avec l'usage—éviter d'inhaler.

Do people believe that smoking is harmful to a person's health? In choosing a sample of people to survey, which group would probably give a biased response? Why?

a. members of a tobacco association

b. members of a medical association

c. every second person walking down the street

d. members of a stop-smoking group

4. In a sample of 25 students at a school, 4 were not born in Canada. Estimate how many of the 650 students at the school were not born in Canada.

5. Use your class as a sample to estimate the number of students in your school.

a. who own a bicycle

b. who wear a wristwatch

c. who live in an apartment

d. who have no brothers or sisters

e. who walk to school

f. who were born

   i. in your community

   ii. in your province **iii.** in Canada

1. Use a calculator to discover a pattern. Then continue the next three lines in the pattern without calculating.

a. 5×5	**b.** $1 \times 9 + 2$	**c.** $2 \times 142\,857$	**d.** $9 \times 12\,345\,679$
5×55	$12 \times 9 + 3$	$3 \times 142\,857$	$18 \times 12\,345\,679$
5×555	$123 \times 9 + 4$	$4 \times 142\,857$	$27 \times 12\,345\,679$

Experimental Probability

Elke performed an experiment. She placed 5 different-colored marbles in a bag. She had everyone in her class draw a marble from the bag. Each time, before the marble was returned to the bag, Elke recorded the result in a tally chart. What is the probability of drawing a black marble?

Color	Tally	Frequency
black	⅂⅂⅂⅂ I	6
red	⅂⅂⅂⅂	5
yellow	⅂⅂⅂⅂ II	7
white	⅂⅂⅂⅂ I	6
green	⅂⅂⅂⅂ III	8

Total 32

The probability of drawing a black marble is $\frac{\text{the number of black marbles drawn}}{\text{the total number of marbles drawn}}$.

$$P(\text{black}) = \frac{6}{32} \text{ or } 0.19 \quad \text{(nearest hundredth)}$$

The probability of drawing a black marble is 0.19.

WORKING TOGETHER

1. Use the tally chart above to find the probability.

   a. P(red)   **b.** P(yellow)

   c. P(white)   **d.** P(green)

2. **a.** Toss a coin 50 times. Record the frequency of heads and tails in a tally chart.

   b. Use the data to find the probability.

   i. P(heads)   **ii.** P(tails)

3. **a.** Toss a paper cup 100 times. Copy and complete the tally chart.

Result	Tally	Frequency
top up		
top down		
on its side		

   b. Use the data to find the probability.

   i. P(on side)   **ii.** P(top up or top down)

1. a. Roll a die 30 times. Copy the tally chart and record the results specified.

Results	Tally	Frequency
4		
odd number		
number less than 3		
number greater than 6		

b. Use the data to find the probability.

  i. P(4)   **ii.** P(odd number)

iii. P(number less than 3)

iv. P(number more than 6)

2. a. Roll two dice 50 times. Copy the tally chart and record the results specified.

Results	Tally	Frequency
totals 7		
totals 11		
totals 2		

b. Use the data to find the probability.

  i. P(totals 7)   **ii.** P(totals 11)

iii. P(totals 2)

3. List all the possible outcomes.

a. tossing a thumbtack

b. rolling a die

c. taking one marble

d. flipping a coin

4. a. Use this net to make a rectangular prism.

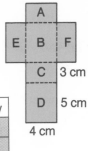

A, E, B, F, C 3 cm, D 5 cm, 4 cm

b. Toss the prism 100 times. Copy and complete the tally chart.

Outcome	Tally	Frequency
A		
B		
C		
D		
E		
F		

c. Use the data to find the probability.

  i. P(A)   **ii.** P(B)   **iii.** P(C)

  iv. P(D)   **v.** P(E)   **vi.** P(F)

5. Draw and then replace a card from a standard deck 50 times. Copy and complete the tally chart recording the results specified.

Result	Tally	Frequency
a diamond		
a king		
queen of hearts		

6. Design and perform an experiment to predict the probability.

a. P(red)   **b.** P(point down)

Try This

1. This evening you are to play two experts in chess at the same time. How can you play so that the probability of your losing both games is 0?

Probability of an Event

Consider Elke's experiment from the previous lesson. By experimenting she found the probability of drawing a black marble from a bag containing one black, one red, one yellow, one white, and one green marble.

She found $P(B) = \frac{6}{32}$ or 0.19.

If the experiment was conducted for a great many draws, the probability would approach the **theoretical probability**.

$$\text{probability} = \frac{\text{number of favorable outcomes}}{\text{number of possible outcomes}}$$

$$= \frac{1}{5} \text{ or } 0.20$$

Find the theoretical probability of first drawing a black marble and then drawing a white marble if the first marble is replaced.

The possible outcomes can be shown in a tree diagram.

First draw	B	R	Y
Second draw	B R Y W G	B R Y W G	B R Y W G
Outcome	(B,B)(B,R)(B,Y)(B,W)(B,G)	(R,B)(R,R)(R,Y)(R,W)(R,G)	(Y,B)(Y,R)(Y,Y)(Y,W)(Y,G)

W
B R Y W G
(W,B)(W,R)(W,Y)(W,W)(W,G)

G
B R Y W G
(G,B)(G,R)(G,Y)(G,W)(G,G)

There are 25 possible outcomes.
There is only 1 favorable outcome.

$$P(B,W) = \frac{1}{25}$$

The theoretical probability can be found by multiplying, without drawing a tree diagram.

$$P(B,W) = P(B) \times P(W)$$
$$= \frac{1}{5} \times \frac{1}{5}$$
$$= \frac{1}{25} \text{ or } 0.04$$

WORKING TOGETHER

1. Use the tree diagram above. Find the probability.

  a. of drawing red twice

  b. of drawing any of the colors twice

  c. of drawing red and green in any order

2. a. Draw a tree diagram to show the outcomes of drawing one of the marbles, *not* replacing it, and drawing another.

  b. What is the probability of drawing a black and then a white marble?

328

1. a. Draw a tree diagram to show the outcomes of tossing the coin and spinning the arrow.

b. Find the probability of tossing heads and spinning red.

2. Find the probability for this roll of two dice.

  a. P(8)   **b.** P(2 or 3)

  c. P(even number)   **d.** P(odd number)

  e. P(number less than 1)

  f. P(factor of 6)

3. a. How many possible outcomes are there when spinning the arrow?

  b. Find the probability.
    i. P(gray)   **ii.** P(blue)
    iii. P(blue or white)   **iv.** P(red)
    v. P(blue or gray or white)

4. a. Draw a tree diagram to show the possible outcomes of spinning the arrow and rolling a die.

  b. Find the probability.
    i. P(yellow,6)   **ii.** P(white or gray,3)
    iii. P(any color,1)
    iv. P(white, an even number)

5. Use multiplication to find each probability in exercise 4**b**.

6. a. Draw a tree diagram to show the possible outcomes of tossing three coins.

  b. Find the probability.
    i. P(H,T,T)   **ii.** P(T,T,T)
    iii. P(H or T, H or T, T)

7. Use multiplication to find each probability in exercise 6**b**.

8. Louisa shuffled 5 cards. She asked Sam to draw one card and then another *without* replacing the first.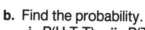
Use multiplication to find the probability.

  a. P(,)   **b.** P(,)   **c.** P( )

9. Keung asked Kay-Anne to draw one marble and then another without replacing the first.

Use multiplication to find the probability.

  a. P(red, green)   **b.** P(blue, red)
  c. P(green, blue)   **d.** P(red, red)

10. a. What is the theoretical probability that a person's birthday is in December?

  b. Find the experimental probability using your classmates as the sample.

KEEPING SHARP

1. Find the value of the expression.

  a. 7 + (−8) **b.** −26 + (−52) **c.** 17 − (−10) **d.** −25 − 5 **e.** −8 − (−3) **f.** −47 − (−65)

  g. −1 − (−2) − (−6) − 8   **h.** −6 + 3 − (−10) + (−47) + 2   **i.** 6 − 7 − 8 − 9 − 10

1. a. Make a tally chart to show the number of letters in each word printed on this page.

b. Display the data in a histogram.

c. Find the mode of the word lengths.

2. Of 25 employees, 15 earn $16 000, 5 earn $20 000, 3 earn $25 000, 1 earns $30 000, and 1 earns $40 000. Find the mean, the median, and the mode of the salaries.

3. The salaries of 19 professional athletes are given.

Salary ($)		
800 000	50 000	30 000
300 000	50 000	30 000
200 000	50 000	30 000
60 000	40 000	30 000
60 000	40 000	30 000
	40 000	30 000
	40 000	30 000

a. Calculate the mean salary.

b. Find the mode of the salaries.

c. Find the median salary.

d. Why is the median salary more meaningful than the mean or the mode?

4. A town council decides to take a survey to find out how many people living in the town use the public library regularly.

a. Should the sample interviews be held in the library or in the supermarket?

b. Of 500 people interviewed, 120 use the library regularly. Estimate how many of the town's population of 10 000 use the library regularly.

5. When a tack is tossed, it can land point up, point down, or on its side.

a. Toss a tack 50 times and record the results in a tally chart.

b. Use the data to find the probability.
   i. P(point up)   **ii.** P(on its side)
   iii. P(point down)
   iv. P(point up or down)

6. a. Draw a tree diagram to show the outcomes of tossing a coin and rolling a die.

b. Find the theoretical probability.
   i. P(H,5)   **ii.** P(H, odd number)
   iii. P(T, number less than 5)

7. Use multiplication to find each probability in exercise **6b**.

8. What is the theoretical probability of picking a vowel?

a. from the letters of the alphabet

b. from the sentence, "The quick brown fox jumped over the lazy dog."

9. A ringette team has won 6 games, tied 3 games, and lost 5 games.

a. What is the probability that the team will win its next game?

b. What is the probability that the team will not lose its next game?

Powers

Recall that 2^4 means $2 \times 2 \times 2 \times 2$.

2^4 is the fourth **power** of 2.

4 is the **exponent**. 2 is the **base**.

A calculator can be used to evaluate powers.

2^4 $\boxed{2}\boxed{\times}\boxed{=}\boxed{=}\boxed{=}$ $\overline{(16.)}$

1. How many times do you press $\boxed{=}$ to evaluate the power? Evaluate.

   a. 3^5 **b.** 5^4 **c.** 6^8 **d.** 7^6 **e.** 4^{10}

   f. 35^3 **g.** 2^{12} **h.** 25^4 **i.** 12^5 **j.** 9^7

A calculator can be used to find what power one number is of another.

What power of 2 is 32?

   $\boxed{32}\boxed{\div}\boxed{2}\underbrace{\boxed{=}\boxed{=}\boxed{=}\boxed{=}\boxed{=}}$ $\overline{(1.)}$ $32 = 2^5$

            5 times to reach 1

2. Copy and complete the statement.

   a. $81 = 3^{\square}$ **b.** $262\,144 = 8^{\square}$ **c.** $1296 = 6^{\square}$ **d.** $3375 = 15^{\square}$

   e. $59\,049 = 9^{\square}$ **f.** $262\,144 = 4^{\square}$ **g.** $6561 = 3^{\square}$ **h.** $15\,625 = 5^{\square}$

3. Evaluate the first six powers of the number.

   a. 3   **b.** 5   **c.** 8   **d.** 11   **e.** 4

4. Find the value. Use memory as necessary.

   a. $3^4 + 2^5$ **b.** $2^6 \div 8$ **c.** $3^5 \times 4^3$ **d.** $2^8 \div 4^4$

5. Explain the results.

   a. $\boxed{4}\boxed{x^2}\boxed{x^2}$ $\overline{(256.)}$ **b.** $\boxed{5}\boxed{\times}\boxed{3}\boxed{=}\boxed{=}\boxed{=}\boxed{=}$ $\overline{(1875.)}$

6. Every five years, Paul earned three times as much per week as he did in the five years before. How old was Paul when he was earning $729 a week if he earned $1 per week when he was 15?

7. The number of amoebas in a container doubled every minute. How many amoebas existed after 10 min if there was originally one amoeba in the container?

331

BASIC Programming IV

A computer is an ideal tool for modelling real situations.
It can be programmed with enough detail that it appears
to be playing a card game or a dice game. In many games
involving chance, programmers often use the **random number function**, **RND**.

A command like PRINT RND (1) or PRINT RND (5) causes a
positive decimal number less than 1 to appear on the screen.

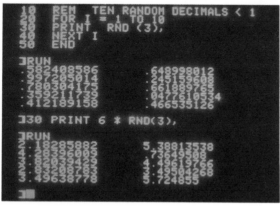

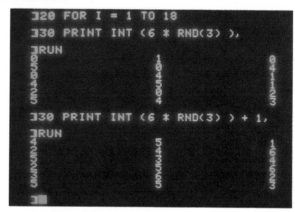

1. a. Explain what is happening in the
photograph above left.

  b. Write a new REM statement in line 10
for the second program.

2. a. Explain what is happening in the
photograph above right.

  b. Write new REM statements in line 10
for the third and fourth programs.

Commands like PRINT INT (6✶RND (1)) + 1 are often used
to model or **simulate** the roll of a die, because they
generate the numbers 1, 2, 3, 4, 5, and 6 at random.

3. If you want to
simulate spinning
this spinner, what
commands would
you use?

4. a. Predict the output for the program at
the right.

  b. Draw a flow chart for this program.

```
10   REM RANDOM COIN TOSS
20   FOR C = 1 TO 30
30   N = INT (2✶RND (1))
35   IF N = 0 THEN PRINT "HEADS",
36   IF N = 1 THEN PRINT "TAILS",
40   NEXT C
50   END
```

This flow chart describes a program to roll one die and keep track of the number of times a six is rolled.

DIE will have the value of 1, 2, 3, 4, 5, or 6 at random.

N keeps track of how many times a six is rolled.

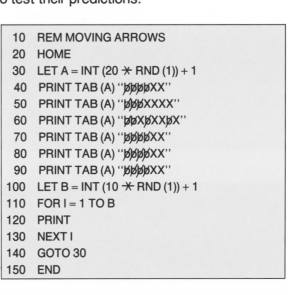

5. Write a BASIC program for this flow chart.

6. Modify the program from exercise 5 to simulate a game between two children. Each rolls a die and the one with the higher number wins. Then they roll 10 times and determine who scores more wins.

7. What is the likelihood that two dice show the same number (for example, 1 and 1, 2 and 2,...,6 and 6)? Work in pairs to roll two dice 30 times, and record how many times a double occurs. Then write a program to simulate rolling two dice 300 times and compare the results.

With the use of the RND function, many experiments can be done through **simulation**. For example, traffic controllers can study how a traffic lane is filled by cars arriving at random intervals; ecologists can study how polluting gases are dispersed in the air; and statisticians can make model situations to test their predictions.

The RND function can also be used to move a figure across the screen.

Line 20 may need to be changed to 20 CLS, depending on the model of microcomputer used.
Line 30 makes an arbitrary tab setting for drawing the arrow. (A command like TAB(14) means move 14 spaces to the right of the left margin.)
Line 100 leaves an arbitrary gap between the printing of two arrows.

8. Modify the program so that you do not have to press the break key to stop the program.

```
10   REM MOVING ARROWS
20   HOME
30   LET A = INT (20 * RND (1)) + 1
40   PRINT TAB (A) "ØØØØXX"
50   PRINT TAB (A) "ØØØXXXX"
60   PRINT TAB (A) "ØØXØXXØX"
70   PRINT TAB (A) "ØØØØXX"
80   PRINT TAB (A) "ØØØØXX"
90   PRINT TAB (A) "ØØØØXX"
100  LET B = INT (10 * RND (1)) + 1
110  FOR I = 1 TO B
120  PRINT
130  NEXT I
140  GOTO 30
150  END
```

Working Backward

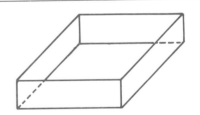

Three tired and hungry hikers had a bag of oranges. After they had fallen asleep one of them awoke, ate $\frac{1}{3}$ of the oranges, and went back to sleep. Later another awoke, ate $\frac{1}{3}$ of the remaining oranges, and went back to sleep. Finally the third hiker awoke and ate $\frac{1}{3}$ of the remaining oranges, leaving 8 in the bag. How many oranges were in the bag originally?

Think. A flow chart might help to understand the problem.

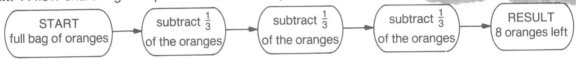

The problem could be solved by guessing and testing. Is there a faster way?

Plan and do. Work backward from the result.

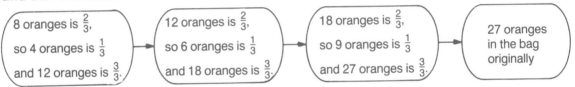

Look back. There were 27 oranges in the bag originally.

Check the solution.

$27 - (\frac{1}{3} \times 27)$ $18 - (\frac{1}{3} \times 18)$ $12 - (\frac{1}{3} \times 12)$

$= 27 - 9$ $= 18 - 6$ $= 12 - 4$

$= 18$ $= 12$ $= 8$ ✓

WORKING TOGETHER

1. A square piece of cardboard has an area of 121 cm². It is made into an open box by cutting a square from each corner and then folding the sides. The volume of the box is 98 cm³. What size of square is cut from each corner?

   a. Draw a small diagram of the cardboard as it appears at the start. Label the dimensions.

   b. What is the formula for the volume of the box?

   c. Guess and test to find the solution. Use a chart to organize your guesses.

   d. Look back to see if your solution is reasonable. Then give a concluding statement.

Length (cm)	Width (cm)	Height (cm)	Volume (cm³)

PROBLEMS

Solve.

1. A triangle has 1 line of symmetry. The perimeter is 19 cm. The length of the shortest side is 5 cm. What are the lengths of the other sides?

2. Five students wrote a history test that they had missed while on a field trip. Their average mark (or mean mark) was 71. If four of the marks were 64, 78, 59, and 81, what was the fifth mark?

3. Nancy filled her truck with 60 L of gasoline. She also spent $2.59 for windshield washer fluid and $1.95 for a can of oil. If she received $9.72 change from two $20 bills, what was the cost of the gasoline per litre?

4. Nathan spent half of his money in one store, and then spent $10 more. In a second store he spent half of his remaining money, and then spent $10 more. Then he had no money left. How much money did he have to start with?

5. One-half of the coins in a wallet are nickels, $\frac{1}{3}$ are pennies, and $\frac{1}{6}$ are dimes. There are 12 nickels. How much money is in the wallet?

6. Miss Wallace made a batch of cookies. Some guests arrived and they ate $\frac{1}{4}$ of the cookies. She gave $\frac{1}{3}$ of the cookies to a neighbor. If Miss Wallace has $2\frac{1}{2}$ dozen cookies left, how many did she make?

7. In a card game, points are lost for cards left in a player's hand at the end of a round. In the last round, Kathy won but Josey lost points. Matt lost half as many points as Josey did. Cynthia lost 1 point, which was half as many as Matt lost. If Josey now has 48 points, how many points did she have before the last round?

8. A bacteria culture doubles its number every hour. There are 262 144 bacteria in the culture at midnight.

   a. What was the bacteria count at noon?

   b. At what time did the lab technician put 1 bacterium in the dish to start the culture?

9. The members of a school academic team competed on a TV quiz show. For each question they answered correctly they received 10 points. For each question they answer incorrectly they lost 15 points. After 20 questions their score was 0. How many questions did they answer correctly?

10. Two 1 L beakers are used in a chemistry experiment. At the start of the experiment, beaker X contains more liquid than beaker Y. From X pour into Y as much liquid as Y already contains. Next, from Y pour into X as much liquid as X now contains. Finally, from X pour into Y as much liquid as Y presently has. Both beakers now contain 800 mL of liquid. How many millilitres of liquid were in each beaker at the start of the experiment?

335

Problem Solving Review

Solve.

1. Grapefruit are piled in the shape of a triangular pyramid. The bottom layer is a triangle with 6 grapefruit on each side. How many grapefruit are in the pile?

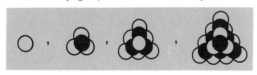

2. The figure has an area of 144 cm². What is the length of its base?

   a. if the figure is a square

   b. if the figure is a rectangle

   c. if the figure is a triangle

3. Marcy remembers paying 85¢ for a bottle of pop when she lived in Drumheller, Alberta. The pop itself cost 35¢ more than the bottle. What was the refund on the bottle worth?

4. Two empty tanks are being filled with gasoline. One tank starts filling at the rate of 175 L/min. Three minutes later the second tank starts filling at the rate of 250 L/min. How long after the second tank starts filling will both tanks contain the same amount of gasoline?

5. An empty pool is being filled with water using 2 hoses. One hose can fill the pool in 24 h. The other hose can fill the pool in 36 h. How long will it take to fill the pool if both hoses are used?

6. An artist received 3¢ for each digit she printed on a page. If she earned $17.37 for a job, how many pages did she number?

7. How many diagonals are there in a dodecagon?

8. At dinner Bill cut smaller pieces of pie for the rest of his family and one large piece of pie for himself. After cutting the pie, $\frac{3}{4}$ of the number of slices to the left of the big slice was 6. How many slices were there altogether?

9. Three pirates dig up a chest of gold coins that they buried many years ago. They decide to divide the treasure the next morning. During the night one greedy pirate sneaks out and divides the coins into three equal groups with one coin left over. He keeps two groups, replaces one group in the chest, and throws the extra coin into the sea for good luck. Later that night a second pirate sneaks out and divides the coins into three groups with one extra coin, keeps two groups, replaces one group, and throws the extra coin into the sea for good luck. Just before sunrise the third pirate repeats the same procedure as his mates. In the morning the three pirates open the chest, divide the coins in three ways with one coin left over, and throw the extra coin into the sea for good luck. What is the least number of coins needed to make this division of the treasure possible?

Chapter Checkup

1. Write a rule that describes the relation. Then list two other ordered pairs.
   a. (z,y), (b,a), (n,m), (t,s)
   b. (3, triangle), (4, quadrilateral), (6, hexagon), (7, heptagon)

2. A plane travels at an average speed of 600 km/h.
   a. Make a table of five values to show the relation between the time and the distance travelled.
   b. Draw a graph.
   c. Estimate the distance travelled.
      i. in 3.5 h   ii. in 6.5 h
   d. Estimate the time required to travel.
      i. 1500 km   ii. 3400 km

3.

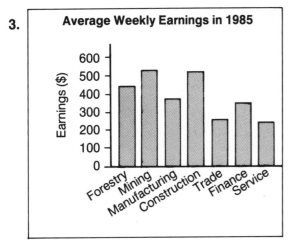

Average Weekly Earnings in 1985

   a. What was the approximate difference in weekly earnings between miners and service workers?
   b. Between which two occupations was the difference in weekly earnings the least? the greatest?
   c. Estimate the average weekly earnings of all the occupations.

4. In 1867 the Conservatives had 101 seats in the House of Commons and the Liberals had 80 seats. No other parties were represented.
   a. Express each party's number of seats as a percent of the total.
   b. Display this data in a circle graph.
   c. Find the number of seats held by each political party in the House of Commons today. Display this in a circle graph.

5. The pulses of various thoroughbred race horses are shown.

Pulse (beats/min)	29	30	31	32	33	34	35	36
Frequency	1	6	8	11	8	5	2	1

   a. Display the data in a histogram.
   b. Find the mean, the median, and the mode of the pulses.

6. An advertising agency wanted to know whether people thought television was useful. The agency put the following advertisement on television.
   "Do you think that television is useful? Please write to..."

   Will this get a representative or a biased sample? Why?

7. Roll a die 50 times and record the results in a tally chart.
   a. What is the experimental probability of rolling a 5?
   b. What is the theoretical probability of rolling a 5?
   c. How do the experimental and theoretical probabilities compare?
   d. Repeat parts a and c for 100 rolls.

Cumulative Checkup

1. Evaluate.

   a. $5 \times 6 - 2^3 \div (3 + 5)$

   b. $3 \times (4 + 4) \div 6 - 12 \div 4$

   c. $\dfrac{8 + 32 \div 4}{3^2 + 4^2 - (5 \times 4 + 3)}$

2. Does the division have zero remainder?

   a. $108 \div 3$ **b.** $532\,104 \div 6$

   c. $7960 \div 5$ **d.** $3888 \div 9$

   e. $13\,988 \div 4$ **f.** $91\,304 \div 8$

3. Find the length of B.

   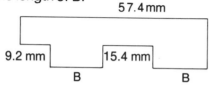

4. Find the perimeter and the area.

   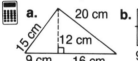

   a. 20 cm, 15 cm, 12 cm, 9 cm, 16 cm
   b. 9.2 cm
   c. 13 m

5. Find the capacity in litres.

   a. Juice 5 cm, 12 cm
   b. Milk 16 cm, 5 cm, 7 cm
   c. Perfume 4 cm, 8 cm, 3.5 cm

6. Write the approximate mass of water in grams, kilograms, or tonnes for the volume.

   a. 7000 cm^3 **b.** 200 cm^3 **c.** 10 m^3

   d. $21\,000 \text{ cm}^3$ **e.** 0.6 m^3 **f.** 32 m^3

7. Find the GCF.

   a. 12, 76 **b.** 36, 64 **c.** 42, 20

   d. 7, 11 **e.** 15, 30 **f.** 24, 40

8. A man has to replace the handle of his pick every 5 a and the head every 6 a. After how many years will the head and the handle wear out at the same time?

9. In a floor hockey game, Marni stopped 7 out of 9 shots on goal. Anna stopped 13 out of 15 shots on goal. Which girl stopped the larger fraction of shots?

10. A house has a floor area of 200 m². Of the area, $\frac{3}{8}$ is bedrooms, $\frac{1}{4}$ is living and dining, $\frac{3}{16}$ is kitchen, $\frac{1}{16}$ is bathroom, $\frac{1}{16}$ is den, and the remainder is halls and closets. Find the area of each region in square metres.

11. Mr. Henderson has to plough 4 fields. If he rents a tractor for $2\frac{1}{2}$ d, what fraction of his fields should he plough each day?

12. Copy and complete.

    a. $\frac{8}{2} = \frac{4}{\square}$ **b.** $3 : 10 = \square : 70$

    c. $\frac{3}{\square} = \frac{2.7}{4.5}$ **d.** $\frac{4.8}{5} = \frac{\square}{2.5}$

13.

    drive wheel 12 teeth, 18 teeth

    a. What is the ratio of the number of teeth on the drive wheel to the number of teeth on the other wheel?

    b. Copy and complete the table.

drive wheel (turns)	1.5	3	6			21
other wheel (turns)				12	18	

14. Use the scale drawing of a flea to find the length of a flea in millimetres.

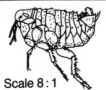

Scale 8 : 1

15. Find the number.

  a. 13% of the number is 69.

  b. 78% of the number is 156.

  c. 56 is 112% of the number.

16. Find the discount and the sale price.

  a.

  b.

  Regular price $19.99
  Discount 15%

  Regular price $8.95
  Discount 25%

17. Calculate the regular price.

  a. 30% discount is $42.

  b. 17% discount is $3.40.

18. Use the Provincial Sales Tax chart on page 216 to calculate the total cost in each province of a portable radio priced at $49.95.

19. How much will be owing at the end of one year if $5000 is borrowed at a simple interest rate of $12\frac{1}{2}$%?

20. Use a protractor to draw an angle with this measure.

  a. 41° **b.** 122° **c.** 166° **d.** 179°

21. Calculate the unknown angle measures.

  a.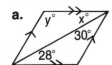

  b.

22. Use compasses and a straightedge to construct a congruent angle.

  a.

  b.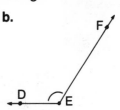

23. Copy and complete.

letter	J		A		C		B	I	K
integer		−3		+1		0			
opposite integer									

24. Write the ordered pair that represents each letter from A to I.

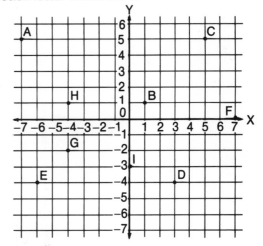

25. Evaluate.

  a. $(+40) + (-7)$ **b.** $(-20) + (-14)$

  c. $(-11) - (+12)$ **d.** $(-4) - (-15)$

  e. $-9 \times (-7)$ **f.** $-11 \times (+6)$

  g. $\frac{-100}{-25}$ **h.** $\frac{-72}{+8}$ **i.** $\frac{+63}{-9}$

339

Construction site managers use equations to calculate the cost of materials and labor on a housing project.

Get Set

1. Which operation, $+, -, \times, \div$, is suggested?

   a. increased by   **b.** product   **c.** less

   d. difference   **e.** quotient **f.** sum

2. Match.

   a. a number increased by 2 $n - 3$

   b. 3 times a number $2 \times n$

   c. a number divided by 2 $3 \times n$

   d. a number less 3 $\frac{2}{n}$

   e. 3 less a number $\frac{n}{2}$

   f. the product of 2 and a number $n + 2$

   g. 2 divided by a number $3 - n$

3. Evaluate.

   a. $8 \times 7 + 6 \times 5$ **b.** $8 \times (7 - 6)$

   c. $8 \times 7 + 5$ **d.** $8^2 + 7 \times 5$

   e. $\frac{5}{7} \times 7$ **f.** $\frac{8 \times 7}{7}$ **g.** $\frac{3}{8} + \frac{2}{8}$

   h. $\frac{3}{8} - \frac{2}{8}$ **i.** $\frac{5}{6} + \frac{1}{8}$ **j.** $\frac{5}{6} - \frac{1}{8}$

   k. $8^2 + 5^2$ **l.** $\frac{35.5}{5}$ **m.** 12×3.1

   n. $17.3 - 8.9$ **o.** $(1.2)^2 + (2.1)^2$

4. Is the sentence true when ▦ is replaced by 12?

   a. ▦ $+ 23 = 35$ **b.** $45 -$ ▦ $= 33$

   c. $6 \times$ ▦ $= 73$ **d.** $\frac{▦}{12} = 1$

5. Complete the number sentence.

   a. ▦ $+ 16 = 33$ **b.** ▦ $- 12 = 45$

   c. $17 +$ ▦ $= 58$ **d.** $35 -$ ▦ $= 12$

   e. ▦ $\times 7 = 56$ **f.** $9 \times$ ▦ $= 108$

   g. $\frac{▦}{11} = 9$ **h.** $\frac{75}{▦} = 3$ **i.** $\frac{▦}{-2} = 1$

6. Find the perimeter.

   a.   **b.**

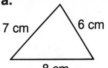 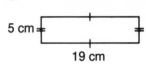

7. a. Write two formulas to use to find the perimeter and the area of a rectangle.

   b. Find the perimeter and the area of a rectangle whose base is 11 cm and whose height is 12 cm.

8. What number would you subtract to have a difference of 0?

   a. 17   **b.** 1418 **c.** $\frac{3}{5}$ **d.** -16.5

9. What number would you add to have a sum of 0?

   a. -38 **b.** $+217$ **c.** $-\frac{7}{8}$ **d.** $+11.4$

10. What number would you divide by to have a quotient of 1?

   a. 44   **b.** 12   **c.** -14 **d.** -9

11. What number would you multiply by to have a product of 1?

   a. $\frac{1}{10}$ **b.** $\frac{-1}{7}$ **c.** $-\frac{1}{11}$ **d.** $\frac{1}{3}$

12. Give the meaning in words.

   a. $>$ **b.** $<$ **c.** $\geq$ **d.** $\leq$

13. List.

   a. four consecutive whole numbers > 7

   b. four consecutive whole numbers < 5

   c. three consecutive integers ≤ 0

   d. three consecutive integers ≥ -7

Words to Mathematics

People with impaired hearing and speaking use sign language to communicate. This language contains symbols that represent letters and words.

G g

R r

telephone

A branch of mathematics called algebra makes use of symbols such as $a, b, c, \ldots, x, y,$ and z, to represent unknown numbers. These symbols are called **variables**.

Just as words can be combined to make phrases and sentences, numbers and variables can be combined to form **expressions**.

Phrase	Variable	Expression
eight **more than** a number	a	$a + 8$
a number **decreased** by two	b	$b - 2$
six **reduced by** a number	d	$6 - d$
four **times** a number	m	$4 \times m$ or $4m$
the **square** of a number	h	h^2
a number **divided by** 5	n	$n \div 5$ or $\frac{n}{5}$
the **reciprocal** of a number	x	$\frac{1}{x}$
ten **added to twice** a number	c	$2c + 10$
three **less than five times** a number	r	$5r - 3$
forty **minus** a number, **divided by** two	f	$\frac{40 - f}{2}$

WORKING TOGETHER

1. Choose the expression for the phrase.

   a. a number diminished by six

   $m - 6$ $\qquad$ $6 - m$ $\qquad$ $\frac{m}{6}$

   b. half of a number

   $g + \frac{1}{2}$ $\qquad$ $\frac{1}{2} - g$ $\qquad$ $\frac{1}{2}g$

   c. the product of four and a number, minus ten

   $10 - 4n$ $\qquad$ $4n - 10$ $\qquad$ $4 \times (n - 10)$

2. List three words that can be represented by the symbol.

   a. $+$ $\qquad$ b. $-$ $\qquad$ c. $\times$ $\qquad$ d. $\div$

3. Translate the expression into words.

   a. $9w$ $\qquad$ b. $a + 11$ $\qquad$ c. $12 - b$

   d. $\frac{n}{4}$ $\qquad$ e. $2y + 3$ $\qquad$ f. $g - 4g$

APPLICATIONS AND EXERCISES

1. Kate knows n sign language symbols. Write an expression for the person.
   a. Ben knows 4 more symbols than Kate.
   b. Sam knows 6 times as many as Kate.
   c. Kyle knows $\frac{1}{2}$ as many as Kate.
   d. Tara knows 6 fewer than Kate.

2. Choose a variable to represent the number. Write an expression.
   a. a number increased by 51
   b. 122 divided by a number
   c. 8 times a number that is subtracted from 37
   d. a number multiplied by itself
   e. $\frac{1}{3}$ of a number reduced by 17
   f. 13 subtracted from the product of 3 and a number
   g. 34 less than double a number

3. Write an expression for the phrase.
   a. the length of a rope divided into 5 equal pieces
   b. 3.14 times the diameter of a plate
   c. twice Joe's batting average less 0.115

4. Translate the expression into words.
   a. $6w$
   b. $9s - 5$
   c. $b - 2$
   d. $(p + 2)^2$
   e. $2h + 3$
   f. $6 \times (1 - k)$
   g. $\frac{3 + e}{14}$
   h. $t + 2t$
   i. $\frac{3m^2}{4}$

5. Mae-Ling and Sue-Ling are twins. Write an expression for the phrase.
   a. the sum of their ages
   b. the sum of their ages 2 a from now
   c. the sum of their ages 5 a ago
   d. the difference of their ages

6. Write an expression for the phrase.
   a. a number added to three times itself
   b. the reciprocal of a number, plus the same number
   c. the cube of a number divided by one less than the same number

7. The length of a soccer field is n metres. The width is 20 m more than half the length. Write an expression for the perimeter of the field.

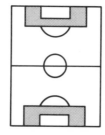

A college student needed $60, so he sent this note to his parents, who loved puzzles.

```
  FORTY
    TEN
  + TEN
  ------
  SIXTY
```

Two weeks later he sent them another note.

```
   SEND
 + MORE
 ------
  MONEY
```

His parents sent the following reply.

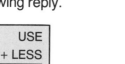

```
   USE
 + LESS
 ------
 SONNY
```

Try This

1. Discover the three addition sentences in the puzzles above. A letter repeated in one puzzle represents the same digit, but can be a different digit in another puzzle.

Substitution

The income from the sale of adult tickets is determined by multiplying 6 times the number of adult tickets sold.

a is the number of adult tickets sold.
$6 \times a$ or $6a$ is an expression for the income.

Ticket prices

Adult	$6.00
Senior	$3.00
Youth	$4.00
Child	$2.00

- What is the income if 55 adult tickets are sold?

  Substitute $a = 55$ in $6a$.

  $$6a$$
  $$= 6 \times (55) \qquad \text{Use parentheses when substituting.}$$
  $$= 330$$

The income from the sale of 55 adult tickets is $330.

- What is the income if 32 child and 45 youth tickets are sold?

  c is the number of child tickets sold and y is the number of youth tickets sold.
  An expression for the income from child and youth ticket sales is
  $$2c + 4y$$

  Substitute $c = 32$ and $y = 45$ in $2c + 4y$.

  $$2c + 4y$$
  $$= 2 \times (32) + 4 \times (45)$$
  $$= 64 + 180$$
  $$= 244$$

The income from the sale of child and youth tickets is $244.

WORKING TOGETHER

1. **a.** Write an expression for the income from the sale of senior and adult tickets.

   b. Calculate the income if 25 senior and 34 adult tickets are sold.

2. Write an expression for the phrase.

   a. two less than a number

   b. eight plus twice a number

3. Evaluate the expressions in exercise 2 if the value of the number is 30.

4. Copy and complete.

   a.

d	$\frac{d}{3}$
0	
3	
6	
12	

   b.

n	$n^2 + 3n$
1	
2	
5	
7	

1. Evaluate $8n - 1$ for this n.

   a. 12   **b.** $\frac{1}{2}$ **c.** 5.5   **d.** 10.2

2. Evaluate $\frac{m}{4} + 3$ for this m.

   a. 16   **b.** 1   **c.** 2.4   **d.** 112

3. Evaluate the expression if $j = 5$.

   a. $17j$ **b.** $0.41j$ **c.** $3j + 2j$

   d. $j^2 + j - 1$ **e.** $26 - 2j$ **f.** $\frac{j}{3} - \frac{2}{3}$

4. Evaluate the expression if $k = 2.7$.

   a. $k + 7$ **b.** $6k$ **c.** $8.4 - k$

   d. $5k + 6$ **e.** $13 - 2k$ **f.** $\frac{5.4}{k}$

5. Evaluate if $p = 3$ and $q = 4$.

   a. $\frac{p}{q}$ **b.** $4p + 3q + 7$

   c. $q - p + 6.3$ **d.** $7p + q^2$

6. Write an expression for the phrase.

   a. the sum of a number and seventeen

   b. ten more than twice a number

   c. nine divided by a number, then increased by six

   d. the quotient of forty-five divided by a number, decreased by five

   e. the product of eleven and a number, subtracted from one hundred

7. Evaluate the expressions in exercise 6 if the value of the number is 9.

8. The area of a circle can be found by multiplying π and the square of the radius.

   a. Which expression can be used?
      i. $\pi \times r$ **ii.** $\pi \times r + r$ **iii.** $\pi \times r^2$

   b. Find the area of a circle when the radius is 11 cm. ($\pi = 3.14$)

9. The circumference of a circle can be found by multiplying π and the diameter.

   a. Write an expression for this.

   b. Find the circumference of a circle when the diameter is 18 cm. ($\pi = 3.14$)

10. Diameters and prices of pizza are shown.

Size Type	Small 26 cm	Medium 36 cm	Large 40 cm	Ex-Large 44 cm
Vegetarian	$5.00	$7.50	$8.25	$10.20
Combo	5.50	8.75	9.50	12.15

    a. Calculate the circumference of each size of pizza to the nearest tenth of a centimetre.

   b. Calculate the area of each size of pizza to the nearest square centimetre.

   c. Calculate the cost per square centimetre of each size and type of pizza. Round to two decimal places.

   d. Based on cost per square centimetre, which size of pizza is the better buy?

11. Evaluate if $e = -3$.

   a. $e + 6$ **b.** $e - (-12)$ **c.** $2e$

   d. $\frac{e}{3}$ **e.** e^2 **f.** $-4e + 5$

Try This

1. Evaluate if $a = -2$, $b = 3$, and $c = -4$. What do you notice?

   a. $a + (b + c)$ and $(a + b) + c$

   b. $a \times (b + c)$ and $a \times b + a \times c$

   c. $\frac{a \times b + a \times c}{a}$ and $b + c$

   d. $(a + b) \times (a - b)$ and $a^2 - b^2$

Collecting Like Terms

The path that a batter can run is in the shape of a diamond.

Determine an expression that represents the length of the path.

Let d represent the distance between consecutive bases in metres.
The length of the path can be found in two ways.

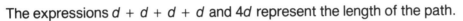

Add the distances.
$d + d + d + d$ OR

Multiply one distance by 4.
$4 \times d = 4d$

The expressions $d + d + d + d$ and $4d$ represent the length of the path.

Because the expressions represent the same length,
$$d + d + d + d = 4d.$$

In $d + d + d + d$, each d is a **term**.
Since the terms have the same variable, they are **like terms**.

Like terms can be added or subtracted.

$2w + 4w = (w + w) + (w + w + w + w)$ OR $2w + 4w = (2 + 4)w$
$\quad\quad\quad = 6w$ $\quad\quad\quad = 6w$

$5y - 3y = (y + y + y + y + y) - (y + y + y)$ OR $5y - 3y = (5 - 3)y$
$\quad\quad\quad = 2y$ $\quad\quad\quad = 2y$

The expression $2x + 7f + 9 + 6x - 3f$ can be simplified by collecting like terms.

$2x + 7f + 9 + 6x - 3f$
$= (2 + 6)x + (7 - 3)f + 9$
$= 8x + 4f + 9$

WORKING TOGETHER

1. Which are like terms?
   $13d \quad 3p \quad 5d \quad 2.1e \quad 2f$
   $10p \quad 13q \quad 4e \quad \frac{1}{2}d \quad \frac{3}{4}f$

2. Simplify.

   a. $n + n$ **b.** $h + 2h$ **c.** $3e + 2e + e$
   d. $8p + 3p$ **e.** $4r - 3r$ **f.** $7x - 2x - 3x$

3. Collect the like terms, then simplify.

   a. $4g + 2 - g + 5 + 7g - 1$
   b. $13 + 3g - 1 + 8g + 4 - g$
   c. $2g + 5g + 11c - 3g - 4c$

4. Evaluate the results from parts **a** and **b** in exercise 3 if $g = 2$.

1. Simplify.

   a. $3n + 4n$ b. $6p - 2p$

   c. $5b + b$ d. $7s - s$

   e. $4k + 4k$ f. $3c - c$

   g. $1.5e + 2.5e$ h. $4j + 5j$

   i. $5f + 2f - f$ j. $5u + u + u$

2. Can the expression be simplified further? Explain.

   a. $4z + 7z$ b. $2x + 8y$

   c. $8z + 4$ d. $12m - 3m$

3. Identify the like terms, then simplify.

   a. $3g + 7g - 9 - g$

   b. $5d + 7 - 2 - 4d$

   c. $5 + 5c - 3c + 1$

   d. $16 + 5k - 2k + 7$

   e. $6z - 2z + 9 + 7z$

   f. $w + 3w + 1 - 2w + 8$

   g. $9r + 3n + 5r + 7 + 4n - 2$

   h. $11y + 5y + 6 - 4y - 1 + 3d$

   i. $7s + 9v + 2e + 6v - 2s - 3v + e$

4. Collect the like terms, then evaluate.

   a. $3s - s$, if $s = 2$

   b. $2x + 4x$, if $x = 1$

   c. $5y + 6y - 3y$, if $y = 3$

   d. $3t + 2 - 2t$, if $t = 0$

   e. $8d + 2d - 3d + 5$, if $d = 8$

   f. $7b + 7b - 14b$, if $b = 4.3$

5. Write an expression for the perimeter.

   a.   b.   c.

6. Find the perimeter of each polygon in exercise 5 if $b = 5$ cm.

7. Collect the like terms, then evaluate if $a = 4$ and $b = 6$.

   a. $3a + 2a + b + 7b$

   b. $6a + 4b - 2b - 3a$

   c. $a + b + 7a + 9b$

8. a. Write an expression that represents the length of the template.

   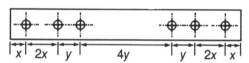

   b. Calculate the length.

   i. if $x = 6$ cm and $y = 8$ cm

   ii. if $x = 1.9$ cm and $y = 2.2$ cm

9. a. Write an expression that represents the perimeter.

   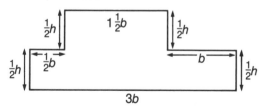

   b. Calculate the perimeter if $h = 2.4$ cm and $b = 5.1$ cm.

Try This

1. Replace the boxes using each digit from 1 to 9 once to make the statement true.

   $\square \times \square\square = \square\square\square = \square\square \times \square$

2. If $\square$ is a positive number less than 10, what value of $\square$ makes $\square$47$\square$0 divisible by 36?

347

Solving Equations by Inspection

Jamie has a mass of 59 kg. He can lift weights equivalent to his own mass.

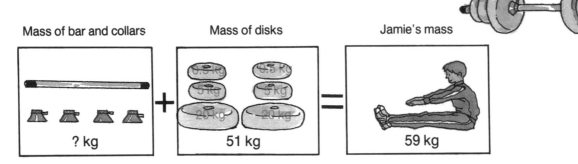

Mass of bar and collars	Mass of disks	Jamie's mass
? kg	51 kg	59 kg

Let m represent the mass of the bar and the collars in kilograms.

$m + 51$ is the combined mass of the bar, the collars, and the disks. $m + 51 = 59$

What is the mass of the bar and the collars?
To determine the mass, find the value for m that makes the sentence true.

$$m + 51 = 59$$
$$\text{Because } 8 + 51 = 59,$$
$$m = 8$$

> What number added to 51 gives 59?

The mass of the bar and the collars is 8 kg.

$m + 51 = 59$ is an **equation**; $m = 8$ is its **solution**.
The above method of solving an equation is called **inspection**.

Solve by inspection.

$$k - 9 = 10$$

> What number minus 9 gives 10?

$$19 - 9 = 10$$

The solution is $k = 19$.

$$7w = 63$$

> What number multiplied by 7 gives 63?

$$7 \times 9 = 63$$

The solution is $w = 9$.

$$\frac{e}{6} = 5$$

> What number divided by 6 gives 5?

$$\frac{30}{6} = 5$$

The solution is $e = 30$.

WORKING TOGETHER

1. Copy and complete.

a. $n + 15 = 21$
$\blacksquare + 15 = 21$
$n = \blacksquare$

b. $19 - m = 16$
$19 - \blacksquare = 16$
$m = \blacksquare$

c. $8y = 112$
$8 \times \blacksquare = 112$
$y = \blacksquare$

d. $\frac{x}{3} = 4$
$\frac{\blacksquare}{3} = 4$
$x = \blacksquare$

1. Is the given value the solution of the equation?

   a. $x + 3 = 13, x = 10$

   b. $3y = 18, y = 54$

   c. $\frac{z}{3} = 8, z = 24$

   d. $10 - p = 6, p = 4$

   e. $r^2 = 144, r = 11$

2. Solve by inspection.

   a. $c + 12 = 18$ b. $n + 11 = 25$

   c. $b - 4 = 16$ d. $m - 8 = 27$

   e. $18 + d = 66$ f. $21 + v = 72$

   g. $24 - v = 5$ h. $33 - w = 19$

3. A rock and 3 one-gram masses balance with 1 fifty-gram mass and 4 one-gram masses. Write and solve an equation to find the mass of the rock.

4. Solve by inspection.

   a. $2a = 30$ b. $\frac{x}{4} = 12$ c. $5x = 100$

   d. $\frac{m}{3} = 20$ e. $8k = 96$ f. $\frac{z}{7} = 5$

5. Solve the pair of equations.

   a. $32 = 4s$ and $4s = 32$

   b. $k + 6 = 9$ and $9 = k + 6$

   c. $7 - b = 3$ and $3 = 7 - b$

   d. $\frac{n}{2} = 12$ and $12 = \frac{n}{2}$

   What conclusion can you make?

6. A weight lifter lifts 280 kg. The mass of the bar and the collars is 25 kg.

   a. Write an equation to represent the mass of the disks. Solve the equation.

   b. About how many times greater is the mass of the disks than the mass of the bar and the collars?

7. Solve.

   a. $6.2 = x - 1.5$ b. $8.5 = m + 1.3$

   c. $7.5 = 0.5n$ d. $h + 12.5 = 17.7$

   e. $8.25 - p = 1.15$ f. $4b = 9.6$

   g. $\frac{d}{3} = 12.25$ h. $3.1 = \frac{y}{9}$

   i. $3j + 2j = 20.25$ j. $2c + c = 0.3$

8. Let n represent the number. Express the sentence as an equation.

   a. The product of a number and 5 is 18.

   b. Twice a number gives a result of 49.

   c. The sum of 16 and a number is 21.8.

   d. A number minus 33 equals 91.

9. Solve the equations in exercise 8.

10. The value of a roll of quarters is $10.00. Write an equation to represent the number of quarters in a roll. Then solve the equation.

11. Repeat exercise 10 for nickels and dimes if a roll of nickels is worth $2 and a roll of dimes is worth $5.

KEEPING SHARP

1. Estimate.

   a. 54×0.26 b. $6.18 + 19.7 + 2$ c. $15 - 3.86$ d. 3.14×2.8

   e. $1.225 \div 3.5$ f. $21.3 - 6.01$ g. $0.0008 \div 0.02$ h. 43.725×0.014

Solving Equations by Systematic Trial

Warren is paid $18/d and $3 for each container he fills. In one day he earns $57. How many containers does Warren fill?

Let c represent the number of containers he fills.

$3 \times c$ or $3c$ represents his earnings from filling containers.
$18 are his earnings for working the day.
$3c + 18$ represents his total earnings for the day.

$$3c + 18 = 57$$

Solve by substituting values for c in the equation.

$3c + 18 = 57$

	c	$3c + 18$	
Try	10	$3 \times (10) + 18 = 48$	low
Try	15	$3 \times (15) + 18 = 63$	high
Try	13	$3 \times (13) + 18 = 57$	✓

$c = 13$ is the solution of the equation.

Warren filled 13 containers.

This method of solving an equation is called **systematic trial**.

Solve by systematic trial.

$3a - 2 = 73$

a	$3a - 2$	
20	$3 \times (20) - 2 = 58$	low
25	$3 \times (25) - 2 = 73$	✓

The solution is $a = 25$.

$2 \times (n + 6) = 96$

n	$2 \times (n + 6)$	
40	$2 \times [(40) + 6] = 92$	low
41	$2 \times [(41) + 6] = 94$	low
42	$2 \times [(42) + 6] = 96$	✓

The solution is $n = 42$.

$\frac{2b}{3} + 5 = 9$

b	$\frac{2b}{3} + 5$	
15	$\frac{2(15)}{3} + 5 = 15$	high
9	$\frac{2(9)}{3} + 5 = 11$	high
6	$\frac{2(6)}{3} + 5 = 9$	✓

The solution is $b = 6$.

WORKING TOGETHER

1. a. Copy and complete the table.

y	$29 - 3y$
5	
6	
7	
8	

   b. What is the solution of the equation $29 - 3y = 8$?

2. Solve by systematic trial.

   a. $11 \times (d - 5) = 66$ **b.** $\frac{30}{k} + 12 = 22$

3. Simplify the left-hand side of the equation. Then solve.   **a.** $2a + 4a + 8 = 44$

   b. $8m + 19 - 3m = 54$

350

APPLICATIONS AND EXERCISES

1. Is $m = 10$ the solution?

    a. $4m + 3 = 43$ **b.** $2m - 1 = 19$

    c. $\frac{m}{5} + 5 = 3$ **d.** $\frac{80}{m} - 2 = 6$

2. "Only one of these equations has $b = 12$ as the solution," claimed Ann. "I disagree!" exclaimed Melanie. "Two equations have 12 as the solution." Who was right, Ann or Melanie?

    a. $2b + 6 = 24$ **b.** $3b - 4 = 14$

    c. $2 \times (b + 5) = 34$ **d.** $\frac{2b}{3} - 2 = 8$

    e. $\frac{b + 16}{2} = 14$ **f.** $\frac{72}{b} + 12 = 7$

3. Copy and complete. Solve the equation.

    a. $14 + 5x = 34$ **b.** $\frac{n}{6} - 2 = 1$

x	$14 + 5x$
1	
4	
5	

n	$\frac{n}{6} - 2$
36	
24	
18	

4. Solve by systematic trial.

    a. $\frac{n}{2} + 3 = 7$ **b.** $2b + 3 = 13$

    c. $3x + 4 = 79$ **d.** $4e - 5 = 35$

    e. $2w - 3 = 18$ **f.** $5h + 3 = 57$

    g. $\frac{s}{4} - 2 = 7$ **h.** $\frac{u}{9} + 6 = 10$

5. Solve by systematic trial.

    a. $2q + 3.6 = 7.2$

    b. $0.1 \times (r + 1.8) = 0.5$

    c. $\frac{m}{3} + 2.4 = 4.8$ **d.** $3p - 2.1 = 4.2$

6. Simplify the left-hand side of the equation. Then solve.

    a. $5a + 3a = 64$

    b. $7b - 4b = 48$

    c. $3d + 4d + 1 = 36$

    d. $12c - 2c + 10 = 40$

    e. $6p + 10 + 3p = 82$

    f. $5m - 4 - 2m = 29$

7. Express as an equation, then solve.

    a. Twice a number, plus 5, equals 25.

    b. A number divided by 2, then added to 5, equals 19.

    c. Two less than a number is divided by 3 to give a result of 7.

8. A taxicab company charges $1.20 plus 25¢ for each kilometre travelled. If a fare is $3.20, what distance was travelled?

    a. Write an equation to represent the situation.

    b. Solve the equation.

A calculator with an automatic constant is useful when solving equations by systematic trial.

1. Solve. Use a calculator to help.

Solve. $4w = 25$

Try. $w = 6$ 4 × 6 = (24) too low

     $w = 6.5$ 6.5 = (26) too high

     $w = 6.25$ 6.25 = (25) ✓

   a. $5k = 66.5$ **b.** $180 \div p = 22.5$ **c.** $5n = 127.5$ **d.** $8q = 100$

   e. $91 \div m = 14$ **f.** $4x = 61$ **g.** $222 \div b = 37$ **h.** $12y = 159$

PRACTICE

1. Write an expression for the phrase.
   a. 81 less than twice a number
   b. a number divided by 5, increased by 6
   c. 29 more than double a number
   d. $\frac{1}{2}$ of a number subtracted from twice the number
   e. the sum of a number and the square of the number
   f. the product of a number and 12, increased by 2

2. Translate the expression into words.
   a. $5m$ b. $9a + 7$ c. $n - 11$
   d. $4 \times (h + 3)$ e. $c + 7c$ f. $\frac{9 + h}{15}$

3. When you purchase a taxable item, the amount of sales tax you pay is the product of the selling price and the sales tax rate. Which expression can be used to calculate the cost of an item when the sales tax is 7%?
   a. $p - 7\%$ b. $p + 7\%$
   c. $0.07p$ d. $p + 0.07p$

4. Evaluate $\frac{3}{v}$ for these values of v.
   a. 2   b. 30   c. 0.5   d. $\frac{7}{2}$

5. Evaluate the expression if $f = 8$.
   a. $12f$ b. $9.3 - f$ c. $f^2 - 1$
   d. $\frac{5f}{2}$ e. $3f + 15.7$ f. $5 + (2f - 1)$

6. Evaluate if $x = 6$ and $y = 4$.
   a. $2x + y$ b. $x^2 - y^2$ c. $\frac{2x}{y} + 1$

7. The volume of a sphere can be found by multiplying $\frac{4}{3}$ times π times the cube of the radius.
   a. Give an expression that can be used to find the volume of a sphere.
   b. Find the volume of a ball when the radius is 4 cm. ($\pi = 3.14$)

8. Simplify.
   a. $8n - 5n$ b. $4q + q$
   c. $m + 2m + 2m$ d. $2a + 4a - 3a$
   e. $3c + 8 + 2c$ f. $5t + d + 2t + 3d$
   g. $6a + 7b + 2a - 3b - a + b$

9. Write an expression for the perimeter.
   a.   b.

10. Solve by inspection or systematic trial.
    a. $2 + b = 15$ b. $6v = 18$
    c. $2n - 3 = 27$ d. $6b + 6 = 18$
    e. $\frac{a}{2} = 14$ f. $6 = m - 5$
    g. $30 = 3x + 6$ h. $19 - v = 3$
    i. $25 - 2d = 1$ j. $2e + 6.2 = 7.8$

11. Express as an equation, then solve.
    a. A number tripled is 57.
    b. Twelve more than a number is 45.
    c. A number divided by 7 is 15.
    d. Eight more than twice a number gives a result of 22.
    e. A number divided by 3 is decreased by 9 to give a result of 4.

Solving Equations

The product of Barry's age and Janet's age, plus 9, is 630.
If Barry is 27, how old is Janet?

Suppose that Janet enters her age on a calculator, multiplies by 27, adds 9, then shows Barry the display.

Barry can find out her age by undoing the sequence of operations on the calculator.

Janet's age is 23. Check the solution by substituting 23 for j in $j \times 27 + 9$. Compare with the expected result, 630.

$j\ \boxed{\times}\ \boxed{27}\ \boxed{+}\ \boxed{9}\ \boxed{=}\ \left(\text{630.}\right)$ $\boxed{-}\ \boxed{9}\ \boxed{\div}\ \boxed{27}\ \boxed{=}\ \left(\text{23.}\right)$

$j \times 27 + 9 = (23) \times 27 + 9$
$= 630\ \checkmark$

To solve equations using a calculator, identify the order of the steps of the equation. Then put the steps in the **reverse order**, using **inverse operations**.

$m + 32 = 56$
$\begin{array}{c} m \\ + \quad 32 \\ \hline 56 \end{array}$ $\begin{array}{c} m \\ - \quad 32 \\ \hline 56 \end{array}$ $\boxed{56}\ \boxed{-}\ \boxed{32}\ \boxed{=}$ $\left(\text{24.}\right)\ m$

$n - 17 = 41$
$\begin{array}{c} n \\ - \quad 17 \\ \hline 41 \end{array}$ $\begin{array}{c} n \\ + \quad 17 \\ \hline 41 \end{array}$ $\boxed{41}\ \boxed{+}\ \boxed{17}\ \boxed{=}$ $\left(\text{58.}\right)\ n$

$\dfrac{h}{6} = 12$
$\begin{array}{c} h \\ \div \quad 6 \\ \hline 12 \end{array}$ $\begin{array}{c} h \\ \times \quad 6 \\ \hline 12 \end{array}$ $\boxed{12}\ \boxed{\times}\ \boxed{6}\ \boxed{=}$ $\left(\text{72.}\right)\ h$

$9k = -54$
$\begin{array}{c} k \\ \times \quad 9 \\ \hline -54 \end{array}$ $\begin{array}{c} k \\ \div \quad 9 \\ \hline -54 \end{array}$ $\boxed{54}\ \boxed{+/-}\ \boxed{\div}\ \boxed{9}\ \boxed{=}$ $\left(\text{-6.}\right)\ k$

Negative numbers stay as negative numbers. Only opposite operations are used.

$6q + 7 = 55$
$\begin{array}{c} q \\ \times \quad 6 \\ + \quad 7 \\ \hline 55 \end{array}$ $\begin{array}{c} q \\ \div \quad 6 \\ - \quad 7 \\ \hline 55 \end{array}$ $\boxed{55}\ \boxed{-}\ \boxed{7}\ \boxed{\div}\ \boxed{6}\ \boxed{=}$ $\left(\text{8.}\right)\ q$

1. Solve the equation using inverse operations.

    a. $m + 56.78 = 89.61$ **b.** $w - 83.12 = 21.79$ **c.** $7.2f = -22.68$

    d. $g \div 0.245 = 20.09$ **e.** $f - 6.64 = -8.43$ **f.** $-9.4t = 34.78$

    g. $7x - 23 = 33$ **h.** $-4k + 9 = 37$ **i.** $6.1y - 3.04 = 17.7$

    j. $\dfrac{3w + 5}{4} = 6.5$ **k.** $\dfrac{2}{3}b = 18$ **l.** $\dfrac{4}{5}z - 3.6 = 2.4$

Solving Equations by Adding and Subtracting

The photograph shows that the scales are balanced. If the same mass is added to both sides or removed from both sides, the scales still balance.

An equation is like balance scales. If a number is added to or subtracted from both sides of an equation, the equation is still a true statement.

The equation $m + 2 = 10$ represents the situation shown on the balance scales.

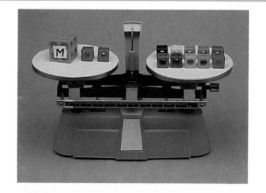

Solve. $m + 2 = 10$

$m + 2 - 2 = 10 - 2$

$m = 8$

Check. Substitute 8 for m in $m + 2$.

$$m + 2 = (8) + 2$$
$$= 10$$

Compare with the expected result, 10.

The solution is $m = 8$.

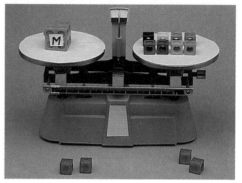

WORKING TOGETHER

1. Copy and complete.

a.

$$x - 3 = 7$$

$$x - 3 + \square = 7 + \square$$

$$x = \bigcirc$$

b.

$$b - 1 = 8$$

$$b - 1 + \square = 8 + \square$$

$$b = \bigcirc$$

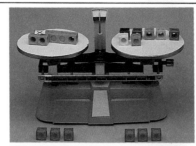

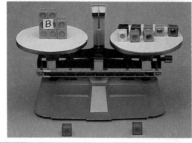

2. Check the answers in exercise 1.

3. Copy and complete.

a. $k + 5 = 8$

$k + 5 - \square = 8 - \square$

$k = \bigcirc$

b. $c - 4 = 9$

$c - 4 + \square = 9 + \square$

$c = \bigcirc$

c. $m - 4 = -3$

$m - 4 + \square = -3 + \square$

$m = \bigcirc$

d. $n + 5 = 3$

$n + 5 - \square = 3 - \square$

$n = \bigcirc$

1. What number should be subtracted from both sides to solve the equation?

 a. $n + 5 = 11$ b. $b + 10 = 25$

 c. $d + 9 = 17$ d. $f + 2 = 19$

 e. $h + 1.7 = 7.8$ f. $m + 8.4 = 16.8$

2. Solve by subtracting 4 from each side. Check by substitution.

 a. $n + 4 = 72$ b. $m + 4 = 16$

 c. $p + 4 = 8.6$ d. $j + 4 = 0$

3. What number should be added to both sides to solve the equation?

 a. $n - 9 = 15$ b. $b - 14 = 22$

 c. $d - 6 = 25$ d. $f - 5 = 61$

 e. $g - 2.5 = 8.7$ f. $m - 1.6 = 1.8$

4. Solve by adding 3 to each side. Check by substitution.

 a. $j - 3 = 52$ b. $y - 3 = 19$

 c. $d - 3 = 16.4$ d. $f - 3 = 0$

5. Solve. Check by substitution.

 a. $r - 7 = 13$ b. $a - 6 = 33$

 c. $x + 12 = 18$ d. $t + 14 = 55$

 e. $m - 8 = 38$ f. $n + 18 = 29$

 g. $y + 21 = 28$ h. $z - 16 = 0$

6. Solve. Check by substitution.

 a. $15 = n + 4$ b. $31 = a + 6$

 c. $32 = m - 8$ d. $44 = b - 15$

 e. $74 = a - 19$ f. $63 = c + 18$

7. Solve.

 a. $b + 12 = 17.5$ b. $r - 18 = 5.6$

 c. $1.6 = r - 9.4$ d. $t + 4.6 = 18.1$

 e. $m - 4.7 = 1.05$ f. $m + 0.43 = 7.25$

 g. $n + \frac{4}{7} = \frac{6}{7}$ h. $b - \frac{1}{5} = \frac{3}{5}$

8. Express as an equation, then solve.

 a. Had Greg swum six more kilometres, he would have covered 35 km. How far did Greg swim?

 b. The cost of the flight increased by $17 to $147. What was the original cost of the flight?

 c. The price of gasoline decreased by 2.1¢/L to 51.6¢/L. What was the original price per litre?

9. Solve. Check by substitution.

 a. $b + 5 = 1$ b. $c + 9 = 4$

 c. $x + 11 = 3$ d. $x + 12 = 8$

 e. $x - 6 = -5$ f. $r - 15 = -2$

 g. $2a - a = 6$ h. $8m - 7m - 6 = -2$

Try
This

1. Solve the equations.

 a. $y + 3.47 = 8.98$ b. $m - 3.96 = 0.02$

 c. $d - 6.12 = -0.79$ d. $211.46 = 206.7 + p$

 e. $k - 4.94 = -0.26$ f. $t + 60.9 = 66.02$

 g. $r - 1.5 = 3.05$ h. $54.28 + x = 60.18$

 i. $-5.18 = j - 9.55$

2. Do the solutions form a Magic Square?

y	m	d
p	k	t
r	x	j

Solving Equations by Multiplying and Dividing

The photograph shows that the scales are balanced.

If the masses on both sides are increased or decreased by the same factor, the scales still balance.

An equation is like balance scales. If both sides of an equation are multiplied by the same factor or divided by the same factor (except 0), the equation is still a true statement.

The equation $2n = 12$ represents the situation shown on the balance scales.

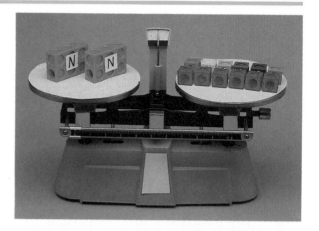

Solve. $2n = 12$

$$\frac{2n}{2} = \frac{12}{2}$$

$$n = 6$$

Check.   Substitute 6 for n in $2n$.

$$2n = 2 \times (6)$$
$$= 12$$

Compare with the expected result, 12.

The solution is $n = 6$.

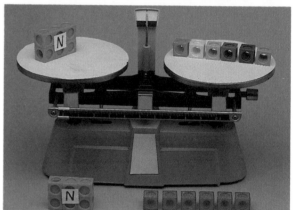

WORKING TOGETHER

1. Copy and complete.

a. $5a = 15$

$\frac{5a}{5} = \frac{15}{\blacksquare}$

$a = \bigcirc$

b. $\frac{c}{7} = 5$

$\frac{c}{7} \times 7 = 5 \times \blacksquare$

$c = \bigcirc$

c. $\frac{b}{4} = 3$

$\frac{b}{4} \times 4 = 3 \times \blacksquare$

$b = \bigcirc$

d. $8 = \frac{m}{6}$

$8 \times \blacksquare = \frac{m}{6} \times 6$

$\bigcirc = m$

2. Check the answers in exercise 1.

3. Copy and complete.

a. $\frac{x}{8} = \frac{3}{2}$

$\frac{x}{8} \times 8 = \frac{3}{2} \times \blacksquare$

$x = \bigcirc$

b. $\frac{r}{4} = \frac{3}{6}$

$\frac{r}{4} \times 4 = \frac{3}{6} \times \blacksquare$

$r = \bigcirc$

c. $\frac{t}{3} = \frac{4}{12}$

$\frac{t}{3} \times 3 = \frac{4}{12} \times \blacksquare$

$t = \bigcirc$

d. $\frac{6}{3} = \frac{m}{2}$

$\frac{6}{3} \times \blacksquare = \frac{m}{2} \times 2$

$\bigcirc = m$

4. Check the answers in exercise 3.

1. What number should both sides be divided by to solve the equation?

   a. $3n = 27$ **b.** $5c = 75$

   c. $8d = 96$ **d.** $11a = 121$

   e. $1.5x = 2.25$ **f.** $1.2y = 10.8$

2. Solve by dividing each side by 6. Check by substitution.

   a. $6c = 96$ **b.** $6b = 84$

   c. $6x = 14.4$ **d.** $0 = 6m$

3. What number should both sides be multiplied by to solve the equation?

   a. $\frac{m}{3} = 16$ **b.** $\frac{n}{5} = 18$ **c.** $\frac{x}{12} = 9$

   d. $\frac{r}{9} = 13$ **e.** $\frac{x}{7} = \frac{5}{2}$ **f.** $\frac{t}{5} = \frac{9}{8}$

4. Solve by multiplying each side by 5.

   a. $\frac{m}{5} = 12$ **b.** $\frac{n}{5} = 14$ **c.** $\frac{r}{5} = 8.1$

   d. $1.3 = \frac{t}{5}$ **e.** $\frac{m}{5} = \frac{7}{2}$ **f.** $\frac{x}{5} = \frac{9}{4}$

5. Solve.

   a. $8y = 56$ **b.** $4t = 56$

   c. $\frac{c}{6} = 15$ **d.** $\frac{x}{11} = 9$

   e. $135 = 5r$ **f.** $44 = \frac{n}{3}$

   g. $\frac{2}{5} = \frac{m}{11}$ **h.** $-72 = -6a$

6. The area of a rectangle is given by the formula $A = bh$, where A is the area, b is the base, and h is the height. Copy and complete the table to find the missing dimensions of the rectangular playing field.

Sport	Area (m²)	Length (m)	Width (m)
basketball	364	26	
soccer	8250		75
volleyball	162		9
women's lacrosse	8227.5	109.7	
baseball infield	750.76	27.4	

7. The average speed of a car is given by the formula $s = \frac{d}{t}$, where s is the speed, d is the distance travelled, and t is the time. Copy and complete the table to find the winning distance travelled for these Le Mans 24 h car races.

Year	Winner's average speed (km/h)	Distance (km)	Time (h)
1978	208.9		24
1983	210.7		24
1984	202.9		24
1985	212.02		24

8. Simplify, then solve. Check by substitution.

   a. $5x + 7x = 132$ **b.** $9b - 3b = 84$

   c. $6m - m = -35$ **d.** $9a + 4a = -39$

KEEPING SHARP

1. Express each fraction as a decimal and as a percent.

   a. $\frac{7}{20}$ **b.** $2\frac{1}{5}$ **c.** $\frac{5}{8}$ **d.** $\frac{1}{3}$ **e.** $\frac{4}{11}$

2. Express each percent as a decimal and as a fraction.

   a. 68%   **b.** $12\frac{1}{2}$%   **c.** $83\frac{1}{3}$%   **d.** 0.5%

Solving Multi-Step Equations

The photograph shows that the scales are balanced.

The equation $2a + 1 = 13$ represents the situation shown on the balance scales.

Solve. $2a + 1 = 13$

Undo the addition by subtracting.

$$2a + 1 - 1 = 13 - 1$$
$$2a = 12$$

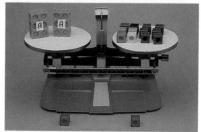

Undo the multiplication by dividing.

$$\frac{2a}{2} = \frac{12}{2}$$
$$a = 6$$

Check. Substitute 6 for a in $2a + 1$.

$$2a + 1 = 2 \times (6) + 1$$
$$= 12 + 1$$
$$= 13$$

Compare with the expected result, 13.

The solution is $a = 6$.

WORKING TOGETHER

1. Copy and complete.
$$3z - 2 = 7$$
$$3z - 2 + 2 = 7 + \square$$
$$3z = \bigcirc$$
$$\frac{3z}{3} = \frac{\bigcirc}{\triangle}$$
$$z = \boxed{}$$

2. Check the answer in exercise 1.

3. Solve. Check by substitution.
   a. $4m - 3 = 17$ **b.** $5c + 2 = 12$

4. Copy and complete. Check the answer.
$$\frac{a}{2} + 3 = 4$$
$$\frac{a}{2} + 3 - 3 = 4 - \square$$
$$\frac{a}{2} = \bigcirc$$
$$\frac{a}{2} \times 2 = \bigcirc \times \triangle$$
$$a = \boxed{}$$

5. Solve. Check by substitution.
   a. $\frac{b}{5} + 6 = 13$ **b.** $\frac{a}{3} - 4 = 3$

1. List in order the operations you would perform to solve the equation.

   a. $3x + 4 = 19$ b. $2m - 7 = 17$

   c. $\frac{b}{5} - 6 = 8$ d. $\frac{c}{8} + 9 = 15$

2. Solve. Check by substitution.

   a. $7x + 2 = 9$ b. $8a + 6 = 22$

   c. $3c - 3 = 24$ d. $9m - 1 = 35$

   e. $10r + 3 = 103$ f. $9x - 8 = 100$

   g. $11b - 44 = 0$ h. $6b + 12 = 12$

   i. $5r + 2.7 = 18.2$ j. $4r - 6.3 = 10.1$

   k. $\frac{n}{7} + 2 = 12$ l. $\frac{t}{3} + 11 = 22$

   m. $\frac{a}{8} - 9 = 21$ n. $\frac{r}{6} - 10 = 20$

   o. $\frac{m}{8} - 19 = 0$ p. $\frac{n}{11} + 47 = 47$

   q. $\frac{x}{5} + 3.7 = 5.2$ r. $\frac{t}{10} - 5.7 = 12.4$

3. The total points scored by a basketball team are determined by the formula $s = 2g + f$, where s is the total points scored, g is the number of field goals made, and f is the number of free throws made. Substitute the given values into the formula $s = 2g + f$. Then solve to complete the table.

Team	Score	Number of field goals	Number of free throws
North	78		24
Innisdale	63	29	
Eastview	54	23	
Central	45		11

4. Typing speed is calculated by the formula $s = \frac{w}{5} - 2e$, where s is the speed in words per minute, w is the number of words typed in 5 min, and e is the number of errors. Substitute the given values into the formula. Then solve to complete the table.

Speed (wpm)	Number of words	Number of errors
35		10
40		8
65	395	

Try This

1. a. Calculate the area of the squares for the right-angled triangles below.

   b. Copy and complete the table.

   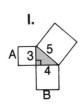
   I.

   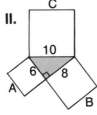
   II.

   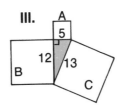
   III.

Figure	Area of square		
	A	B	C
I			
II			
III			

2. a. Find the area of A plus the area of B for each figure.

   b. How does this sum compare with the area of C?

   c. State a relationship between the area of the square on the **hypotenuse** and the areas of the squares on the other two sides.

359

Pythagoras and Equations

Pythagoras, a Greek scholar, showed that, for any
right-angled triangle, the area of the square on the
hypotenuse equals the sum of the areas of the squares
on the other sides.

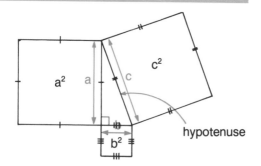

He expressed this relationship as an equation.
$$c^2 = a^2 + b^2$$

Many problems involving right-angled triangles
can be solved with this equation.

How long is the slanted board that helps
support the wall?

Let c represent the length in metres.
Since the triangle has a right angle:

$$c^2 = a^2 + b^2 \qquad c = \blacksquare$$
$$c^2 = (4)^2 + (3)^2 \qquad a = 4$$
$$c^2 = 16 + 9 \qquad b = 3$$
$$c^2 = 25$$
$$c = \sqrt{25}$$
$$c = 5 \qquad \text{The board is 5 m long.}$$

Another construction company uses a 6 m board to support a 4 m wall. What is the distance,
to the nearest tenth of a metre, from the base of the wall to the bottom of the board?

Let b represent the distance in metres.

$$c^2 = a^2 + b^2 \qquad c = 6$$
$$(6)^2 = (4)^2 + b^2 \qquad a = 4$$
$$36 = 16 + b^2 \qquad b = \blacksquare$$
$$20 = b^2$$
$$\sqrt{20} = b$$
$$4.58 \doteq b \qquad \text{The distance is about 4.6 m.}$$

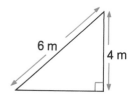

WORKING TOGETHER

1. State the length of the hypotenuse.

a.

b.

c.

2. Write an equation to show how the sides
are related. Then solve for the unknown.

a.

b.

360

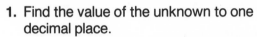
1. Find the value of the unknown to one decimal place.

   a. $c^2 = 2^2 + 3^2$ **b.** $c^2 = 9^2 + 10^2$

   c. $12^2 = 7^2 + b^2$ **d.** $15^2 = 11^2 + b^2$

   e. $8^2 = a^2 + 2^2$ **f.** $10^2 = a^2 + 1^2$

2. Calculate the length of the unknown side to the nearest tenth of a centimetre.

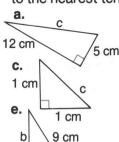
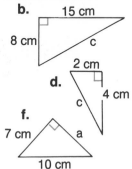
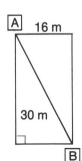

a. 12 cm, c, 5 cm

b. 15 cm, 8 cm, c

c. 1 cm, c

d. 2 cm, c, 4 cm

e. b, 1 cm, 9 cm, 5 cm

f. 7 cm, a, 10 cm

3. a. Find the distance from A to B by walking around the outside of the field.

   b. Find the shortcut distance across the field from A to B.

   c. How much shorter is the shortcut?

A, 16 m, 30 m, B

4. What is the straight-line distance the ball travels when it is thrown from third base to first base?

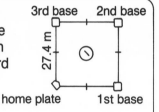
3rd base   2nd base   27.4 m   home plate   1st base

5. A 5 m ladder is placed against a building. How high up the wall does it reach?

   a. if the foot of the ladder is 1 m from the base of the building

   b. if the foot of the ladder is 2 m from the base of the building

6. Part of Jane's gymnastics floor routine is shown in the diagram. What distance does she cover to the nearest tenth of a metre?

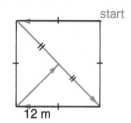
start, 12 m

7. Computer chips are produced on silicon wafers.

   a. What is the diameter of the wafer to the nearest tenth of a centimetre?

   b. What is the area?

1.9 cm, 1.9 cm

Computers working along with video machines can produce very realistic simulations. A flight simulator, used to train pilots, consists of a model of a cockpit with computer-controlled video screens mounted in the windows. When the computer receives commands from the pilot, the graphics change instantly.

Computers working along with mechanical parts can perform industrial tasks. Robots, used to manufacture cars in an assembly line, consist of a swivel arm fitted with an interchangeable "hand" (spray gun or welder). The arm and hand are controlled by computer. Running different programs can vary the tasks.

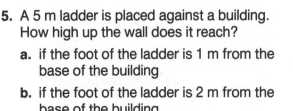

1. What advantages does using a flight simulator have over flying in a real jet?

2. What advantages are there to having these tasks performed by robots?

Solving and Graphing Inequations

Airlines check that each piece of luggage has a mass of 32 kg or less. $m \leq 32$

If the mass of a piece of luggage is more than 32 kg, the passenger is charged for the extra mass. $m > 32$

$m \leq 32$ and $m > 32$ are **inequations.**

An inequation is like unbalanced scales.

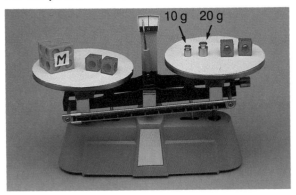

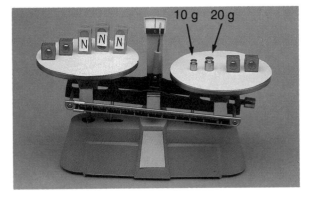

$m + 2 > 32$ represents the above situation.

Solve and graph using whole numbers.

$$m + 2 > 32$$
$$m + 2 - 2 > 32 - 2$$
$$m > 30$$

For $m > 30$, $m = \{31, 32, 33, 34, \ldots\}$

$$\begin{array}{ccccc} \bullet & \bullet & \bullet & \bullet & \bullet \\ 30 & 31 & 32 & 33 & 34 \end{array} \longrightarrow$$

$3n + 2 \leq 32$ represents the above situation.

$$3n + 2 \leq 32$$
$$3n + 2 - 2 \leq 32 - 2$$
$$\frac{3n}{3} \leq \frac{30}{3}$$
$$n \leq 10$$

For $n \leq 10$, $n = \{0, 1, 2, 3, 4, 5, 6, 7, 8, 9, 10\}$

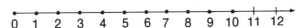

0 1 2 3 4 5 6 7 8 9 10 11 12

WORKING TOGETHER

1. Match the inequation with its graph.

a. $m > 3$

b. $m < 3$

c. $m \leq 3$

d. $m \geq 3$

i. 0 1 2 3 4 5 6 7

ii. 0 1 2 3 4 5 6 7

iii. 0 1 2 3 4 5 6 7

iv. 0 1 2 3 4 5 6 7

2. a. Choose the correct inequation for the sentence "An integer increased by 7 is greater than 4."

   i. $n + 7 \geq 4$ **ii.** $n + 7 < 4$ **iii.** $n + 7 > 4$

   b. Solve the inequation chosen in part **a**.

   c. List four integers that satisfy the inequation in part **b**.

   d. Graph the solution of part **b** using integers.

1. Solve and graph using whole numbers.

   a. $2 + s < 7$ **b.** $m - 4 < 5$

   c. $2d \geq 8$ **d.** $\frac{t}{2} \leq 6$ **e.** $2b + 1 > 7$

   f. $\frac{w}{3} + 2 < 5$ **g.** $3n + 2n > 5$

2. Give two inequations that are true for the graph.

   a. 0 1 2 3 4 5 6 7 8 9 10 11 12

   b. 10 11 12 13 14 15 16

3. Express as an inequation.

   a. A number plus 3 is less than 11.

   b. The product of a number and 4 is less than or equal to 18.

   c. The quotient of a number divided by 2, increased by 1, is greater than 2.

4. Solve and graph the inequations in exercise 3 using whole numbers.

5. **a.** Write an expression for the perimeter of the triangle.

   b. The perimeter is less than 24 cm. Express this as an inequation.

   c. Solve and graph the inequation.

   d. List three possible lengths for the sides.

6. **a.** Write an expression for the width of the entire glued board.

   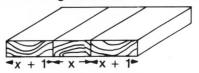

   $x + 1$ x $x + 1$

   b. The width must be 29 cm or less. Express this as an inequation.

   c. Solve and graph the inequation.

   d. List three possible widths for the smaller board.

7. A tour bus can carry a maximum of 52 people, including 3 staff members.

   a. Give an inequation for the number of tourists that can ride in the bus.

   b. Solve and graph the inequation.

8. Solve and graph using integers.

   a. $r - 2 < 6$ **b.** $t + 5 > 1$

   c. $2m \leq 4$ **d.** $\frac{k}{3} \leq 2$

   e. $8 + b \leq 12$ **f.** $3x + 4 < -16$

   g. $2z - 6 > -6$ **h.** $3c - c < 6$

9. Express as an inequation.

   a. A number increased by 6 is less than 1.

   b. A number doubled and then decreased by 2 is less than or equal to 0.

10. Solve and graph the inequations in exercise 9 using integers.

Try This

1. x, y, and a represent positive integers. Is the statement true?

   a. $x^2 > y^2$, if $x > y$ **b.** $\frac{1}{x} > \frac{1}{y}$, if $x > y$ **c.** $ax > ay$, if $x > y$ **d.** $\frac{x}{a} > \frac{y}{a}$, if $x > y$

2. Repeat exercise 1 where x, y, and a represent negative integers.

1. Solve. Check by substitution.

a. $x + 29 = 36$ **b.** $t - 30 = 48$

c. $26 + a = 53$ **d.** $m - 12 = 41$

e. $75 = b - 11$ **f.** $38 = c + 12$

g. $49 = m - 11$ **h.** $57 = n + 6$

2. Solve.

a. $z + 0.6 = 9.7$ **b.** $m + 1.8 = 0.7$

c. $x - 3.8 = 4.4$ **d.** $c - 9.6 = 17.08$

e. $c + \frac{1}{2} = \frac{1}{8}$ **f.** $m - \frac{1}{3} = \frac{3}{8}$

g. $\frac{3}{7} + x = \frac{4}{5}$ **h.** $\frac{5}{8} + n = \frac{11}{12}$

i. $\frac{2}{5} = c - \frac{1}{2}$ **j.** $\frac{4}{9} = m + \frac{1}{4}$

3. Solve.

a. $7d = 140$ **b.** $9a = 108$

c. $\frac{c}{5} = 9$ **d.** $\frac{x}{12} = 8$

e. $\frac{m}{5} = \frac{3}{7}$ **f.** $\frac{t}{2} = \frac{5}{11}$

g. $123 = 3z$ **h.** $\frac{2}{5} = \frac{r}{8}$

4. Simplify, then solve. Check by substitution.

a. $3x - 2x = 4$ **b.** $7a - 6a - 4 = 8$

c. $9x + 2x = 33$ **d.** $8b + b = 45$

e. $7a - a = 42$ **f.** $5c - 2c = -21$

5. List in order the operations you would perform to solve the equation.

a. $3y - 3 = 24$ **b.** $2r + 4 = 20$

c. $\frac{p}{21} + 9 = 11$ **d.** $\frac{n}{2} - 9 = 6$

e. $1.6 + \frac{u}{12} = 1.7$ **f.** $25 = 15g - 20$

6. Solve the equations in exercise 5.

7. The cost of a phone call can be determined by the formula $c = 54 + 40\,m$, where c is the cost of the call in cents and m is the length of the call in minutes. Find the length of the call for the given cost.

a. 254¢   **b.** 174¢   **c.** 334¢   **d.** 454¢

8. Find the value of the unknown to one decimal place.

a. $c^2 = 5^2 + 12^2$ **b.** $c^2 = 6^2 + 8^2$

c. $4^2 = a^2 + 1^2$ **d.** $9^2 = 5^2 + b^2$

9. Calculate the length of the unknown side to the nearest tenth of a millimetre.

a. 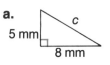   **b.**

c.   **d.**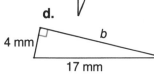

10. A ladder 6 m long is placed against a building so that the foot of the ladder is 3 m from the wall. Draw a diagram. Then calculate, to the nearest tenth of a metre, how high up the wall the ladder reaches.

11. Solve and graph using whole numbers.

a. $4m < 19$ **b.** $6p + 2 > 38$

c. $2h + 1 \le 15$ **d.** $3k + 4 \ge 13$

12. Solve and graph using integers.

a. $q + 7 \le 13$ **b.** $e + 4 > 2$

c. $4 + r > 3$ **d.** $8 + 2f < 16$

Wind Chill Factor

The temperature outside is not the only factor used to determine how "cold" it is. The main concern is the speed at which our bodies lose heat. Other factors, especially the wind speed, also affect how cold it is.

To determine the wind chill factor on a cold day, follow the temperature across the graph and the wind speed up the graph until the two lines intersect. The approximate wind chill factor can be found using the labelled curves. At –10°C and a wind speed of 32 km/h, the point of intersection lies between 1500 W/m² (watts per square metre) and 1625 W/m², or approximately 1570 W/m². Since exposed flesh freezes at 1625 W/m², this reading indicates that extreme caution should be used when travelling or working outdoors.

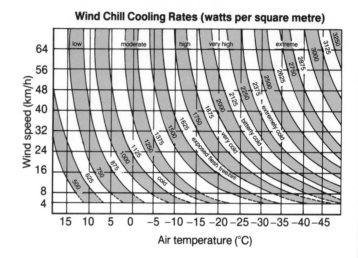

Wind Chill Cooling Rates (watts per square metre)

1. Find the approximate wind chill factor for the temperature.

   a. –20°C and a wind speed of 24 km/h

   b. –5°C and a wind speed of 48 km/h

2. Name at least two possible combinations of temperature and wind speed that would produce a wind chill factor of approximately 2000 W/m².

3. The morning weather report says it is –15°C and the wind is from the northwest at 40 km/h. Do you think it is wise to go out to play in the snow?

4. Would the weather be suitable for an afternoon of cross-country skiing in Churchill, Manitoba, during January?

Examples of Wind Chill Factors

Wind chill factor (W/m²)	Comments
600	Conditions considered comfortable when dressed in wool underwear, socks, mitts, ski boots, ski headband, and thin cotton windbreaker suit, and while skiing over level snow at 5 km/h.
1000	Pleasant conditions for outdoor travel cease on overcast days.
1200	Pleasant conditions for outdoor travel cease on clear, sunlit days.
1400	Freezing of human flesh begins, depending on degree of activity, amount of solar radiation, character of skin, and circulation. Travel and life in temporary shelters becomes disagreeable.
2000	Conditions for outdoor travel become dangerous. Exposed areas of the face will freeze in less than 1 min for the average individual.
2300	Exposed areas of the face will freeze within $\frac{1}{2}$ min for the average individual.

	Average Monthly Wind Chill Factor		
Location	December	January	February
Regina, Sask.	1320	1450	1390
Winnipeg, Man.	1370	1490	1400
Churchill, Man.	1680	1740	1720
Toronto, Ont.	1030	1110	1110

Inside a Computer

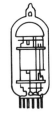

A computer is an **electronic** machine that handles information and helps people solve problems. There have been several major changes in electronic computers during the past 40 years. Each change has ushered in a new **generation** of computers.

1ST GENERATION 1946
The first electronic computer was the ENIAC. It worked using over 18 000 **vacuum tubes**, and weighed over 30 t! First-generation computers could perform about 1000 calculations per second.

Vacuum Tube

2ND GENERATION 1958
Transistors were invented and replaced vacuum tubes in computers. As a result, computers became smaller, more reliable, and more efficient. Second-generation computers could perform about 10 000 calculations per second.

Transistor

3RD GENERATION 1964
The **integrated circuit** was developed on the surface of a **tiny silicon chip**. Each chip could replace circuits with 70 transistors. Computers became much smaller and faster. Third-generation computers could perform about 10^6 calculations per second.

Actual-Size Chip

4TH GENERATION 1976
The first **microcomputer** was produced. Scientists developed a method of putting thousands of integrated circuits on one tiny chip. These chips are smaller and less expensive to make than the third-generation chips. Fourth-generation computers became even smaller and faster, and could perform about 10^8 calculations per second.

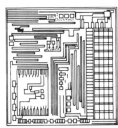

Enlarged Chip

1. About how many times faster was each generation of computers than the previous generation?

2. Some computers today can add 1 million pairs of 8-digit numbers in 1 s. About how long would it take you to do this manually?

3. As computers developed during the past, they became smaller, faster, more reliable, and less expensive. What do you think computers will be like in the future?

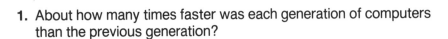

Many chips in their protective plastic casings are visible inside a microcomputer. The most important chip is the **microprocessor**. It controls how information moves in the system, and also performs the calculations.

The other chips constitute the memory.
RAM stands for Random Access Memory. This is the area where information that you input is stored.
ROM stands for Read Only Memory. This is the area where the manufacturer stores all the operating information. It can never be changed.

input/output ports

microprocessor

ROM

RAM

power supply

4. What happens to RAM and ROM?

   a. when you change a program

   b. when you switch off the computer

5. Why do you think most software runs only on the model of microcomputer it was designed for?

A computer system has 5 main parts that work together.

for input   input unit

for processing   memory unit ←→ control unit ←→ arithmetic unit

for output   output unit

6. a. Explain how the components in the photograph above fit in with the diagram at left.

   b. What part is the CPU?

Today many appliances and electronic games contain microprocessors. They are each programmed to perform a specific task: some microwaves can start, cook, and stop at scheduled times, new cameras can automatically adjust the focus for a shot, modern sewing machines can follow pre-programmed stitching patterns. →

7. a. What other everyday devices contain microprocessors?

   b. Are these devices real computers? Explain.

Using Algebra

An ant walks completely around the edge of a picnic table and travels 4.5 m. If the table is twice as long as it is wide, how long is each side?

Think. The problem could be solved by guessing and testing. Is there a faster way?

Plan and do. Choose a variable to represent the length of one side. Let *w* represent the width of the table in centimetres. The length is twice the width, or $2w$. Draw a diagram to organize the information.
Then write an equation and solve it.

$$2w + w + 2w + w = 450$$
$$6w = 450$$
$$w = 75$$

The width of the picnic table is 75 cm.

Look back. Does the above statement answer the question? Give a concluding statement. Check if the answer works in the original problem.

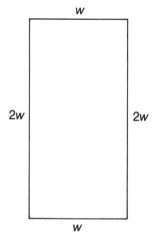

WORKING TOGETHER

1. Zelda said to a friend, "I have two brothers, Zeke and Zachary. I am three years younger than Zeke. Zachary is two years older than I am."

   a. Copy and complete the chart of their ages.

Zeke	Zelda	Zachary
z		

   b. Who is the youngest? Who is the oldest?

   c. If the sum of all their ages is 23, how old are they?

2. The sum of two consecutive whole numbers is 67.

   a. Write and solve the equation.

   b. What are the two numbers?

3. A number gives the same result when it is multiplied by 3 as when 3 is added to it.

   a. Write an equation.

   b. What is the number?

   c. Is the answer the same if 5 is the factor and the addend? Explain.

PROBLEMS

Write an equation to solve the problem.

1. The sum of three consecutive whole numbers is 36. What are the numbers?

2. The sum of two consecutive integers is −5. What are the integers?

3. On a test Daniel answered four times as many questions correctly as he did incorrectly. If he answered 40 questions, how many did he answer incorrectly?

4. Henri is two years older than Stu. Marta is five years older than Henri. The sum of their ages is 36. How old is Stu?

5. The small squares in figure A and figure B are congruent. If the perimeter of figure A is 96 cm, what is the perimeter of figure B?

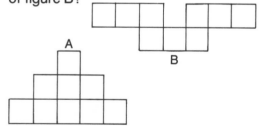

6. The perimeter of an isosceles triangle is 21.0 cm. One side is 4.5 cm longer than either of the other sides. What are the lengths of the two other sides?

7. The perimeter of a rectangle is 50 cm. The length is 3 cm greater than the width. What is the area of the rectangle?

8. Darlene earned $16 more than Sue. Sue earned $10 more than Roger. Together they earned $66. How much money did each person earn?

9. At the end of a school day a Grade 1 teacher had 19 crayons left. In the morning, 15 crayons had been given out, and at recess 13 crayons had been returned. After lunch, 12 crayons had been given out. How many crayons did the teacher have at the start of the day?

10. Phil's age is 5 more than the sum of the ages of the twins Barb and Bonnie. Phil is 27. How old are Barb and Bonnie?

11. A bag of dimes and quarters contains 356 coins. There are 3 times as many dimes as quarters. How many of each type of coin are in the bag?

12. A certain number of pennies and twice as many nickels are worth 77¢. How many pennies and nickels are there?

13. The sum of the ages of two children is 11. In five years one child will be twice as old as the other. What are their ages now?

14. The average mark on a test for a class of 35 students was 61. The average mark obtained by the 15 girls in the class was 65. What was the average mark obtained by the boys?

369

Problem Solving Review

Solve.

1. A rope 30 m in length is cut into 4 pieces so that each piece is twice the length of the previous piece. How long is each piece?

2. How many rectangles can be drawn by joining the dots in this 2 × 10 array?

   • • • • • • • • • •

   • • • • • • • • • •

3. Jean-Paul ate $\frac{1}{3}$ of a pizza, Maureen ate $\frac{1}{4}$, and Claus ate the remaining amount, which was worth $3. How much was the pizza worth?

4. A tractor is pulling two floats in a parade. The tractor is half as long as the first float. The second float is as long as the tractor and first float combined. The total length of the tractor and the two floats is 24 m. What is the length of the tractor and each float?

5. The area of a right-angled isosceles triangle is 8 cm². What is the perimeter of the triangle?

6. The sum of two consecutive whole numbers is equal to the next prime number greater than 89. What are the numbers?

7. One angle of a triangle is twice as large as the smallest angle, and the third angle is three times as large as the smallest angle. What is the measure of the smallest angle?

8. What is the area of the shaded region in square units?

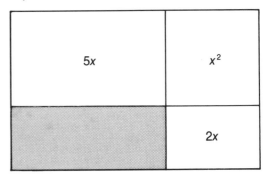

9. Five people can make 5 sandwiches in 5 min. How many people are needed to make 30 sandwiches in 30 min?

10. Sofia can rake the yard in $\frac{1}{2}$ h. Juan can do the same job in 20 min. How long would it take both of them, working together, to rake the yard? What assumptions are you making?

11. If there are fourteen different flavors of ice cream, how many different double-scoop ice cream cones are possible?

Chapter Checkup

1. Write an expression for the phrase.

   a. 25 decreased by a number

   b. 8.7 plus the product of a number and 4

   c. 19 minus the product of a number and 3

2. Evaluate the expression if $r = 9$.

   a. $6r$ b. $\frac{r}{2} + 1$ c. $r + r^2$

   d. $12r - 5$ e. $\frac{10r}{3} + r$ f. $r(3r - 1)$

3. a. Write an expression that can be used to find the area of a triangle.

   b. Find the area of a triangle when the base is 17.5 cm and the height is 15.2 cm.

4. Simplify.

   a. $20n + 13n$ b. $16a - 7a$

   c. $d + 8d + d$ d. $9s - s - s$

   e. $2b + 4 + 3b + 6$ f. $3r - r + 7 + 2r$

   g. $v + w - v + w$

   h. $10z + t + 2z - 3t$

5. Collect the like terms, then evaluate.

   a. $12e - 7e$, if $e = 2$

   b. $8w + 2 + w$, if $w = 1.1$

   c. $12r - 6r + r$, if $r = 10$

6. Solve.

   a. $4m = 32$ b. $\frac{n}{5} = 1$

   c. $19 = x + 9$ d. $2a + 3 = 17$

   e. $\frac{m}{7} = \frac{8}{5}$ f. $\frac{d}{5} - 4 = 8$

   g. $3x + 5x = 72$ h. $9c - 5c = 48$

7. Express as an equation, then solve.

   a. Eight more than a number is divided by 3 to give a result of 6.

   b. A number doubled is reduced by 5 to give a result of 15.

   c. Five less than a number, divided by 2 is 6.

8. It costs $1.50 for the first hour and $0.50 for each additional half hour to park in a parking lot. Mr. Fell paid $4.50.

   a. Write an equation to represent the situation.

   b. Solve the equation to determine how long Mr. Fell was parked.

9. Find the length of the unknown side to one decimal place.

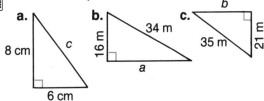

10. Solve and graph the inequations using whole numbers.

   a. $n + 1 > 10$ b. $8 + n \le 12$

   c. $3n \ge 12$ d. $2n - 1 > 9$ e. $\frac{n}{3} \le 1$

11. An elevator can safely transport a maximum of 920 kg at one time. The elevator operator has a mass of 65 kg, and the average mass of a Grade 8 student is 45 kg.

   a. Give an inequation that can be used to show how many Grade 8 students can ride the elevator.

   b. Solve and graph the inequation.

371

Cumulative Checkup

1. Express as a single power, then evaluate.

   a. $7^5 \div 7^3$ **b.** $2^{10} \div 2^3$

   c. $29^{14} \div 29^{13}$ **d.** $10^8 \div 10^2$

2. Multiply only if the product is greater than 1500.

   a. $\begin{array}{r} 79 \\ \times\,19 \\ \hline \end{array}$ **b.** $\begin{array}{r} 45.2 \\ \times\,38 \\ \hline \end{array}$ **c.** $\begin{array}{r} 28.4 \\ \times\,41.6 \\ \hline \end{array}$

   d. $\begin{array}{r} 3.74 \\ \times\,450 \\ \hline \end{array}$ **e.** $\begin{array}{r} 39.6 \\ \times\,42.3 \\ \hline \end{array}$ **f.** $\begin{array}{r} 149.9 \\ \times\,13.7 \\ \hline \end{array}$

3. Find the area to the nearest tenth.

   a. rectangle, base 7.6 m, height 8.4 m

   b. triangle, base 12.4 cm, height 6.8 cm

   c. parallelogram, base 40 cm, height 32 cm

   d. square, side 7.5 m

   e. circle, diameter 17 cm

4. Copy and complete for water.

	Volume	Capacity	Mass
a.	7 cm³		
b.	8000 cm³		
c.	80 cm³		
d.	8 m³		
e.		4 mL	
f.		400 mL	
g.		4 L	
h.		4 kL	
i.			3 t
j.			30 kg

5. Copy and use > or < to make a true statement.

   a. $2\frac{1}{4} \bigcirc \frac{11}{4}$ **b.** $2\frac{1}{2} \bigcirc \frac{7}{3}$ **c.** $4\frac{1}{4} \bigcirc \frac{14}{3}$

6. List two equivalent fractions.

   a. $\frac{3}{5}$ **b.** $\frac{8}{10}$ **c.** $\frac{8}{7}$ **d.** $\frac{18}{12}$

7. Find the result.

   a. $\frac{4}{5} + \frac{7}{10}$ **b.** $\frac{2}{3} \div \frac{3}{4}$ **c.** $4\frac{7}{8} - 1\frac{1}{4}$

8. Jean read $7\frac{1}{2}$ pages of a novel in 15 min. How many pages did she read per minute?

9. Express as a ratio in simplest form.

   a. 18 min to 1 h   **b.** 1 mm to 1 m

   c. 4 kg to 24 g   **d.** 4 cm to 1.2 mm

10. In the election for grade representative, Shirma received 6 votes for every 8 votes that Erica received. Shirma received 39 votes.

    a. How many votes did Erica receive?

    b. How many students voted if Shirma and Erica were the only candidates?

11. Which can of soup is more economical?

    a. 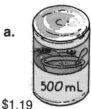   **b.**

    500 mL   300 mL

    $1.19   59¢

12. The scale on a map is 5 cm to 1 km.

    a. Find the distance on the map for the actual distance on the ground.

       i. 6 km   **ii.** 2.5 km   **iii.** 3.2 km

    b. Find the actual distance on the ground for the distance on the map.

       i. 10 cm   **ii.** 7.5 cm   **iii.** 22 cm

13. About 18% of the graduates enter college. There are 450 graduates. How many enter college?

14. Mark received 24 out of 32 on his mathematics test. What percent did he get on the test?

15. Last year, a pair of jeans cost $24. This year the same pair of jeans costs $27. What is the percent increase in cost?

16. Find the discount and the sale price.

a.    **b.**

Regular price $50   Regular price $27
Discount 20%   Discount 5%

17. Calculate the total cost of each article in exercise 16 if the sales tax is 8%.

18. Use compasses and a straightedge to copy △MOP.

  a. by SSS   **b.** by SAS   **c.** by ASA

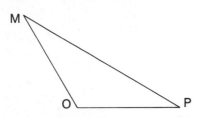

19. a. Use a protractor to draw the angle.

   i. 36°   **ii.** 116°   **iii.** 154°

  b. Bisect each angle.

  c. Write the measure of one of the smaller angles in each bisected angle.

20. Solve for x.

a. 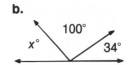   **b.**

21. In golf, a score of +3 means 3 strokes above par. What does the following score represent?

  a. +7   **b.** 0   **c.** −2   **d.** −8

22. Mark coordinate axes on grid paper.

  a. Graph the points with coordinates (2, 0), (1, 1), (0, 2), (−1, 1), (−2, 0), (−1, −1), (0, −2), (1, −1), (2, 0).

  b. Connect the points in order. What have you drawn?

23. Evaluate.

  a. $16 + (−2) + (−5) − (−11)$

  b. $15 ÷ (−3) + (3) × (−6)$

  c. $(−3)^3 + [16 ÷ (−4)]^2$

24. Express as a decimal.

  a. 10^{-1} **b.** 10^{-3} **c.** 10^{-5} **d.** 10^{-7}

25. Express in standard form.

  a. $1.6 × 10^{-2}$ **b.** $2.7 × 10^{-4}$

  c. $5.4 × 10^{-6}$ **d.** $8.15 × 10^{-8}$

26.

Earth's Surface	
water	72%
land with vegetation	16%
other land	12%

  a. Display this data in a circle graph.

  b. What is covering the land that is not covered with vegetation?

12/Transformations

Professional movers use many properties of transformations. Moving awkward shapes often involves combinations of translations, reflections, and rotations.

Get Set

1. How many different shapes are used to make this tiling pattern?

   a. 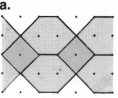   b.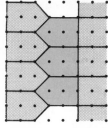

2. Use the pair of shapes to sketch a tiling pattern. Trace the shapes or cut copies from colored paper.

3. Can the shape be used to make a tiling pattern? If so, use cutouts to sketch the pattern.

   a.   b. 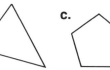   c.

4. Is the red figure a slide, flip, or turn image of the black figure?

   a.    b.

   c.   d.

5. Is the red line a line of symmetry?

   a. 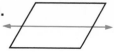   b.

   c.   d.

6. Wriite the ratio of the lengths.

   a. ——————   ————————————

   b. ——————————   ——————

7. Copy and complete.

   a. $\frac{5}{8} = \frac{\square}{32}$ b. $\frac{9}{21} = \frac{3}{\square}$

   c. $\frac{2.2}{6} = \frac{15.4}{\square}$ d. $\frac{1.6}{7.2} = \frac{0.4}{\square}$

   e. $\frac{2.1}{2.7} = \frac{7}{\square}$ f. $\frac{3.5}{4} = \frac{\square}{8}$

8. Express in lowest terms.

   a. $\frac{30}{40}$ b. $\frac{15}{60}$ c. $\frac{21}{30}$

   d. $\frac{24}{28}$ e. $\frac{32}{40}$ f. $\frac{72}{90}$

9. Copy the figure onto grid paper. Is your picture an enlargement or a reduction?

   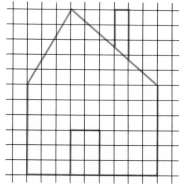

375

Congruent Figures

Riita made a design for a dance poster by cutting out a cardboard pattern, placing it in different positions, and tracing around it.

The figures are **congruent** because they have the same size and shape.

Finding the Matching Vertices and Sides

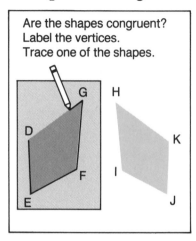

Are the shapes congruent?
Label the vertices.
Trace one of the shapes.

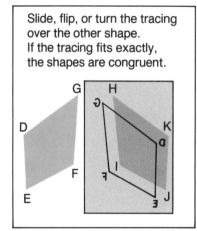

Slide, flip, or turn the tracing over the other shape.
If the tracing fits exactly, the shapes are congruent.

Matching Vertices

D	K
E	J
F	I
G	H

Matching sides

DE	KJ
EF	JI
FG	IH
GD	HK

Quadrilateral DEFG is congruent to quadrilateral KJIH.

WORKING TOGETHER

1. Does the colored shape slide, flip, or turn to match the other?

   a.

   b.

   c.

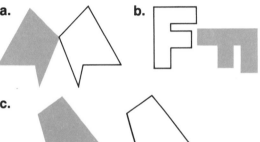

2. Use tracing paper to find which red shape is congruent to the green shape. List the matching vertices and sides.

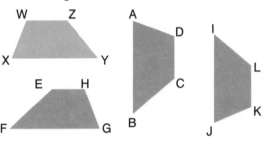

376

1. Use tracing paper to decide if figure A is congruent to figure B.

a.
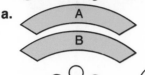

b.

2. Use tracing paper to find congruent figures.

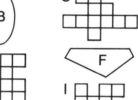

3. Find congruent shapes. List the matching vertices and sides.

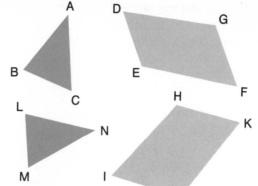

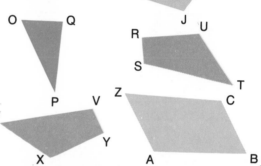

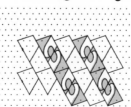

When congruent copies of one figure are placed side by side to cover a flat surface completely, the pattern is a **tessellation**.

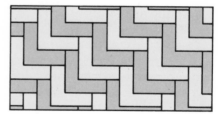

Try This

1. Any triangle or quadrilateral can be used to make a tessellation. Create a tessellation on dot paper. Draw a design in the congruent figures.

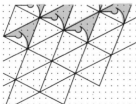

Translations

To centre the picture on the screen, the operator must move it to the left and up. An arrow shows the distance and direction of the motion. The motion is called a **translation**.

Identifying a Translation Image

Trace △ABC.	Slide the tracing left 4 units.	Then slide the tracing up 2 units.
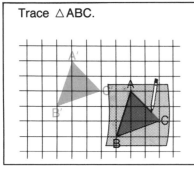	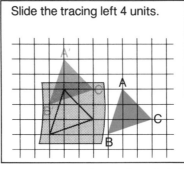	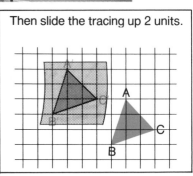

Each point of △ABC **maps onto** a corresponding point of △A'B'C'.

A → A'   B → B'   C → C'

(triangle A prime, B prime, C prime)

△A'B'C' is a **translation image** of △ABC.
△A'B'C' is **congruent** to △ABC.

The translation can be described by a **translation arrow**.
The vector is written as $(\overrightarrow{-4, 2})$.

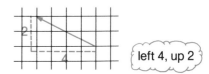

(left 4, up 2)

WORKING TOGETHER

1. Compare the lengths of corresponding sides and the sizes of corresponding angles of △ABC and △A'B'C'.

2. Does this show $(\overrightarrow{2, -3})$?

   a.   b.   c.

3. a. Copy the figures onto grid paper. Then draw a translation arrow for the translation.

   b. Write the vector that describes the translation.

1. Does the picture suggest a translation?

a.

b.

c.

2. Copy the figures onto grid paper. Use tracing paper to determine whether the blue figure is a translation image of the black figure.

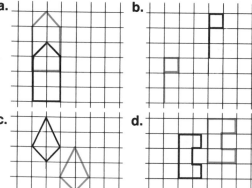

3. a. Draw a translation arrow for each translation in exercise 2.

   b. Write the vector that describes each translation.

4. Use grid paper to show.

   a. $(\overrightarrow{2,3})$ **b.** $(\overrightarrow{2,-3})$ **c.** $(\overrightarrow{-2,3})$

   d. $(\overrightarrow{-2,-3})$ **e.** $(\overrightarrow{4,0})$ **f.** $(\overrightarrow{0,-1})$

5.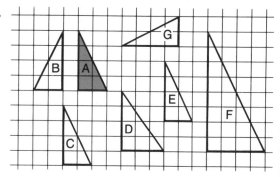

   a. Without tracing paper, decide which figures are translation images of A.

   b. Write the vector for each translation.

   c. Explain why each of the other figures is not a translation image.

Try This

In a word transformation, one letter may be changed at a time, but each new word must be a true word. For example, TWO → TEN.

step 1	TWO
step 2	TOO
step 3	TON
step 4	TEN

1. Perform the word transformation.

   a. BARN → FIRE   **b.** FALL → DOWN   **c.** DEAD → LIVE

   d. COLD → ZERO   **e.** SICK → WELL

Drawing Translation Images

Draw the translation image of a triangle for $(\overrightarrow{-3,2})$.

Tracing Method

Trace △ABC. Slide the tracing left 3 units.	Then slide it up 2 units. Mark the vertices by pressing with a sharp pencil.	Remove the tracing. Join the vertices. Label them A′, B′, and C′.

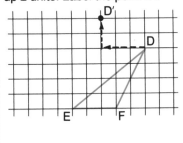

$$△ABC → △A'B'C' \text{ for } (\overrightarrow{-3,2}).$$

Counting Method

From D count left 3 units and up 2 units. Label the point D′.	Follow the count for E and for F. Label the points E′ and F′.	Join D′, E′, and F′.

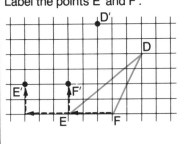 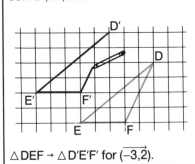

$$△DEF → △D'E'F' \text{ for } (\overrightarrow{-3,2}).$$

How are a figure and its translation image alike?

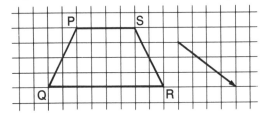

APPLICATIONS AND EXERCISES

1. Copy the diagram onto grid paper. Use tracing paper to draw the image for the translation arrow shown. Label the points.

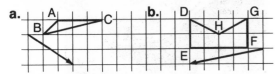

2. Copy the diagram onto grid paper. Write the vector that describes the translation arrow. Draw the translation image by using the counting method. Label the points.

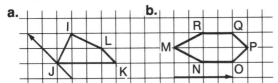

3. Copy the diagram onto grid paper. Draw the translation image.

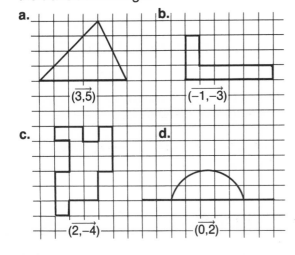

4. a. Mark coordinate axes on grid paper. Draw and label a triangle with coordinates A(2,3), B(1,1), C(4,0).

b. Draw $\triangle$ A'B'C' for $(\overrightarrow{3,4})$.

c. Write the coordinates of A', B', C'.

5. a. Mark coordinate axes on grid paper. Draw and label a parallelogram with coordinates E(9,6), F(7,4), G(11,4), H(13,6).

b. Draw parallelogram E'F'G'H' for $(\overrightarrow{-5,1})$.

c. Write the coordinates of E', F', G', H'.

6. Each piece is shown in its starting position on a chessboard.

♔ King
♕ Queen
♖ Rook
♗ Bishop
♘ Knight
♙ Pawn

Use an 8 by 8 square grid to show the positions of the pieces after each move in this chess game.

a. First move: Player moves the white Pawn in front of the King's Bishop $(\overrightarrow{0,2})$.

b. Second move: Player moves the black Pawn in front of the King $(\overrightarrow{0,-1})$.

c. Third move: Player moves the white Pawn from the first move $(\overrightarrow{0,1})$.

KEEPING SHARP

1. Simplify.

a. $3m + 9 + 2m$

b. $4g + 6h - 3g + 1h$

c. $4a + 2b + 6a - 1b$

d. $3p - 4p + 6q - 2q + 1$

e. $3c - 8d + 9c + 2d$

f. $14 - 3n + 2 - 5n$

Reflections

One French horn is the **reflection image** of the other.

Identifying a Reflection Image

Mark two dots on the **reflection line**.
Trace △ABC and the two dots.

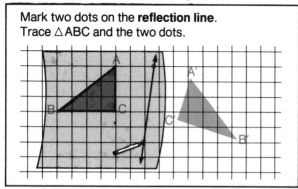

Flip the tracing over.
Match the two pairs of dots.

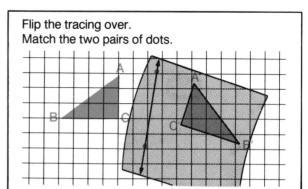

Each point of △ABC maps onto a corresponding point of △A'B'C'.

A → A'   B → B'   C → C'

△A'B'C' is a **reflection image** of △ABC. △A'B'C' is **congruent** to △ABC.

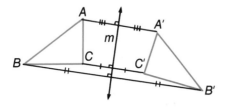

Each point and its image are the same perpendicular distance from the reflection line.

A Mira can be placed on line *m* to check the reflection.

WORKING TOGETHER

1. a. Copy the diagram onto grid paper. Use tracing paper to determine whether the blue figure is a reflection image of △GHI.

b. Label the points.

c. How many units from the reflection line is each point of a pair?

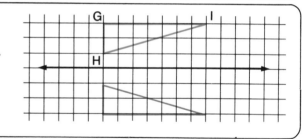

1. Does the picture suggest a reflection?

a.

b.

c.

2. Copy the figures onto grid paper. Use tracing paper to determine whether the blue figure is an image of the black figure for the reflection line shown.

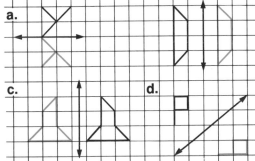

3. Sketch the reflection line for the word AMBULANCE to show the image.

a. ɅWꓭU⅃Ɐreal (AMBULANCE reflected)

b. ƎↃИA⅃UꓭMA (AMBULANCE reflected)

c. How is the word written on the front of an ambulance? Why is it written this way?

4. Copy the figures onto grid paper. Use tracing paper to find the reflection line. Draw the line. Label the points of the reflection image.

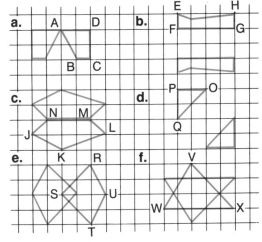

5. Copy the figures from exercise 4 onto grid paper. Use a Mira to find the reflection line. Draw the line.

The widespread use of computers has created a new kind of criminal.

1. Is this a crime? Discuss.

a. A bank employee, with access to the main computer, arranges for the small amounts of money left over after rounding to be transferred to a special account.

b. A person gets a computer video game for her/his birthday, and manages to copy the program. Copies of the disk are given to several friends.

Drawing Reflection Images

Draw the image for the given reflection line.

Tracing Method

Mark two dots on the reflection line. Trace △ ABC and the two dots.	Flip the tracing. Match the two pairs of dots. Mark the vertices by pressing with a sharp pencil	Remove the tracing. Join the vertices. Label them A′, B′, and C′.

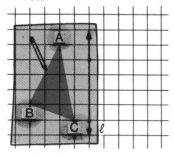
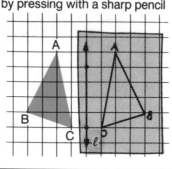
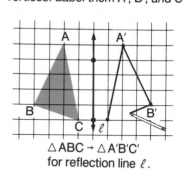

△ ABC → △ A′B′C′
for reflection line ℓ.

Counting Method

From M, count the number of units to the reflection line. Count as many units on the opposite side of line r. Mark the image point M′.	Follow the same steps for N and O.	Join M′, N′, and O′.

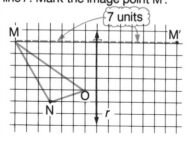

7 units

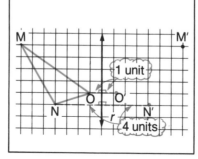

1 unit

4 units

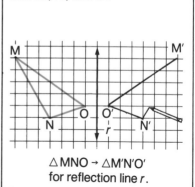

△ MNO → △ M′N′O′
for reflection line r.

How are a figure and its reflection image alike?

WORKING TOGETHER

1. Copy the diagram onto grid paper. Use tracing paper to draw the reflection image. Label the points.

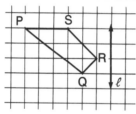

2. Copy the diagram from exercise 1 onto grid paper. Draw the reflection image by counting. Label the points.

3. Copy the diagram from exercise 1 onto grid paper. Use a Mira to draw the reflection image. Label the points.

1. Copy the diagram onto grid paper. Use tracing paper to draw the image for the reflection line shown. Label the points.

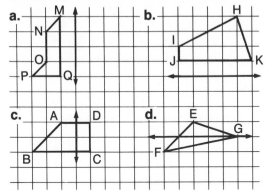

2. Copy the diagram onto grid paper. Draw the reflection image by counting. Label the points.

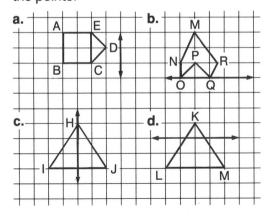

3. Copy the diagram onto grid paper. Use a Mira to draw the image for the reflection line shown.

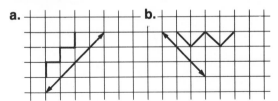

4. Copy and draw the reflection image.

   a. REFLECTION ←→   b. REFLECTION ↕

5. a. Mark coordinate axes on grid paper. Draw and label a rectangle with coordinates A(−3,6), B(−3,4), C(1,4), D(1,6).

   b. Draw rectangle A′B′C′D′ using the X-axis as the reflection line.

   c. Draw rectangle A″B″C″D″ using the Y-axis as the reflection line.

6. a. Mark coordinate axes on grid paper. Draw and label a parallelogram with coordinates M(−2,3), N(−4,−2), O(4,−2), P(5,3).

   b. Draw parallelogram M′N′O′P′ using the X-axis as the reflection line.

   c. Draw parallelogram M″N″O″P″ using the Y-axis as the reflection line.

1. Use a straightedge and a blank piece of paper. Draw a diagonal of the page. Draw a large triangle on one side of the diagonal. Then use compasses and a straightedge to construct the reflection of the triangle using the diagonal as the reflection line.

The perpendicular distance to the line is the same for a point and its image.

Try This

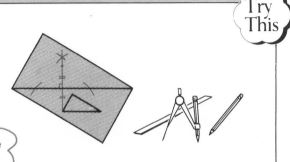

385

PRACTICE

1. Use tracing paper to find congruent figures. List the matching vertices and sides.

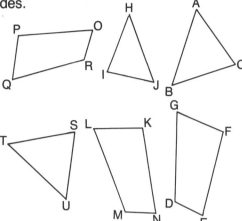

2. Use grid paper to show.

   a. $\overrightarrow{(-5,-1)}$ **b.** $\overrightarrow{(0,4)}$ **c.** $\overrightarrow{(7,2)}$

3. **a.** Copy the figures onto grid paper. Draw the translation arrow or the reflection line that maps the figure onto its image.

   b. Label the points.

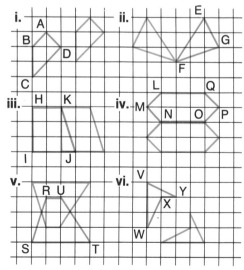

   c. Write the vector that describes each translation.

4. Copy the diagram onto grid paper. Draw the translation image or the reflection image.

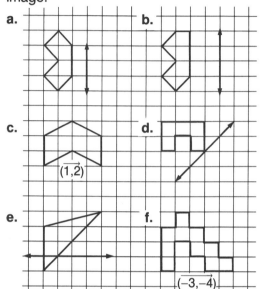

5. **a.** Mark coordinate axes on grid paper. Draw and label a triangle with coordinates A(3,6), B(1,3), C(7,3).

   b. Draw △A′B′C′ for $\overrightarrow{(4,-2)}$.

   c. Write the coordinates of A′, B′, and C′.

6. **a.** Mark coordinate axes on grid paper. Draw and label a parallelogram with coordinates A(−2,4), B(−4,−1), C(3,−1), D(4,3).

   b. Draw parallelogram A′B′C′D′ using the Y-axis as the reflection line.

   c. Draw parallelogram A″B″C″D″ using the X-axis as the reflection line.

7. Which symbol follows in the sequence?

Angles of Incidence and Reflection

Try This

It is a law of science that for a reflection, the **angle of incidence** equals the **angle of reflection**.

A billiard player can predict the path of a ball before hitting it. When a billiard ball strikes the cushion, the angle of incidence equals the angle of reflection.

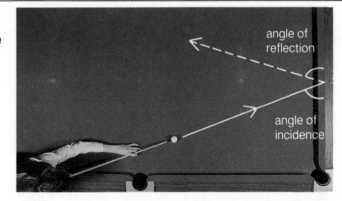

If a ball is hit at a 45° angle on a standard-size billiard table, the ball hits the midpoint of the longer side, then rebounds. The ball goes directly into the corner.

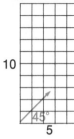 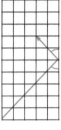 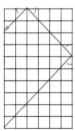 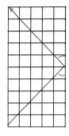

If a ball is hit at a 45° angle on a table with this shape, → the ball rebounds six times before it goes into the corner. At each rebound, the angle of incidence equals the angle of reflection.

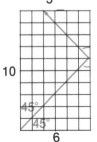 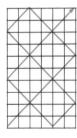

1. On graph paper, make a diagram of the table. Use the same number of units of length and width as shown. Draw the path of the ball as far as it can go. If the ball ends up in a corner, mark the corner with a large dot.

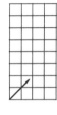 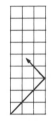 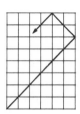 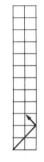

2. On which table does the ball have the simplest path?

Rotations

Each blade of the ceiling fan is like a **rotation image** of the other blades.

Each blade rotates about a **rotation centre**.

Two blades attached at the centre suggest a **rotation angle**.

The rotation centre is the vertex of the rotation angle.

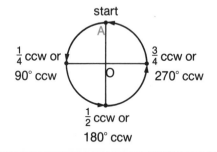

Identifying a Rotation Image

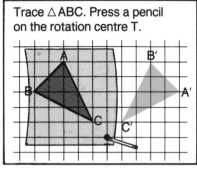

Trace △ABC. Press a pencil on the rotation centre T.

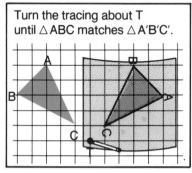

Turn the tracing about T until △ABC matches △A'B'C'.

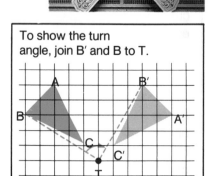

To show the turn angle, join B' and B to T.

△ABC maps onto △A'B'C' through a $\frac{1}{4}$ or 90° turn about T.

△A'B'C' is the **rotation image** of △ABC.

△A'B'C' is **congruent** to △ABC.

Point A can be rotated clockwise.

start

A

$\frac{3}{4}$ cw or 270° cw

$\frac{1}{4}$ cw or 90° cw

$\frac{1}{2}$ cw or 180° cw

Point A can be rotated counterclockwise.

start

A

$\frac{1}{4}$ ccw or 90° ccw

$\frac{3}{4}$ ccw or 270° ccw

$\frac{1}{2}$ ccw or 180° ccw

WORKING TOGETHER

1. **a.** Copy the diagram onto grid paper. Then use tracing paper to rotate △RST about centre T to match the blue triangle.

   b. Label the corresponding vertices.

   c. Draw a rotation angle.

   d. Name the rotation angle.

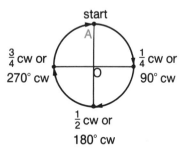

2. Which rotation angle is $\frac{3}{4}$, or 270°, cw?

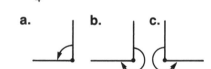

   a.   **b.**   **c.**

APPLICATIONS AND EXERCISES

1. Does the picture suggest a rotation?

a.

b.

c.

2. Match the symbol with its meaning.

a. $\frac{1}{4}$ ccw **b.** 180° cw **c.** $\frac{1}{2}$ ccw

d. $\frac{3}{4}$ cw **e.** $\frac{3}{4}$ ccw **f.** 90° cw

g. 270° cw **h.** 180° ccw **i.** $\frac{1}{2}$ cw

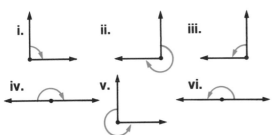

i.   ii.   iii.

iv.   v.   vi.

3. Write the corresponding rotation angle in a counterclockwise direction.

a. 90° cw **b.** $\frac{1}{2}$ cw **c.** 270° cw

4. Name the rotation angle for the turn of the minute hand on a clock.

a. 12:00 to 12:45 **b.** 2:00 to 2:15

c. 7:30 to 8:00 **d.** 11:45 to 12:30

5. Copy the diagram onto grid paper. Use tracing paper to perform the rotation about centre T. Label the vertices.

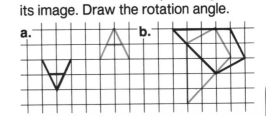

6. a. Draw each rotation angle in exercise 5.

b. Name each rotation angle.

7. Copy the figures onto grid paper. Find the rotation centre that maps the figure onto its image. Draw the rotation angle.

1. To find the answer to the Music Trivia question, calculate the expression following it. Then rotate the display 180°.

a. What is Bruce Springsteen known as? 503 × 11 − 25

b. What is the Electric Light Orchestra often called? (3 − 0.956) ÷ 2.8

2. Work backward to create Music Trivia questions.

Drawing Rotation Images

Tracing Method

<table>
<tr>
<td>

Trace △ABC. Mark a dot E on the beginning arm of the rotation angle. The rotation angle is 270° ccw.

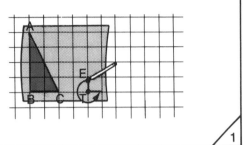

1
</td>
<td>

Press a pencil on the turn centre. Turn the tracing until the dot E is on the other arm of the rotation angle.

2
</td>
</tr>
<tr>
<td>

Mark the vertices by pressing with a sharp pencil.

3
</td>
<td>

Remove the tracing. Join the vertices. Label them A′, B′, and C′.

△ABC → △A′B′C′ for a rotation of 270° ccw about centre T.

4
</td>
</tr>
</table>

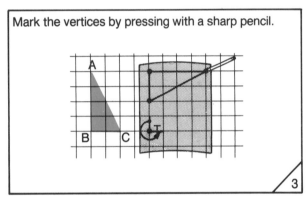

How are a figure and its reflection image alike?

WORKING TOGETHER

1. Copy the diagram onto grid paper. Name the rotation angle, then use tracing paper to draw the rotation image. Label the points.

   a.
   b.

2. Compare the lengths of corresponding sides and the sizes of corresponding angles of LMNO and L′M′N′O′.

3. Copy the diagram onto grid paper. Draw the image for the rotation angle about centre T.

   a. $\frac{1}{2}$ ccw
   b. $\frac{3}{4}$ cw

   c. 90° cw

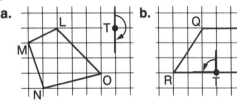

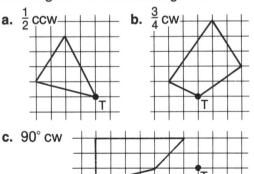

APPLICATIONS AND EXERCISES

1. Copy the diagram onto grid paper. Name the rotation angle. Draw the rotation image.

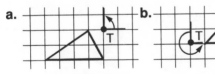

a.   b.

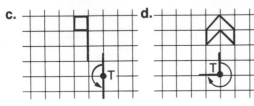

c.   d.

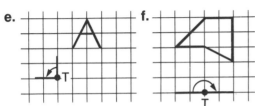

e.   f.

2. Three turns are required to open a combination lock. Give the combination of the lock for these turns. Start at 0.

   a. $2\frac{1}{2}$ cw, $1\frac{1}{4}$ ccw, $\frac{1}{2}$ cw

   b. $2\frac{3}{4}$ cw, 1 ccw, $\frac{3}{4}$ cw

   c. $2\frac{1}{4}$ cw, $1\frac{1}{2}$ ccw, $\frac{1}{2}$ cw

3. Copy the diagram onto grid paper. Draw the image for the rotation angle.

   a. 270° cw   **b.** 90° ccw

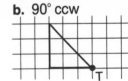

   c. 180° cw   **d.** 90° cw

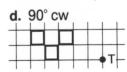

   e. $\frac{1}{2}$ ccw   **f.** $\frac{3}{4}$ ccw

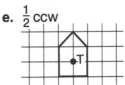

4. **a.** Mark coordinate axes on grid paper. Draw and label a rectangle with coordinates A(–5,3), B(–5,1), C(–2,1), D(–2,3).

   b. Draw the image for a 90° ccw rotation about the origin (0,0).

   c. Label each corresponding point and give its coordinates.

5. **a.** Mark coordinate axes on grid paper. Draw and label a polygon with coordinates A(0,4), B(–2,2), C(–2,0), D(–2,–2), E(0,–4), F(2,–2).

   b. Draw the image for a 180° cw rotation about the origin.

   c. Label each corresponding point and give its coordinates.

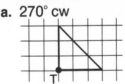

KEEPING SHARP

1. Express the fraction as a decimal.

   a. $\frac{7}{10}$ **b.** $\frac{1}{100}$ **c.** $\frac{11}{20}$ **d.** $\frac{2}{5}$ **e.** $\frac{3}{4}$

   f. $\frac{3}{8}$ **g.** $\frac{3}{16}$ **h.** $\frac{1}{3}$ **i.** $\frac{1}{11}$ **j.** $\frac{1}{9}$

2. Express the decimal as a fraction.

   a. 0.001   **b.** 0.017   **c.** 0.375

   d. 0.125   **e.** $0.\overline{3}$ **f.** $0.\overline{1}$

   g. $1.\overline{6}$ **h.** $0.\overline{45}$ **i.** $0.\overline{027}$

Identifying the Transformations

The Dutch artist M.C. Escher used a variety of transformations to create his famous designs.

The bulldogs are congruent. They are translated in one line. Then a reflection and a rotation begin the next line.

© M. C. Escher Heirs C/O Cordon Art—Baarn—Holland.

A tracing of bulldog A can be reflected, then rotated, to map onto bulldog B.

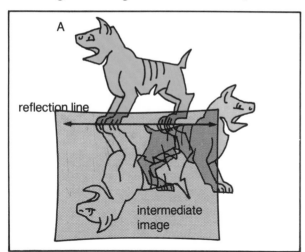

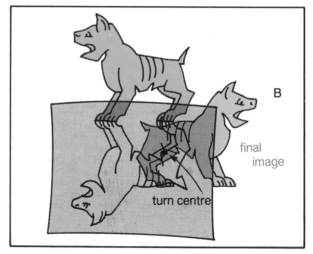

WORKING TOGETHER

1. Copy the diagram onto grid paper. Show the transformations that map the black figure onto its final blue image. Draw the translation arrow, reflection line, or rotation centre. Then label the points.

a.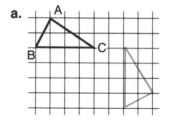

b.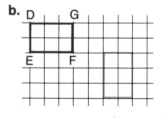

392

1. What transformations are suggested?

   a. moving furniture into a new house

   b. playing both sides of a record

   c. raising a flag up a flagpole

2. Copy the figures onto grid paper. Show the transformations that map the figure onto its final image. Label the points.

   a. 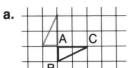   **b.**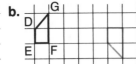

3. Describe the transformations used to create this Escher design.

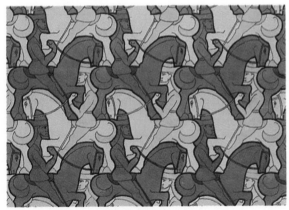

© M. C. Escher Heirs C/O Cordon Art—Baarn—Holland.

4. Copy the diagram onto grid paper. Draw the intermediate image and the final image.

   a. 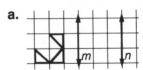   **b.**

   i. reflection about *m*   **i.** reflection about *k*

   ii. reflection about *n*   **ii.** $(\overrightarrow{-1,-4})$

   c. 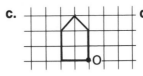   **d.**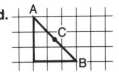

   i. 180° cw about O   **i.** reflection about $\overline{AB}$

   ii. $(\overrightarrow{4,3})$ **ii.** 90° ccw about C

   e. 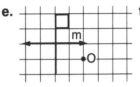   **f.**

   i. reflection about *m*   **i.** $(\overrightarrow{-1,-2})$

   ii. 270° cw about O   **ii.** reflection about ℓ

5. Describe a single translation, reflection, or rotation, if any, that maps each figure from exercise 4 onto its final image.

1. a. Copy the diagram onto square dot paper.

   b. Show the least number of possible motions required to move the boat into the boathouse.

Try This

Symmetry

One half of the butterfly appears identical to the other half. A mirror could be placed so that part of the butterfly and its reflection appear to form the entire butterfly.

The butterfly possesses **reflectional symmetry**. The line on which the mirror is placed is a **line of symmetry**.

Reflectional Symmetry—Tracing Method

Trace the figure. Fold the shape to test if the two halves match.

  line of symmetry

The letter M has reflectional symmetry or line symmetry.

Mira Method

Place a Mira on the figure so that the reflection of one part of the figure matches the other part.

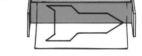

The shape has reflectional symmetry or line symmetry.

The flower below can be rotated about a point to a new position and appear identical.

The flower possesses **rotational symmetry**. The centre of rotation is the **point of symmetry**.

Rotational Symmetry—Tracing Method

Trace the figure. Press a pencil on the centre and rotate the tracing until the tracing and the original coincide again.

point of symmetry

This tracing maps onto the original twice in a 360° turn. The order of rotational symmetry for N is 2.

WORKING TOGETHER

1. Trace the letter.
   a. Turn the tracing about the centre. Then write the order of rotational symmetry.
   b. Fold to find the lines of symmetry. Draw them.

1. Trace the shape. Draw all the lines of symmetry and write the order of rotational symmetry.

   a.  **b.**

   c.  **d.**

2. Does the shape suggest reflectional symmetry, rotational symmetry, both, or neither?

   a. human face **b.** human hand

   c. star **d.** heart shape

   e. ceiling fan **f.** snowflake

3. Write the capital letters of the English alphabet that have this symmetry.

   a. vertical line symmetry

   b. horizontal line symmetry

   c. horizontal and vertical line symmetry

   d. rotational symmetry **e.** no symmetry

4. Use the steps in exercise 3 to investigate the symmetry of the letters or symbols.

   a. capital letters of the Greek alphabet

   b. astronomy symbols

5. Trace the regular polygon. Draw the lines of symmetry. Mark the point at their intersection. Test whether this is a centre of rotational symmetry. Write the order of rotational symmetry.

   a. **b.** **c.**

   d.   **e.** 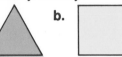 **f.**

6. **a.** How are the number of equal sides, the number of equal angles, the number of lines of symmetry, and the order of rotational symmetry related for each regular polygon in exercise 5?

   b. Write the number of lines of symmetry and the order of rotational symmetry of other regular polygons.

Try This

Many crossword puzzles have rotational symmetry.

1. Copy this puzzle. Shade in the least number of squares in order for the puzzle to have rotational symmetry of order 4.

   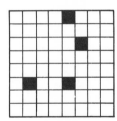

2. Examine crossword puzzles in newspapers and magazines. Try to find three examples with rotational symmetry. Try to find a puzzle that does not have rotational symmetry. Try to find a puzzle that has line symmetry.

Similar Figures

This poster comes in two sizes. The posters are **similar**.

Similar objects have the same shape, but need not be the same size.

Finding Properties of Similar Figures

△ABC and △DEF are similar. Place a tracing of △ABC onto △DEF with ∠A at ∠D. Compare the angles. Measure, then compare, the lengths of the sides.	Repeat with ∠B on ∠E.	Repeat with ∠C on ∠F.
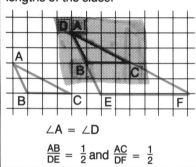	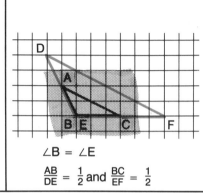	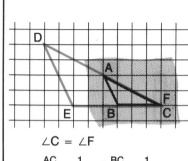
∠A = ∠D	∠B = ∠E	∠C = ∠F
$\frac{AB}{DE} = \frac{1}{2}$ and $\frac{AC}{DF} = \frac{1}{2}$	$\frac{AB}{DE} = \frac{1}{2}$ and $\frac{BC}{EF} = \frac{1}{2}$	$\frac{AC}{DF} = \frac{1}{2}$ and $\frac{BC}{EF} = \frac{1}{2}$

For a pair of similar figures
- corresponding angles are equal.
- ratios of the lengths of corresponding sides are equal. This is a **scale ratio**.

WORKING TOGETHER

1. Place a tracing of △PQR onto △STU.

   a. Move the tracing to find the pairs of corresponding angles.

   b. Name the pairs of corresponding sides.

   c. Measure the lengths of the corresponding sides in millimetres. Then write the ratios.

   d. What is the scale ratio?

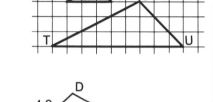

2. △ABC is similar to △DEF.

   a. Find the scale ratio.

   b. Find the length of the unknown sides.

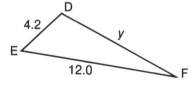

1. Trace figure A. Use the tracing to find which figures are similar to A. Explain why each of the other figures is not.

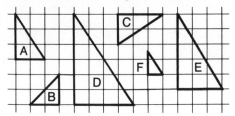

2. △KLM and △PON are similar.

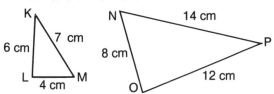

   a. Name the pairs of corresponding angles.

   b. Write the ratios of the lengths of the corresponding sides.

   c. Write the scale ratio.

3. Find the scale ratio. Then calculate the unknown length for the pair of similar triangles.

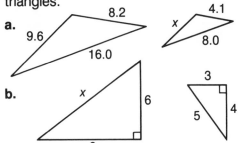

4. The mixing bowls in a set are similar. Their diameters are 15 cm, 20 cm, and 25 cm. The depth of the largest bowl is 15 cm.

   a. Find the scale ratio.

   b. How deep are the other bowls?

5. Lana and Sim measured the length of each other's shadow at the same time of day. Lana, who is 150 cm tall, cast a shadow 100 cm long. Sim cast a shadow 120 cm long. Sim drew this diagram to calculate his height.

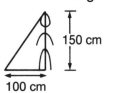

   a. Explain why the triangles are similar.

   b. Find the scale ratio.

   c. Find Sim's height, s.

6. A metre stick casts a shadow 150 cm long. At the same time of day, a flagpole's shadow is 675 cm long.

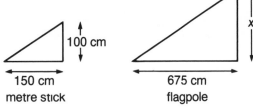

   a. Find the scale ratio.

   b. Find the height, x, of the flagpole.

The height of a tall object can be found by using similar triangles.

Try This

1. Use a metre stick and shadows to calculate the height.

   a. of your school's flagpole

   b. of a tall tree in the schoolyard

Dilatations

A projector transfers the picture from the
slide to the screen. The image has the
same shape but a different size.

A transformation that changes the
size of a figure but not its shape
is a **dilatation**.

A figure can be enlarged using a point outside or inside the figure as a **centre of enlargement**.

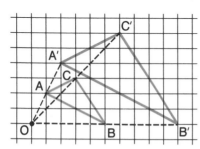

△ A′B′C′ is an enlarged image.

Point O is the
centre of enlargement.

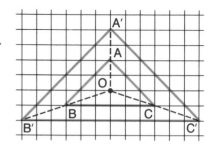

Measure, then compare, the lengths of the corresponding sides of △A′B′C′ and △ABC.

$$\frac{A'C'}{AC} = \frac{2}{1} \qquad \frac{A'B'}{AB} = \frac{4.6}{2.3} \text{ or } \frac{2}{1} \qquad \frac{B'C'}{BC} = \frac{4}{2} \text{ or } \frac{2}{1}$$

Therefore $\dfrac{\text{the length of a side for } \triangle A'B'C'}{\text{the length of a side for } \triangle ABC} = \dfrac{2}{1}$ ⟨image/original⟩

To construct the enlarged image, multiply the length of each side of the original
figure by a **scale factor**. The scale factor of △A′B′C′ is 2.

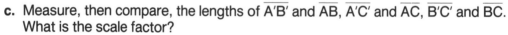

WORKING TOGETHER

1. **a.** Measure, then compare, the lengths of $\overline{OA'}$ and $\overline{OA}$, $\overline{OB'}$ and $\overline{OB}$, $\overline{OC'}$ and $\overline{OC}$.

   b. How does each ratio compare with the scale factor?

2. Copy the diagram onto grid paper.

   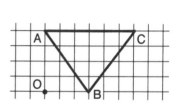

   a. Draw a dotted line between O and each vertex. Then
   extend each dotted line to 3 times its length.

   b. Label the corresponding end points A′, B′, and C′.
   Join A′, B′, and C′.

   c. Measure, then compare, the lengths of $\overline{A'B'}$ and $\overline{AB}$, $\overline{A'C'}$ and $\overline{AC}$, $\overline{B'C'}$ and $\overline{BC}$.
   What is the scale factor?

1. Copy the diagram onto grid paper.

    a. Label the points of the enlarged image.

    b. Name the pairs of corresponding sides.

    c. Measure, then compare, the lengths of the corresponding sides.

    d. Write the scale factor.

    e. Measure, then compare, the lengths of $\overline{OA'}$ and $\overline{OA}$, $\overline{OB'}$ and $\overline{OB}$, $\overline{OC'}$ and $\overline{OC}$. How does each ratio compare with the scale factor?

2. Copy the diagram onto grid paper. Draw the image about the centre for the scale factor shown.

    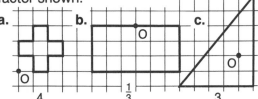

3. Copy and complete the table for each pair of figures from exercise 2.
   What conclusions can you make?

	Perimeter		Area	
	original	image	original	image
a.				
b.				
c.				

4. a. Mark coordinate axes on grid paper. Draw and label a rectangle with coordinates P(1,6), Q(1,1), R(4,1), S(4,6).

   b. Multiply each coordinate value by 2. Write the new coordinates and name them P', Q', R', and S'. Plot these and draw the image, figure P'Q'R'S'.

   c. Measure, then compare, the lengths of the corresponding sides.

   d. Where is the centre of enlargement?

   e. Write the scale factor.

   f. How does the scale factor compare with the number by which each coordinate value was multiplied?

   g. Draw an enlargement of rectangle PQRS about the centre (0,0) with scale factor 3.

5. Mark coordinate axes on grid paper. Draw and label a triangle with coordinates A(6,3), B(12,6), C(6,12). Use the method in exercise 4 to draw the dilatation image about the centre (0,0) with this scale factor.

   a. 2   **b.** $\frac{1}{3}$ **c.** $\frac{1}{2}$

6. A school photograph 4 cm wide by 5.5 cm long is enlarged to be 12 cm wide.

   a. What is the scale factor?

   b. How long is the picture?

Try This

1. Copy and use the figure to make a tessellation on square grid paper.

2. Draw the same tessellations on a distorted grid.

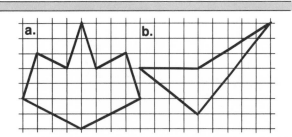

1. Draw the rotation angle.

   a. 90° ccw   **b.** $\frac{1}{2}$ ccw   **c.** 270° ccw

2. Write the corresponding rotation angle in a clockwise direction for each angle in exercise 1.

3. Copy the diagrams onto grid paper. Then use tracing paper to rotate the red figure to match the blue figure. Label the vertices.

  a. 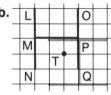   **b.**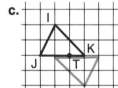

  c. 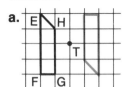   **d.**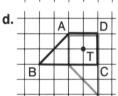

4. a. Draw each rotation angle in exercise 3.

  b. Name each rotation angle.

5. Copy the diagram onto grid paper. Draw the rotation image.

  a. 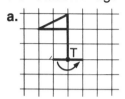   **b.**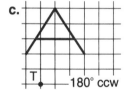
                                     270° cw

  c. 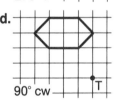   **d.**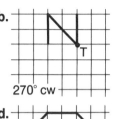
       180° ccw   90° cw

6. a. Mark coordinate axes on grid paper. Draw a trapezoid with coordinates A(−2,2), B(−3,−2), C(3,−2), D(2,2).

  b. Draw the image for a 90° cw rotation about the origin (0,0).

  c. Label each point and give its coordinates.

7. a. Mark coordinate axes on grid paper. Draw and label a square with coordinates A(−2,2), B(−2,−2), C(2,−2), D(2,2). Place a dot at the origin to show the rotation centre.

  b. Describe the images after a rotation of 90° cw, 180° cw, 270° cw, and 360° cw.

  c. What is the order of rotational symmetry of a square?

8. Copy the figures onto grid paper. Draw the intermediate and the final image.

  a. 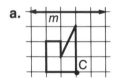   **b.**

  i. 90° ccw about C   **i.** reflection about *n*

  ii. reflection about *m*   **ii.** $\overrightarrow{(-2,3)}$

9. The canisters in the set are similar. Find the unknown measurements.

10. Copy the diagram onto grid paper. Draw the image using the scale factor and the centre.

Sequences and Patterns

The automatic constant can be used to calculate consecutive powers of a number.

$\boxed{2}$ $\boxed{\times}$ $\boxed{=}$ $\boxed{=}$ $\boxed{=}$ $\boxed{=}$ $\boxed{=}$

2, 2, 4, 8, 16, 32, 64,

Memory can be used to add consecutive powers. $2^1 + 2^2 + 2^3 + 2^4 + 2^5 + 2^6$

$\boxed{2}$ $\boxed{M+}$ $\boxed{\times}$ $\boxed{=}$ $\boxed{M+}$ $\boxed{=}$ $\boxed{M+}$ $\boxed{=}$ $\boxed{M+}$ $\boxed{=}$ $\boxed{M+}$ $\boxed{=}$ $\boxed{M+}$ $\boxed{MR}$ ⟨ 126. ⟩

---

1. a. Use the multiplication constant to generate consecutive powers of 3 from 3^1 to 3^8. Record the ones digit of each power.

  b. What sequence is formed by the ones digits of $3^1, 3^2, 3^3, 3^4, 3^5, 3^6, 3^7, 3^8, \ldots$?

  c. What are the ones digits of $3^{24}, 3^{33}$, and 3^{38}?

2. a. Use the multiplication constant to generate consecutive powers of 7 from 7^1 to 7^8. Record the tens and ones digits of each power.

  b. What sequence is formed by the tens and ones digits of $7^1, 7^2, 7^3, 7^4, 7^5, 7^6, 7^7, 7^8, \ldots$?

  c. What are the tens and ones digits of $7^{24}, 7^{33}$, and 7^{38}?

3. a. Check that each equation is true.
$1 \times 2 = \frac{1 \times 2 \times 3}{3}$, $1 \times 2 + 2 \times 3 = \frac{2 \times 3 \times 4}{3}$, $1 \times 2 + 2 \times 3 + 3 \times 4 = \frac{3 \times 4 \times 5}{3}$

  b. Extend the pattern. $1 \times 2 + 2 \times 3 + 3 \times 4 + 4 \times 5 = \boxed{}$
  Check that it is true.

  c. Use the pattern to evaluate $1 \times 2 + 2 \times 3 + 3 \times 4 + \ldots + 10 \times 11$.

  d. Use the pattern to evaluate $1 \times 2 + 2 \times 3 + 3 \times 4 + \ldots + 40 \times 41$.

4. a. Complete, expressing each sum as a square.
$1^3 = 1^2$, $\quad 1^3 + 2^3 = 1 + 8$, $\quad 1^3 + 2^3 + 3^3 = \blacksquare$, $\quad 1^3 + 2^3 + 3^3 + 4^3 = \blacksquare$
$\qquad\qquad\qquad\qquad = 9$
$\qquad\qquad\qquad\qquad = 3^2$

  b. Use the sequence to evaluate $1^3 + 2^3 + 3^3 + \ldots + 9^3 + 10^3$.

5. a. Complete, expressing each result as a square.
$1 \times 2 \times 3 \times 4 + 1 = 24 + 1$, $\quad 2 \times 3 \times 4 \times 5 + 1 = \blacksquare$, $\quad 3 \times 4 \times 5 \times 6 + 1 = \blacksquare$
$\qquad\qquad\qquad\qquad = 25$
$\qquad\qquad\qquad\qquad = 5^2$

  b. Use the sequence to evaluate $10 \times 11 \times 12 \times 13 + 1$.

Computers and Farming

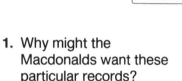

Cows and computers seem to have little in common, but computers are helping people to run their farms more efficiently.

The Macdonalds own and operate a large dairy farm. The software they use with their computer is designed to record the milk yield of each cow, and the quantity and composition of its feed.

1. Why might the Macdonalds want these particular records?

Each cow wears an identification collar—an electronic tag worn around the neck. At the feeding station, a hood over the feeding trough "reads" the tag and sends the information to the computer. The program causes some of the diet for that cow to be released. This happens each time the cow comes to the feeding station, until the entire daily ration has been released.

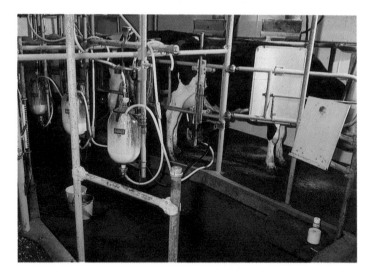

In the automated milking parlor, the milk flow from each cow is monitored. The computer program calculates and records the total volume of milk supplied by each cow at each milking.

After each milking, the computer prints out the record of the milk yield.
The more milk a cow produces, the more highly concentrated grain it requires.
This is the expensive ingredient in the feed. The computer uses the milk-yield figures to adjust the feed allotment for the next day, so that the high milk producers are fed a richer diet.

2. **a.** What do you think is the advantage of using this kind of computer system?

   b. Discuss any disadvantages that might arise in this kind of operation.

   c. How could this type of operation be used in chicken farming?

The MacConneys run a cattle feedlot and use special computer software to manage the operation.

Farmers often send their cattle to the feedlot to be fattened before they are sold. At any one time a feedlot may have up to 9000 head of cattle. Cattle are usually handled in groups of 100, and each group spends 3 to 4 months on the feedlot.

The overall performance of the feedlot is measured by finding, for each group of cattle, the ratio of

$$\frac{\text{cost of feed and medical supplements}}{\text{gain in weight}} .$$

3. What data would you expect to find in the MacConneys' computer?

4. If clients are charged a flat rate plus $1.50/kg of weight gained per month, how could the computer be used to print monthly invoices?

5. How could this type of operation be used on a pig feedlot?

Computers are also changing the way in which livestock are sold.

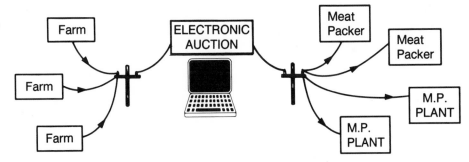

Farmers with livestock to sell send the details to the auctioneer by computer. This information is sent to prospective buyers. At a pre-arranged time the auction begins. The auctioneer sends out a signal and bidders have 15 s to type a bid. Buyers may continue to bid until no one wishes to bid higher. The name of the highest bidder and that bid are recorded by computer.
Later, farmers are told who bought their livestock and at what price.
The livestock are moved from the farm directly to the buyer.

6. a. Discuss how livestock auctions were run in the past.

   b. What are some advantages and disadvantages in running the auctions by the old method and by the electronic method?

Logical Thinking

"Who did it?" snarled Mr. Scrooge, when he found his window was broken. Only one of the children is telling the truth. Who broke the window?

Think. If only one of them is telling the truth, the rest must be lying.

Plan and do. Try each one in turn to see if it is possible for he or she to be telling the truth while the other two are lying.

Trial 1 – If Kim is telling the truth, she did not do it.
Buster is lying, so Kyle did not do it.
Kyle is lying, so Buster must be telling the truth. ⎫ not possible

Trial 2 – If Buster is telling the truth, Kyle did it.
Kim is lying, so she did it. ⎫ not possible
Kyle is lying, so Buster must be telling the truth.

Trial 3 – If Kyle is telling the truth, Buster is lying.
Buster is lying, so Kyle did not do it.
Kim is lying, so she broke the window.

Look back. Review the solution process. Then give a concluding statement.

WORKING TOGETHER

1. Sue Brown, Jim Green, and Sam Black are standing in a line. One is wearing a brown coat, one a green coat, and one a black coat. "Have you noticed," said the person with the green coat, "that none of us is wearing the color of coat that matches our name." "You're right," said Sue.

   a. Copy and complete the table.
   b. What color of coat was each person wearing?

Person	Coat Color		
	Brown	Green	Black
Sue Brown	no		
Jim Green		no	
Sam Black			no

Solve. Drawing diagrams or making a chart may be helpful.

1. Yolanda, Pam, and Arlene ran the 100 m sprint at the school field day. Yolanda did not finish third and Pam did not finish second. However, Pam finished 0.8 s ahead of the girl in the blue shorts. In what order did they finish?

2. The police knew that either a white or a yellow car was used in a robbery. The twins Chet and Christie saw the robbery, and Chet told the police which color the car was. Later Christie told a reporter that Chet said the car was white. If one of the twins always tells the truth and the other always lies, what color was the robbers' car?

3. Wanda, Bob, and Melissa rode through the fairgrounds on a bicycle, a skateboard, and a motorcycle. The bicycle rider was a girl. Wanda ran out of gas. What was each person riding?

4. Bill, Art, and Raymond each have two part-time jobs. These include sales clerk, musician, painter, taxi driver, waiter, and gardener. What two jobs does each have?
   The taxi driver took Bill and the sales clerk to a concert.
   The painter painted the sales clerk's apartment.
   The taxi driver does not know where the gardener works.
   The musician and the gardener go skiing with Bill.
   Raymond lives in the same apartment building as the painter and Art.
   Raymond goes out with the sales clerk's sister.

5. Amy, Mary, and Edna are sisters. Amy is not the oldest. The youngest sister is taller than Amy. The oldest sister uses the telephone more often than Mary. Name the sisters in the order of their ages.

6. How can you use four rods that measure 2 cm, 5 cm, 7 cm, and 9 cm to measure a length of 1 cm?

7. Two tomatoes weigh the same as a cucumber and a carrot. A cucumber weighs the same as 5 carrots. How many carrots weigh the same as one tomato?

8. In a model train layout, the tunnel through the mountain is 1 m long. If the model train is also 1 m in length and travels at the rate of 60 m/min, how long does it take for the train to pass completely through the tunnel?

9. Five adults and two children want to cross a river. The only way across is a raft that carries either 1 adult or 2 children. How many times must the raft cross the river?

10. **a.** Seven objects are identical in appearance, but one is slightly heavier than the rest. How can you use an equal arm balance to determine which object is heavier in just two weighings?

    b. How many weighings are needed for 9 objects? 12 objects?

11. A 16 L container is full of gasoline. How can the gasoline be divided equally using 11 L and 6 L cans?

Problem Solving Review

Solve.

1. Wilbur has 8 identical brown socks and 12 identical black socks in a drawer.

   a. If he reaches inside the drawer without looking, what is the least number of socks he must take out to ensure that he has a pair?

   b. What if there are also 4 identical blue socks in the drawer?

2. If the length of a dinosaur skeleton is 20 m plus half its own length, how long is it?

3. Mr. Cook, Mr. Plumber, and Mr. Carpenter were talking. "It's strange," said Mr. Cook, "that none of us has an occupation corresponding to his name." "That's true," said the man who was a carpenter. "Yet the three of us are a cook, a plumber, and a carpenter." What are the occupations of Mr. Cook, Mr. Plumber, and Mr. Carpenter?

4. What is the least number of marbles that the bag can contain? The number of marbles in the bag can be shared equally among 2, 3, 4, 5, or 6 children.

5. Each girl in a group of 50 girls has blonde or red hair, and blue or green eyes. Fourteen have blue eyes and blonde hair, 31 have red hair, and 18 have green eyes. How many girls have green eyes and red hair?

6. A dollar was changed for 16 coins, which were nickels and dimes. How many nickels and how many dimes were there?

7. Darrell is five years older than Gord. Courtney is two years younger than Darrell. Bob is Courtney's twin brother. If Darrell is 28, how old is each of the others?

8. Each colored region of the target is worth a different number of points. The sum of the points for the red and blue regions is 11, the sum for the blue and yellow regions is 19, and the sum for the red and yellow regions is 16. How many points are assigned to each region?

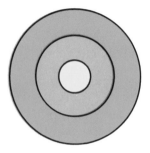

9. Three different views of a cube are shown.

   Which shape is opposite this face?

   a.   **b.**   **c.**

10. What four masses can you use with an equal arm balance to find the mass of any object from 1 kg to 40 kg in whole numbers of kilograms?

Chapter Checkup

1. Which figures are congruent? List the matching vertices and sides.

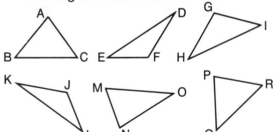

2. Draw the translation arrow on grid paper for the vector.

  a. $(\overrightarrow{-1,8})$ **b.** $(\overrightarrow{0,7})$ **c.** $(\overrightarrow{4,-5})$

3. a. Name the figures that are translation images of A. Write the vector that describes each translation.

  b. Explain why each of the other figures is not a translation image.

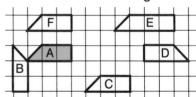

4. Copy the diagram onto grid paper. Draw the translation image.

5. a. Mark coordinate axes on grid paper. Draw a triangle with coordinates A(1,4), B(0,2), C(3,0).

  b. Draw △A′B′C′ for $(\overrightarrow{-2,3})$.

  c. Write the coordinates of A′, B′, and C′.

6. a. Mark coordinate axes on grid paper. Draw a parallelogram with coordinates A(−2,4), B(−4,1), C(−2,1), D(0,4).

  b. Draw parallelogram A′B′C′D′ using the X-axis as the reflection line.

  c. Draw parallelogram A″B″C″D″ using the Y-axis as the reflection line.

7. Name the clockwise and counter-clockwise rotation angles that map the figure onto its image about centre T.

  a.   **b.**

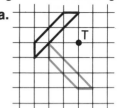 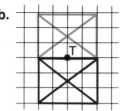

8. Copy the figures onto grid paper. Which transformations map figure ABCD onto its final image? Draw the intermediate image and label the points.

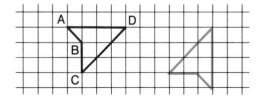

9. Trace the logo. Draw the lines of symmetry and find the order of rotational symmetry.

10. A 1.0 m fence pole casts a shadow 1.4 m long. At the same time of day, a tree casts a shadow 10.0 m long.

  a. Draw a diagram to show the similar triangles.

  b. How tall is the tree?

407

Cumulative Checkup

1. a. Copy and complete the sequence.

$$81 \times 9 = \square$$
$$882 \times 9 = \square$$
$$8883 \times 9 = \square$$

b. Predict the product of 88 884 × 9. Check the result using a calculator.

c. Use the shortcut to find the product of 888 885 × 9.

2. Find the result.

a. 0.86 × 0.001   **b.** 8.86 ÷ 1000

c. 193.4 ÷ 0.01   **d.** 21.7 × 1000

e. 0.0093 ÷ 0.0001 **f.** 4.15 × 0.01

3. Copy and complete.

a. 37 mm = □ cm   **b.** 890 cm = □ m

c. 1200 m = □ km   **d.** 3.1 m = □ cm

e. 14.2 cm = □ mm   **f.** 0.9 km = □ m

4. Find the area of the figure.

a.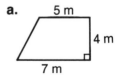

b.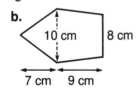

5. Find the volume and the capacity of the aquarium. Then find the approximate mass of the water that fills the aquarium.

a.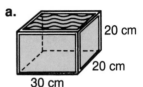

b.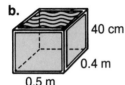

6. Ahmed took $\frac{3}{4}$ h to cut the grass and $\frac{1}{3}$ h to trim the shrubs. How long did it take him to do both jobs?

7. Express as a mixed number in lowest terms.

a. $\frac{17}{5}$ **b.** $\frac{31}{4}$ **c.** $\frac{36}{9}$ **d.** $\frac{28}{8}$

8. A store sells a radio for $1\frac{2}{5}$ times the wholesale price of $25.50.

a. Find the selling price of the radio.

b. Find the profit on each radio sold.

9. Copy and complete.

a. $\frac{1.7}{2.5} = \frac{\square}{10}$ **b.** $\frac{0.36}{\square} = \frac{36}{19}$ **c.** $\frac{\square}{1.4} = \frac{10}{35}$

10. The drive wheel of a gear has 48 teeth and the other wheel has 36 teeth.

a. Write the ratio of the number of teeth on the drive wheel to the number of teeth on the other wheel in simplest form.

b. When the drive wheel is turned 100 times, how many times does the other wheel turn?

11. A 6 mm stack of paper contains 54 sheets. How many sheets would be in a 10 cm stack?

12. It took Pat $4\frac{1}{2}$ h to drive 270 km.

a. Find her average speed in kilometres per hour.

b. At that speed, how far can she drive in $8\frac{1}{4}$ h?

13. A house sold for $85 000 three years ago. This year the same house sold for $120 000. What is the % increase over the three years?

14. Mr. Simms borrowed $1350 for 4 months. The interest rate was 12%.

  a. How much was the interest?

  b. What amount did he pay the bank at the end of 4 months?

15. Find the missing number.

  a. 14% of the number is 52.

  b. 120% of the number is 36.

  c. 7% of the number is 49.

16. a. Use compasses and a ruler to construct $\triangle$BOX with BO = 9 cm, OX = 6 cm, and BX = 10 cm.

  b. Construct the right bisector of each side. Extend these lines to meet at a point P.

  c. Centre P, radius PB, draw a circle.

17. Express in scientific notation.

  a. 0.0075   **b.** 0.8351   **c.** 198.52

  d. 0.000 089 **e.** 45 000 000

18. Arrange from least to greatest.

  a. $\frac{3}{8}, -\frac{5}{6}, -\frac{7}{8}, -1\frac{2}{3}$ **b.** −0.1, −1, −0.01

19. Write an expression for the phrase.

  a. 12 added to twice a number

  b. three times a number decreased by 6

  c. the number divided by 6, then reduced by 7

20. Write a mapping rule for the relation. List two other ordered pairs.

  a. (1,1), (2,2), (3,3), (4,4), (5,5)

  b. (0,0), (1,$\frac{1}{3}$), (2,$\frac{2}{3}$), (3,1), (4,1$\frac{1}{3}$)

21. A ship is travelling at 15 km/h.

  a. Make a table of values to show the relation between the time and the distance travelled each hour for 8 h.

  b. Draw a graph of the relation.

  c. Use the graph to find the distance travelled in the time.

  i. 2.5 h   **ii.** 3.5 h   **iii.** 4.5 h

22. Simplify.

  a. $20n + 13n$ **b.** $19a - 12a$

  c. $d + 6d + d$ **d.** $19m - m - m$

  e. $v + g + 2v + 4g$

  f. $16 + 4c - 11 + 8c$

23. Collect the like terms, then evaluate.

  a. $7n + 8n - 10n + 2$, if $n = 2$

  b. $5a + (a + 3) - 4a - 3$, if $a = 6$

  c. $2m + 4p + 6m - 2p$, if $m = -5$ and $p = -2$

24. Solve. Check by substitution.

  a. $3a - 2 = 13$ **b.** $5h + 7 = 42$

  c. $\frac{k}{4} = 9$ **d.** $\frac{c}{3} - 3 = 3$

  e. $\frac{y}{8} + 6 = 8$ **f.** $3m + 4m = 84$

25. Find the value of c to one decimal place.

  a. $c^2 = 8^2 + 15^2$ **b.** $c^2 = 5^2 + 5^2$

  c. $c^2 = 7^2 + 13^2$ **d.** $c^2 = 9^2 + 2^2$

26. Calculate the length of the unknown side to the nearest tenth of a centimetre.

  a.   **b.**   **c.**

5 cm c 12 cm   5 cm   2 cm a 25 cm b 65 cm

Extra Practice

Set 1 (Use after page 7.)

1. Estimate.

   a. $\begin{array}{r} 36\,089 \\ +\,52\,118 \\ \hline \end{array}$ b. $\begin{array}{r} 47\,913 \\ +\,26\,047 \\ \hline \end{array}$ c. $\begin{array}{r} 9\,412 \\ 17\,108 \\ +\,28\,412 \\ \hline \end{array}$ d. $\begin{array}{r} 103\,218 \\ -\,58\,865 \\ \hline \end{array}$ e. $\begin{array}{r} 68\,458 \\ -\,9\,536 \\ \hline \end{array}$

2. Evaluate.

   a. $841 + 916$ b. $1096 + 538$ c. $7177 - 3065$ d. $4482 - 625$

   e. $1906 + 4135 + 8177$ f. $10\,405 - 8991$ g. $21\,412 + 61\,105 + 8707$

Set 2 (Use after page 11.)

1. Estimate.

   a. $\begin{array}{r} 937 \\ \times\,48 \\ \hline \end{array}$ b. $\begin{array}{r} 278 \\ \times\,19 \\ \hline \end{array}$ c. $\begin{array}{r} 9412 \\ \times\,27 \\ \hline \end{array}$ d. $31\,\overline{)\,59\,106}$ e. $47\,\overline{)\,346\,812}$

2. Calculate.

   a. 814×74 b. 209×108 c. $16\,\overline{)\,7232}$ d. $21\,\overline{)\,16\,443}$

3. Which numbers are divisible by 2? by 5? by 4? by 8?

   a. $10\,476$ b. 1240 c. $89\,207$ d. $92\,105$ e. $18\,824$ f. $71\,488$

Set 3 (Use after page 13.)

1. Make a factor tree to find the prime factorization.

   a. 50   b. 42   c. 81   d. 90   e. 160   f. 200   g. 270

2. Divide by prime factors to find the prime factorization.

   a. 36   b. 45   c. 56   d. 64   e. 150   f. 220   g. 550

Set 4 (Use after page 19.)

1. Express as a single power. Then evaluate.

   a. $9 \times 9 \times 9$ b. $3 \times 3 \times 3 \times 3$ c. $11 \times 11 \times 11 \times 11 \times 11$

   d. $7^6 \div 7^2$ e. $9^5 \times 9^7$ f. $8^7 \times 8^{12}$ g. $10^5 \times 10^6$ h. $3^{11} \div 3^9$

2. Evaluate.

   a. $\sqrt{64}$ b. $\sqrt{121}$ c. $\sqrt{10\,000}$ d. $\sqrt{7 \times 7 \times 2 \times 2}$ e. $\sqrt{2 \times 2 \times 3 \times 3 \times 6 \times 6}$

Set 5 (Use after page 21.)

1. Find two more terms in the sequence.
   a. 1, 5, 25, 125
   b. 3, 9, 27, 81
   c. 2, 7, 12, 17
   d. 8, 18, 28, 38
   e. 1, 4, 9, 16
   f. 1, 8, 27, 64
   g. 1, 12, 123, 1234
   h. 1, 11, 121, 1331

2. a. Copy and complete.

$$1 + 2 + 1 = \blacksquare$$
$$1 + 2 + 3 + 2 + 1 = \blacksquare$$
$$1 + 2 + 3 + 4 + 3 + 2 + 1 = \blacksquare$$

   b. Study the pattern in part **a**. What shortcut can be used to find the sum?
   c. Find this sum. 1 + 2 + 3 + 4 + 5 + 6 + 7 + 8 + 7 + 6 + 5 + 4 + 3 + 2 + 1

Set 6 (Use after page 25.)

1. Evaluate.
   a. $6 \times 4 - 8$
   b. $15 \div 3 + 2$
   c. $1 + 24 \div 4 - 3$
   d. $4^2 - 3 \times 5$
   e. $27 + (8 \times 3 - 3^2)$
   f. $48 \div (16 - 4 \times 2) \times 6 - 6$
   g. $\frac{(5 + 8) \times 4 - 2^5}{12 + 0 \times 3 - 2}$

2. Copy. Use parentheses, if necessary, to make a true statement.
   a. $16 - 12 \times 5 = 20$
   b. $48 \div 16 + 8 = 2$
   c. $40 \div 20 - 12 \times 5 = 1$
   d. $38 + 4 - 2 \times 6 = 30$
   e. $4 \times 4 + 3 \div 3 - 2 = 15$
   f. $18 - 15 \div 3 \times 5 + 2^2 = 9$

3. Evaluate mentally.
   a. $36 + 42 + 24$
   b. $83 + 45 - 23$
   c. $6 \times 22 \times 5$
   d. $13 \times 25 \times 4$
   e. 29×16

Set 7 (Use after page 41.)

1. Use > or < to make a true statement.
   a. $5.07 \bigcirc 5.7$
   b. $0.08 \bigcirc 0.07$
   c. $7.92 \bigcirc 8.13$
   d. $5.462 \bigcirc 5.452$
   e. $10.9 \bigcirc 10.08$
   f. $3.2 \bigcirc 3.199$

2. Arrange in order from greatest to least.
   a. 0.123, 0.321, 0.231
   b. 27.372, 30.2, 27.4
   c. 9.7, 90.07, 0.97
   d. 7.2, 7.24, 7.42, 4.72

Set 8 (Use after page 43.)

1. Estimate.

a.	b.	c.	d.	e.
371.95	917.42	1816.4	642.15	2812.8
+ 148.47	+ 339.13	+ 907.13	− 115.06	− 395.17

2. Evaluate.

a.	b.	c.	d.	e.
	0.026			
271.95	0.89	417.42	1.749	275
− 118.47	+ 9.8	− 329.173	+ 17.08	− 2.75

Set 9 (Use after page 45.)

1. Evaluate.

   a. 13.4×10
   13.4×100
   13.4×1000
   $13.4 \times 10\,000$

   b. $13.4 \div 10$
   $13.4 \div 100$
   $13.4 \div 1000$
   $13.4 \div 10\,000$

   c. 13.4×0.1
   13.4×0.01
   13.4×0.001
   13.4×0.0001

   d. $13.4 \div 0.1$
   $13.4 \div 0.01$
   $13.4 \div 0.001$
   $13.4 \div 0.0001$

2. Calculate.

   a. 0.74×0.1 **b.** 1000×0.0504 **c.** $12.5 \div 0.001$ **d.** $0.915 \div 100$

Set 10 (Use after page 51.)

1. Estimate.

   a. $\begin{array}{r} 75.9 \\ \times\, 0.05 \\ \hline \end{array}$ **b.** $\begin{array}{r} 145.31 \\ \times\, 0.04 \\ \hline \end{array}$ **c.** $\begin{array}{r} 7.48 \\ \times\, 0.97 \\ \hline \end{array}$ **d.** 9.7×12.4 **e.** $135.7 \div 2.3$

2. Multiply only if the product is greater than 70.

   a. $\begin{array}{r} 14.7 \\ \times\, 5.6 \\ \hline \end{array}$ **b.** $\begin{array}{r} 22.91 \\ \times\, 1.14 \\ \hline \end{array}$ **c.** $\begin{array}{r} 62.9 \\ \times\, 1.8 \\ \hline \end{array}$ **d.** $\begin{array}{r} 11.23 \\ \times\, 5.12 \\ \hline \end{array}$ **e.** $\begin{array}{r} 745.2 \\ \times\, 0.15 \\ \hline \end{array}$

3. Catie is paid $4.50/h. Find her earnings for the hours of work.

   a. 23 h   **b.** 31 h   **c.** 27.5 h   **d.** 29.5 h   **e.** 35.5 h

---

Set 11 (Use after page 55.)

1. Copy. Then place the decimal point in the quotient.

   a. $587.7 \div 9 = 653$ **b.** $16.555 \div 7 = 2365$ **c.** $1.428 \div 3 = 476$

2. Rewrite with a whole number divisor. Round the quotient to the nearest tenth.

   a. $2.4 \overline{)\, 0.7946}$ **b.** $0.72 \overline{)\, 1.173}$ **c.** $11.6 \overline{)\, 31.8}$ **d.** $2.01 \overline{)\, 112.07}$ **e.** $83.692 \div 2.5$

Set 12 (Use after page 57.)

1. Express in scientific notation.

   a. 9011   **b.** 178 003   **c.** 192.3   **d.** 879.41   **e.** 154 000 000

2. Express in standard form.

   a. 6.3×10^4 **b.** 1.14×10^2 **c.** 9.07×10^5 **d.** 8.007×10^3 **e.** 1.3×10^6

3. Light travels 1 073 600 000 km/h. In scientific notation, how far does it travel in one day?

Set 13 (Use after page 71.)

1. Copy and complete.

   a. 4 m = ☐ cm   **b.** 3 km = ☐ m   **c.** 5 cm = ☐ mm   **d.** 1.9 m = ☐ cm

   e. 2.4 km = ☐ m   **f.** 7.2 cm = ☐ mm   **g.** 14 mm = ☐ cm   **h.** 219 cm = ☐ m

   i. 350 m = ☐ km   **j.** 72.1 m = ☐ km   **k.** 1.2 mm = ☐ cm   **l.** 9.8 cm = ☐ m

---

Set 14 (Use after page 75.)

1. Copy and complete.

	Regular polygon	Length of one side	Number of sides	Perimeter
a.	hexagon	2.4 cm		
b.	pentagon			715 m
c.	square	4 km		
d.	octagon			18.4 cm
e.	decagon	14.6 mm		

2. Find the perimeter of the picture frame.

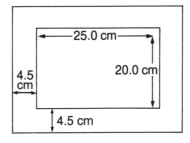

Set 15 (Use after page 77.)

1. What is the circumference of a circular swimming pool with a diameter of 3.6 m?

2. A tennis ball has a diameter of 6 cm. What is its circumference?

3. Find the perimeter of the figure.

   a.

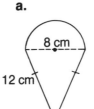

   b.

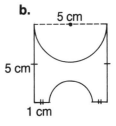

Set 16 (Use after page 79.)

1. Copy and complete the chart for rectangles.

	Base	Height	Area in cm²	Area in m²
a.	17.3 m	200 cm		
b.	25 cm	0.25 m		
c.	11.1 cm	0.29 m		
d.	140 cm	230 cm		

2. A regulation soccer field has a minimum length of 100 m and a maximum length of 130 m. It has a minimum width of 50 m and a maximum width of 100 m.

   a. What is the least possible area of a regulation soccer field?

   b. What is the greatest possible area?

Set 17 (Use after page 87.)

1. Find the area. □ represents 1 cm².

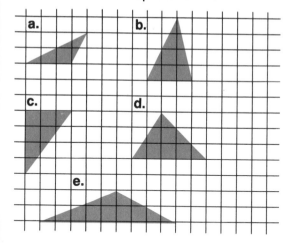

2. Copy and complete the chart for triangles.

	Base	Height	Area
a.	2.5 m	3.2 m	
b.	7.46 cm		37.3 cm²
c.		12.3 cm	104.55 cm²
d.	2 m	2 m	

3. Find the area of the shaded region.

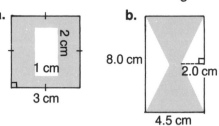

Set 18 (Use after page 89.)

1. Find the area. □ represents 1 cm².

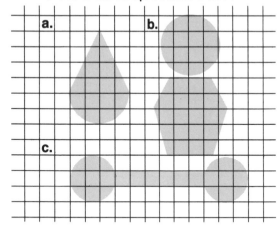

2. Copy and complete the chart for circles.

	Diameter	Radius	Area
a.	2 m		
b.		5 cm	
c.	50 mm		
d.		12 m	

3. Find the area of the shaded region.

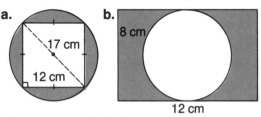

Set 19 (Use after page 91.)

1. Copy and complete.

    a. 200 mm² = ▓ cm²

    b. 0.5 km² = ▓ ha   **c.** 2.5 m² = ▓ cm²

    d. 4 ha = ▓ km²   **e.** 5900 cm² = ▓ m²

2. The length of one side of a square field is 110 m. Find the area of the field.

3. A town covers a rectangular area 10 km by 5 km. Find the area of the town in square metres and in hectares.

Set 20 (Use after page 105.)

1. Match the polyhedron with its net.

a. 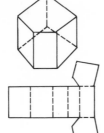   **b.** 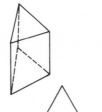   **c.**   **d.**

i.   **ii.**   **iii.**   **iv.**

Set 21 (Use after page 111.)

1. Sketch the faces of the polyhedron. Then find the surface area.

a.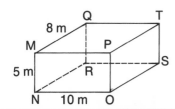

8 m Q T M P S 5 m R N 10 m O

b.

6 cm 4 cm

2. Sketch the surfaces of the cylinder. Then find the surface area to the nearest tenth.

a.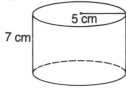

5 cm 7 cm

b.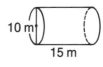

10 m 15 m

Set 22 (Use after page 117.)

1. Find the volume of the prism.

a.

1.0 m 0.4 m 0.7 m

b.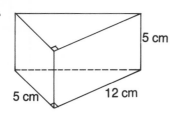

5 cm 5 cm 12 cm

2. Each cube in an ice cube tray has sides of length 2.1 cm. The tray holds 12 cubes. What is the total volume of ice that can be made at one time?

3. Find the volume of the cylinder to the nearest tenth.

FRESH MINTS 1.0 cm 11.2 cm

Set 23 (Use after page 121.)

1. Copy and complete.

	a.	b.	c.	d.
Volume	7500 cm³	▨cm³	▨cm³	▨m³
Capacity	▨L	▨mL	▨mL	3 kL
Mass	▨kg	350 g	2.1 kg	▨t

2. A circular swimming pool has a radius of 2 m. How many litres of water are needed to fill the pool to a depth of 1.2 m?

3. A rectangular water tank is 1.8 m long, 1.5 m wide, and 1.2 m deep. Find the mass of the water that the tank can hold.

415

Set 24 (Use after page 135.)

1. Find all the factors of the number.
   a. 18　　**b.** 30　　**c.** 42　　**d.** 50　　**e.** 64　　**f.** 100　　**g.** 190　　**h.** 225

2. Find the GCF of the pair.
   a. 15, 24　　**b.** 18, 30　　**c.** 21, 36　　**d.** 48, 35　　**e.** 84, 96　　**f.** 30, 105

3. List the first five multiples of the number.
   a. 2　　**b.** 6　　**c.** 7　　**d.** 8　　**e.** 9　　**f.** 10　　**g.** 15

4. Find the LCM of the pair.
   a. 4, 6　　**b.** 5, 7　　**c.** 12, 21　　**d.** 8, 12　　**e.** 4, 14　　**f.** 15, 20

Set 25 (Use after page 137.)

1. Copy and complete.
   a. $\frac{2}{3} = \frac{8}{\square}$　　**b.** $\frac{3}{5} = \frac{\square}{20}$　　**c.** $\frac{24}{3} = \frac{8}{\square}$　　**d.** $\frac{9}{2} = \frac{36}{\square}$　　**e.** $\frac{6}{32} = \frac{\square}{16}$　　**f.** $\frac{15}{9} = \frac{5}{\square}$

2. Express in lowest terms.
   a. $\frac{12}{18}$　　**b.** $\frac{24}{18}$　　**c.** $\frac{35}{45}$　　**d.** $\frac{20}{75}$　　**e.** $\frac{8}{36}$　　**f.** $\frac{16}{20}$　　**g.** $\frac{42}{24}$

3. List two equivalent fractions for the fraction.
   a. $\frac{1}{3}$　　**b.** $\frac{3}{5}$　　**c.** $\frac{4}{1}$　　**d.** $\frac{7}{2}$　　**e.** $\frac{12}{18}$　　**f.** $\frac{24}{9}$　　**g.** $\frac{92}{24}$　　**h.** $\frac{27}{36}$

Set 26 (Use after page 141.)

1. Copy and use >, <, or = to make a true statement.
   a. $\frac{15}{20} \bigcirc \frac{3}{4}$　　**b.** $\frac{5}{8} \bigcirc \frac{9}{16}$　　**c.** $\frac{12}{7} \bigcirc \frac{18}{11}$　　**d.** $\frac{6}{5} \bigcirc \frac{15}{12}$　　**e.** $\frac{5}{6} \bigcirc \frac{20}{24}$

2. Arrange from greatest to least.
   a. $\frac{3}{4}, \frac{2}{3}, \frac{5}{6}$　　**b.** $\frac{5}{8}, \frac{9}{16}, \frac{3}{4}$　　**c.** $\frac{3}{10}, \frac{2}{5}, \frac{9}{20}$　　**d.** $\frac{8}{5}, \frac{7}{4}, \frac{13}{10}$　　**e.** $\frac{9}{4}, \frac{15}{7}, \frac{19}{14}$

3. Find the LCM of the denominators.
   a. $\frac{3}{4}, \frac{5}{16}$　　**b.** $\frac{1}{3}, \frac{2}{9}$　　**c.** $\frac{3}{8}, \frac{2}{5}$　　**d.** $\frac{3}{5}, \frac{1}{7}$　　**e.** $\frac{3}{4}, \frac{5}{6}$　　**f.** $\frac{4}{9}, \frac{5}{6}$

4. Find the result.
   a. $\frac{5}{7} + \frac{1}{7}$　　**b.** $\frac{8}{9} - \frac{4}{9}$　　**c.** $\frac{5}{6} - \frac{2}{3}$　　**d.** $\frac{3}{10} + \frac{1}{6}$　　**e.** $\frac{11}{12} - \frac{3}{4}$　　**f.** $\frac{1}{4} + \frac{1}{2} + \frac{1}{5}$

Set 27 (Use after page 147.)

1. Express as a fraction.

 a. $4\frac{2}{5}$ **b.** $5\frac{2}{3}$ **c.** $7\frac{1}{8}$ **d.** $3\frac{4}{9}$ **e.** $8\frac{3}{5}$ **f.** $1\frac{11}{12}$ **g.** $9\frac{3}{10}$ **h.** $10\frac{8}{9}$

2. Express as a mixed number with the fraction in lowest terms.

 a. $\frac{15}{12}$ **b.** $\frac{24}{9}$ **c.** $\frac{32}{6}$ **d.** $\frac{17}{5}$ **e.** $7\frac{10}{8}$ **f.** $3\frac{16}{6}$ **g.** $5\frac{14}{10}$ **h.** $1\frac{9}{4}$

3. Find the result.

 a. $4\frac{1}{6} + 5\frac{4}{6}$ **b.** $3\frac{3}{4} - 2\frac{1}{2}$ **c.** $5\frac{3}{10} + 3\frac{1}{2}$ **d.** $4\frac{1}{2} + 3\frac{3}{4}$ **e.** $4\frac{7}{12} - 1\frac{2}{3}$

Set 28 (Use after page 149.)

1. Multiply.

 a. $\frac{1}{4} \times \frac{1}{4}$ **b.** $\frac{3}{4} \times \frac{4}{9}$ **c.** $\frac{17}{5} \times 2$ **d.** $\frac{7}{18} \times \frac{9}{2}$ **e.** $\frac{8}{5} \times \frac{5}{8}$

 f. $3\frac{1}{3} \times \frac{3}{10}$ **g.** $4\frac{1}{4} \times 3$ **h.** $2\frac{1}{3} \times 4\frac{1}{2}$ **i.** $3\frac{2}{5} \times 3\frac{1}{3}$ **j.** $4\frac{1}{6} \times 8\frac{2}{5}$

Set 29 (Use after page 151.)

1. Divide.

 a. $\frac{4}{5} \div \frac{7}{3}$ **b.** $\frac{3}{5} \div \frac{9}{10}$ **c.** $1 \div \frac{5}{9}$ **d.** $\frac{2}{3} \div \frac{2}{3}$ **e.** $\frac{11}{5} \div 11$ **f.** $\frac{8}{3} \div 16$

 g. $1\frac{3}{4} \div \frac{1}{4}$ **h.** $5\frac{1}{2} \div \frac{7}{8}$ **i.** $4\frac{1}{2} \div \frac{27}{4}$ **j.** $6\frac{2}{3} \div 7\frac{1}{6}$ **k.** $4\frac{1}{3} \div 8\frac{2}{3}$ **l.** $3\frac{3}{4} \div 4\frac{1}{2}$

Set 30 (Use after page 155.)

1. Express as a decimal.

 a. $\frac{7}{10}$ **b.** $\frac{63}{100}$ **c.** $\frac{7}{8}$ **d.** $\frac{3}{20}$ **e.** $\frac{11}{2}$ **f.** $\frac{31}{40}$ **g.** $\frac{11}{16}$ **h.** $7\frac{3}{5}$

2. Express using bar notation.

 a. $0.444\ldots$ **b.** $0.173\,173\ldots$ **c.** $3.181\,818\ldots$ **d.** $12.0333\ldots$ **e.** $1.972\,727\ldots$

 f. $\frac{5}{6}$ **g.** $\frac{7}{9}$ **h.** $\frac{4}{3}$ **i.** $\frac{5}{11}$ **j.** $\frac{7}{24}$ **k.** $3\frac{1}{6}$ **l.** $8\frac{2}{3}$ **m.** $\frac{11}{9}$

3. Express as a fraction or a mixed number in lowest terms.

 a. 0.12 **b.** 0.125 **c.** $0.\overline{8}$ **d.** $0.8\overline{1}$ **e.** $0.\overline{39}$ **f.** $0.\overline{153}$

 g. $2.1\overline{8}$ **h.** $5.\overline{6}$ **i.** $36.\overline{36}$ **j.** $3.1\overline{5}$ **k.** $1.0\overline{9}$ **l.** $4.9\overline{45}$

Set 31 (Use after page 171.)

1. Write two equivalent ratios for the ratio.
   a. 15 to 12 **b.** 4:9 **c.** 1.8:6 **d.** 13:26:39 **e.** 4 to 16 to 20 **f.** $\frac{15}{36}$

2. Express as a ratio in simplest form.
   a. 12 min to 1 h **b.** 450 g to 1 kg **c.** 60¢ to $3 **d.** 1 m to 1 km
   e. 27 mm:54 cm **f.** 45 s:12 min:1 h **g.** 9 d to 3 weeks **h.** 750 mL to 1.5 L

3. Lemonade is made by mixing 3 cans of water with 1 can of frozen concentrate. Copy and complete the table to show equivalent ratios.

concentrate (cans)	1			9	
water (cans)		12	18		36
total solution (cans)					

Set 32 (Use after page 175.)

1. Copy and complete.
   a. $\frac{3}{\square} = \frac{1}{2}$ **b.** $\frac{\square}{8} = \frac{9}{24}$ **c.** $\frac{1}{25} = \frac{\square}{100}$ **d.** $\frac{6}{\square} = \frac{3}{4}$ **e.** $\frac{1.4}{1.6} = \frac{\square}{2.4}$ **f.** $\frac{\square}{1.2} = \frac{1.2}{1.6}$

2. Copy and complete by estimating.
   a. $\frac{11}{5} \doteq \frac{32}{\square}$ **b.** $\frac{13}{7} \doteq \frac{\square}{58}$ **c.** $\frac{7}{8} \doteq \frac{79}{\square}$ **d.** $\frac{5}{12} \doteq \frac{\square}{100}$ **e.** $\frac{21}{16} \doteq \frac{100}{\square}$

3. **a.** Which wheel turns faster? →
   b. Copy and complete the table.

drive wheel	5	10			125		
other wheel	8		32	96		240	1000

Set 33 (Use after page 179.)

1. Express as a unit rate.
   a. 350 km travelled in 7 h **b.** 30 beats in 25 s **c.** 260 words typed in 5 min

2. A plane flies 850 km/h. How far does it fly in the time?
   a. 3 h **b.** 5 h **c.** $\frac{1}{2}$ h **d.** 1.5 h **e.** 4 h **f.** 6 h

3. Wally earns $196 for working 20 h.
   a. What is his hourly rate of pay? **b.** How much would he earn for working 40 h?
   c. How many hours would he have to work to earn $279.30?

Set 34 (Use after page 181.)

1. Find the unit price to the nearest cent.
   a. $3.95 for 12 apples
   b. $6.99 for 24 cans of juice
   c. $54.75 for 4 tickets

2. Two brands of chicken pot pies are on sale. Brand X sells at 5 for $2.25 and Brand Y at 6 for $2.99. Which is the better buy? What assumptions are you making?

Set 35 (Use after page 185.)

1. Express the scale as a ratio.
   a. 1 cm to 1 km
   b. 1 cm to 1 mm
   c. 1 mm to 20 m
   d. 1 cm to 15 m
   e. 1 cm to 30 km

2. Use the scale 1 cm to 50 m to find the height of a scale drawing of the building.

Building	Approximate height (m)
Fenwick Towers (Halifax, N.S.)	90
Place Victoria (Montréal, Que.)	190
Vancouver Square (Vancouver, B.C.)	180

Set 36 (Use after page 203.)

1. Express the number as a percent.
   a. $\frac{3}{4}$ b. $\frac{3}{5}$ c. $\frac{3}{10}$ d. $\frac{3}{50}$
   e. $\frac{7}{20}$ f. $2\frac{1}{4}$ g. $\frac{347}{1000}$ h. $\frac{81}{300}$

2. What fraction of the diagram is shaded? Express this as a percent.

   a.   b.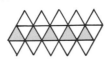

3. Express the percent as a decimal.
   a. 15%   b. 50%   c. 5%
   d. 0.5%   e. 500%   f. $55\frac{1}{2}$%
   g. $24\frac{1}{4}$%   h. $30\frac{1}{2}$%   i. $140\frac{1}{2}$%

4. Express the decimal as a percent.
   a. 0.71   b. 0.02   c. 0.002   d. 0.2
   e. 0.375   f. 0.99   g. 3.15   h. 1
   i. 100   j. 0.1   k. 0.333   l. 0.6

5. Copy and complete.

	Fraction	Decimal	Percent
a.		0.01	
b.			10%
c.			25%
d.			37.5%
e.	$\frac{15}{25}$		
f.		0.65	
g.	$\frac{21}{50}$		
h.	$\frac{4}{5}$		
i.		1.3	

Set 37 (Use after page 209.)

1. Estimate.
   a. 25% of 202   b. 20% of 300
   c. 1% of 78.5   d. $37\frac{1}{2}$% of 160
   e. 15% of 620   f. 107% of 923
   g. 0.5% of 250   h. 60% of 5.4

2. Calculate the percents in exercise 1.

3. If 562 000 000 000 barrels of oil were produced in Canada, how many barrels would come from Saskatchewan or Alberta?

Canadian Oil Sources

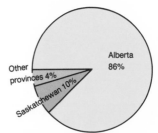

Set 38 (Use after page 213.)

1. Express the fraction as a decimal, then as a percent.

   a. $\frac{7}{8}$ **b.** $\frac{9}{4}$ **c.** $\frac{17}{20}$ **d.** $\frac{18}{16}$ **e.** $1\frac{3}{8}$

2. Express the fraction as a decimal to the nearest thousandth. Then express the decimal as a percent.

   a. $\frac{4}{11}$ **b.** $\frac{5}{7}$ **c.** $\frac{4}{15}$ **d.** $1\frac{5}{16}$ **e.** $\frac{7}{11}$

3. Find the percent.

   a. What percent of 1 h is 12 min?
   b. What percent is 200 g of 400 g?
   c. What percent of $1 is 65¢?
   d. What percent of 1 km is 1 m?
   e. What percent of 1 L is 300 mL?

4. Copy and complete. Check each answer.

   a. 20% of a number is 13.
   1% of the number is △.
   100% of the number is ▣

   b. 125% of a number is 115.
   1% of the number is △.
   100% of the number is ▣

5. Decide if the missing number is greater or less than the given number. Find the missing number, then check the answer.

   a. 15% of a number is 102.
   b. 110% of a number is 550.
   c. 1% of a number is 6.
   d. 256 is 16% of a number.
   e. 200% of a number is 1024.

Set 39 (Use after page 219.)

1. A store is having a 10% off sale on everything in the store. Find the sale price.

   a. jeans, regular price $25.00
   b. shorts, regular price $16.95
   c. tennis shirt, regular price $13.00
   d. running shoes, regular price $19.95

2. Melissa bought a calculator that cost $25. Her bill was $26.50. How much was the sales tax? Express this as a percent.

3. Calculate the simple interest on this deposit.

   a. $500 at 12% for 1 a
   b. $2500 at 18% for 6 months

Set 40 (Use after page 237.)

1. Name.

   a. parallel lines
   b. perpendicular lines
   c. a right angle
   d. an obtuse angle
   e. an acute angle
   f. a straight angle

2. Classify the angle.

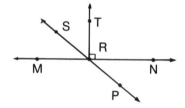

   a. ∠PRM **b.** ∠TRN **c.** ∠SRM
   d. ∠SRT **e.** ∠PRN **f.** ∠SRN

Set 41 (Use after page 241.)

1. What is the measure of the complementary angle for this angle?

   a. 10°   **b.** 22°   **c.** 48°   **d.** 79°

2. What is the measure of the supplementary angle for this angle?

   a. 10°   **b.** 40°   **c.** 110°   **d.** 130°

3. Name.

   a. alternate interior angles

   b. co-interior angles

   c. corresponding angles

4. Calculate the unknown angle measures.

   a.   **b.**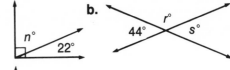

   c.   **d.**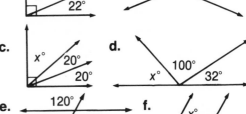

   e. 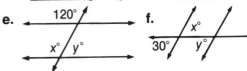   **f.**

Set 42 (Use after page 243.)

1. Classify the triangle in two ways.

   a.   **b.**

   c.   **d.**

      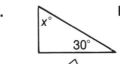

2. Calculate the unknown angle measure.

   a.   **b.**

   c.   **d.**

   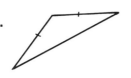

   e.   **f.**

Set 43 (Use after page 245.)

1. Classify the quadrilateral.

   a.   **b.**   **c.**

   d.   **e.**   **f.**

   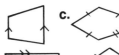

2. What quadrilateral has the property?

   a. four equal sides   **b.** one right angle

   c. opposite sides equal and parallel

   d. exactly one pair of parallel sides

   e. four equal sides and a right angle

3. Calculate the unknown angle measures.

   a.   **b.**

      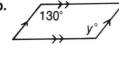

   c.   **d.**

      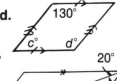

   e.   **f.**

      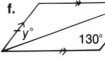

Set 44 (Use after page 251.)

1. Use compasses and a straightedge to construct the line segment.

   a. congruent to AB   A ——————— B

   b. twice the length of AB

   c. three times the length of AB

2. Use a protractor to draw the angles.

   a. 30°   **b.** 50°   **c.** 80°   **d.** 150°

3. Use compasses and a straightedge to copy each angle from exercise 2.

4. Construct an angle congruent to ∠MON.

   a. using a protractor

   b. using compasses and a straightedge

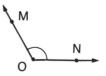

Set 45 (Use after page 253.)

1. List the three matching parts for the pair of triangles. Then write the congruence statement using SSS, SAS, or ASA.

   a.

   b.

   c.

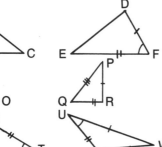

2. Use compasses and a straightedge to construct a triangle with sides the length of *r*, *s*, and *t*.

   r ——————

   s ——————————

   t ————————————

3. Use compasses, a ruler, and a protractor to construct this triangle.

   a. △CAT, CA = 7 cm, ∠ACT = 50°, and ∠CAT = 70°

   b. △MUD, MU = 5 cm, MD = 6 cm, and ∠UMD = 110°

Set 46 (Use after page 255.)

1. **a.** Use a protractor to draw the angle.

   i. 20°   **ii.** 120°   **iii.** 90°   **iv.** 57°

   b. Bisect each angle.

2. Copy line segment AB. Then divide it into four congruent segments.

   A ——————————————— B

3. **a.** Use compasses and a straightedge to construct △ABC.

   b. Construct the perpendicular bisector of each side of the triangle.

   c. Extend the bisectors to meet at D.

   d. With centre D, radius DA, draw a circle.

Set 47 (Use after page 261.)

1. Use compasses and a ruler to construct the figure.

   a. parallelogram, sides 5 cm and 3 cm   **b.** square, sides 6 cm

Set 48 (Use after page 277.)

1. Copy and use > or < to make a true statement.

   a. +7 ◯ −7   **b.** 0 ◯ −5   **c.** −8 ◯ −3   **d.** −2 ◯ −9   **e.** +3 ◯ +9

   f. −8 ◯ +8   **g.** −5 ◯ +10   **h.** −1 ◯ −3   **i.** −4 ◯ +11   **j.** +6 ◯ 0

2. Arrange from least to greatest.

   a. +4, −1, +2, −6, 0, +8, −7   **b.** −2, −8, +3, −5, −12. +10   **c.** −4, +3, −5, 0, +6, −6

Set 49 (Use after page 281.)

1. Evaluate.

   a. (+7) + (−5) + (−12)   **b.** (−8) + (−7) + (+6)   **c.** (+9) + (+11) + (−12)

   d. (−7) + (−4) + (+6) + (+5)   **e.** (−6) + (+3) + (+5) + (−4)   **f.** (+2) + (−3) + (−1) + (+9)

Set 50 (Use after page 283.)

1. Write the opposite integer.

   a. −7   **b.** +9   **c.** −11   **d.** −4   **e.** +15   **f.** 12   **g.** 17   **h.** 0

2. Copy and complete.

   a. (−4) − (−2) = (−4) + ▢   **b.** (+9) − (−2) = (+9) + ▢   **c.** (−3) − (+7) = (−3) + ▢

   d. (+6) − (+11) = (+6) + ▢   **e.** (−11) − (−14) = (−11) + ▢   **f.** (+2) − (−8) = (+2) + ▢

3. Evaluate.

   a. (+8) − (−2)   **b.** (+11) − (−15)   **c.** (−8) − (−3)   **d.** (+5) − (+9)   **e.** (−2) − (+8)

Set 51 (Use after page 289.)

1. Is the product positive or negative?

   a. +11 × (+2)   **b.** 8 × 7   **c.** −8 × (+2)   **d.** +7 × (−8)   **e.** −4 × (−3)

2. Find the quotient.

   a. −12 ÷ (−3)   **b.** +9 ÷ (−9)   **c.** −42 ÷ (+7)   **d.** +40 ÷ (+10)   **e.** −18 ÷ (−18)

   f. +15 ÷ (−5)   **g.** −100 ÷ (+4)   **h.** −21 ÷ (−7)   **i.** $\frac{0}{-5}$ **j.** $\frac{-16}{+8}$

Set 52 (Use after page 291.)

1. Evaluate.

   a. −7 × (−8) ÷ (+2)   **b.** +4 × (−9) + (−1)   **c.** −36 ÷ (−9) × (+3)   **d.** [(+9) − (−3)] ÷ (−6)

   e. (+5) × (−6) + (+5) × (+6)   **f.** (−4) × (+4) − (−4) × (+5)   **g.** (+4) × (−1) − (+4) × (−3)

   h. $(-2)^3$ + (−12) ÷ (−6)   **i.** $[(-4)^2 ÷ (-8)] ÷ (-4)$ **j.** $[(-3)^3 − (-2)] ÷ (+5)$

423

Set 53 (Use after page 293.)

1. Express in scientific notation.
   a. 0.000 000 915   **b.** 0.0093   **c.** 8.15   **d.** 0.875   **e.** 19 142

2. Express in standard form.
   a. 1.42×10^{-2} **b.** 2.07×10^{-1} **c.** 3.99×10^{-4} **d.** 1.6×10^{-5} **e.** 9.05×10^{0}

Set 54 (Use after page 295.)

1. Copy and use > or < to make a true statement.
   a. $-\frac{2}{3} \bigcirc \frac{3}{2}$ **b.** $-\frac{2}{7} \bigcirc -\frac{5}{7}$ **c.** $0 \bigcirc -\frac{3}{4}$ **d.** $-7.5 \bigcirc -5.2$ **e.** $-0.5 \bigcirc -5$

2. Express as the quotient of two integers.
   a. 0.3   **b.** $0.\overline{3}$ **c.** $1\frac{7}{8}$ **d.** $-0.\overline{2}$ **e.** 1.7   **f.** $0.\overline{55}$ **g.** -0.75

3. Arrange from least to greatest.
   a. $\frac{3}{4}, -0.5, 1.1$ **b.** $-2\frac{1}{5}, -2.3, -\frac{21}{10}$ **c.** $-\frac{7}{8}, -1\frac{1}{7}, 0.4, -2.\overline{2}$

Set 55 (Use with Chapter 10.)

1.

Name	Age (a)	Height (cm)
Kevin	11	140
Michelle	8	115
Paul	9	145
Mark	6	118
Troy	7	120

   a. Write a rule that describes the relation (Kevin, Paul), (Michelle, Mark), (Paul, Troy), (Michelle, Troy). List two other ordered pairs for this relation.

   b. Write a rule that describes the relation (Kevin, Paul), (Mark, Troy), (Michelle, Kevin), (Mark, Paul). List two other ordered pairs for this relation.

2. Write a rule for the relation. Then list four other ordered pairs.
   a. (4, 12), (5, 15), (7, 21), (0, 0)
   b. (1, 1), (2, 8), (3, 27), (4, 64)

3. Copy and complete the table. Write a rule.

   a.

0	0
4	
5	1
7	1.4
20	4
	18

   b.

1	4
3	10
7	22
	28
	40
15	

4. **a.** A train travelled 840 km from Calgary to Vancouver at an average speed of 120 km/h. Copy and complete the table to show its progress.

Time (h)	Distance (km)	Ordered pair
0	0	(0, 0)
1	120	(1, 120)
2		

   b. Draw a graph of the relation.

Set 56 (Use after page 343.)

1. Write an expression for the phrase.
   a. 27 less than a number
   b. the sum of 27 and the square of a number

2. Translate the expression into words.
   a. $a + 5$ b. $9 - a$ c. $\frac{a}{6}$ d. $5 \times (a - 7)$ e. $3a + 8$ f. $\frac{a}{2} - 11$

Set 57 (Use after page 347.)

1. Evaluate $3n + 5$ for these values of n.
   a. 2   b. 8   c. 10   d. $\frac{1}{3}$ e. $\frac{2}{3}$ f. 7.8   g. -2

2. Evaluate the expression if $m = 4$.
   a. $12m$ b. $0.25m$ c. $47 - 3m$ d. $\frac{m}{2} - \frac{1}{4}$ e. $m^2 + 2m - 1$

3. Simplify.
   a. $3m + 8m$ b. $12a - 3a$ c. $6x + 5x - 3x - 4x$ d. $2m + 3a + m + a$

4. Collect the like terms. Then evaluate.
   a. $5a + 2 + 3a$, if $a = 11$ b. $6t + 15 + 3t - 4$, if $t = 2$ c. $8r - 3r - 2r$, if $r = 0.9$

Set 58 (Use after page 349.)

1. Is the given value the solution of the equation?
   a. $x + 17 = 29, x = 12$ b. $m - 4 = 35, m = 31$ c. $3a = 33, a = 11$

2. Express as an equation, then solve.
   a. The sum of a number and 6 is 19.
   b. A number decreased by 7 is 24.
   c. The product of 3 and a number is 84.
   d. A number divided by 6 is 13.

Set 59 (Use after page 351.)

1. Copy and complete. Solve the equation.

   a. $2a + 1 = 75$

a	$2a + 1$
30	
35	
40	

   b. $48 - 3c = 21$

c	$48 - 3c$
5	
7	
10	

2. Express as an equation, then solve.
   a. Twice a number, decreased by 1 is 13.
   b. Three times a number divided by 2 is 18.
   c. Eight times a number increased by 13 is 48.
   d. Two less than a number divided by 3 is 25.

425

Set 60 (Use after page 357.)

1. Solve. Check by substitution.

   a. $m + 7 = 33$ 　　 **b.** $n - 22 = 5$ 　　 **c.** $15a = 60$ 　　 **d.** $n - 19 = 11.3$

   e. $\frac{b}{11} = 6$ 　　 **f.** $3.9 = m - 5.7$ 　　 **g.** $\frac{r}{7} = 5.7$ 　　 **h.** $\frac{t}{6} = \frac{5}{2}$

2. Express as an equation, then solve.

   a. A number less 3.9 is 2.8. 　　 **b.** A number divided by 22 is 9.

   c. Twice a number increased by three times the number is 105.

Set 61 (Use after page 359.)

1. Solve. Check by substitution.

   a. $7a + 2 = 51$ 　　 **b.** $4t - 9 = 39$ 　　 **c.** $5m - 8 = 52$ 　　 **d.** $3x + 4.3 = 19.6$

   e. $\frac{b}{3} + 8 = 37$ 　　 **f.** $\frac{x}{2} - 7 = 42$ 　　 **g.** $\frac{b}{10} - 9.6 = 1.8$ 　　 **h.** $\frac{c}{9} + 11.2 = 11.2$

2. Express as an equation, then solve.

   a. Four times a number less 3 is 57. 　　 **b.** Six less than 5 times a number is 19.

   c. A number divided by 4, then increased by 8 gives 24.

Set 62 (Use after page 361.)

1. State the length of the hypotenuse.

   a. 　　 **b.** 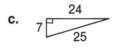 　　 **c.** 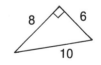 　　 **d.**

2. Calculate the length of the unknown side to the nearest tenth of a metre.

   a. 　　 **b.** 　　 **c.** 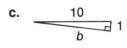 　　 **d.**

Set 63 (Use after page 363.)

1. Solve. Graph the solutions using whole numbers.

   a. $a + 7 \le 12$ 　　 **b.** $m - 11 < 2$ 　　 **c.** $\frac{b}{3} \ge 5$ 　　 **d.** $3c > 27$ 　　 **e.** $2b - 8 > 32$

2. Express as an inequation, then solve.

   a. The sum of 8 and a number is less than or equal to 21. 　　 **b.** A number reduced by 5 is greater than or equal to 12.

Set 64 (Use after page 385.)

1. Draw the translation arrow on grid paper for the vector.

   a. $(4, \vec{1})$ **b.** $(-1, \vec{-4})$ **c.** $(-4, \vec{1})$

   d. $(4, \vec{-1})$ **e.** $(-1, \vec{0})$ **f.** $(0, \vec{4})$

2. Copy the figures onto grid paper. Draw the translation arrow, then write the vector that describes the translation of the black figure onto its red image.

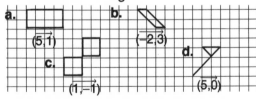

3. Copy the diagram onto grid paper. Draw the translation image.

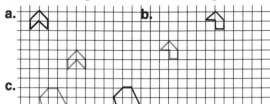

4. Copy the figures onto grid paper. Draw the reflection line.

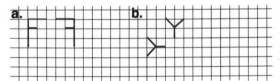

5. Copy the diagram onto grid paper. Draw the reflection image. Label the points.

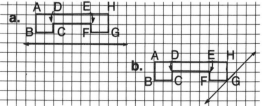

6. Copy the figures onto grid paper. Draw the translation arrow or the reflection line that maps the black figure onto its red image.

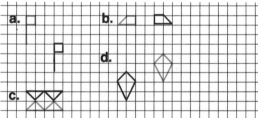

Set 65 (Use after page 391.)

1. Copy the figures onto grid paper. Draw and name the rotation angle.

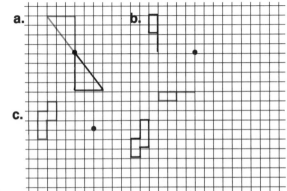

2. Copy the diagram onto grid paper. Draw the image for the rotation angle with centre A.

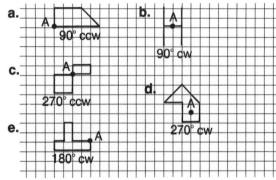

Set 66 (Use after page 395.)

1. Use tracing paper. Fold and find the number of lines of symmetry.

   a.   **b.**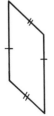

   c.    **d.**

2. Use tracing paper. Find the order of rotational symmetry of the figure.

   a.   **b.**

3. Trace the logo. Draw any lines of symmetry and give the order of rotational symmetry.

   a.   **b.**   **c.**

Set 67 (Use after page 399.)

1. Are the figures similar?

   a.

   b. Aa   **c.**

   d.   **e.**

   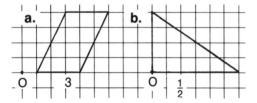

2. Similar figures can be drawn on grids of different sizes. Find the scale ratio of these figures.

   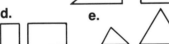

3. Copy the diagram onto grid paper. Draw the image about the centre for the scale factor.

4. Write the scale factor for the dilatation.

   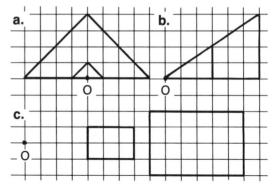

5. Draw coordinate axes on grid paper.

   a. Draw and label a rectangle with coordinates A(2, 1), B(7, 1), C(7, –2), D(2, –2).

   b. Multiply each coordinate value by 2. Give the new coordinates and name them A′, B′, C′, and D′. Plot these points and draw the image, figure A′B′C′D′.

   c. Find the scale factor of the enlargement about the centre (0, 0).

428

Glossary

Acute angle: an angle whose measure is greater than 0° but less than 90°.

Acute-angled triangle: a triangle whose angles are all acute angles.

Addition: 9 + 13 + 7 = 29

addends   sum

Adjacent angles: angles that share a common vertex and a common ray.

Alternate interior angles: angles a, d or b, c

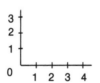

Altitude (of a triangle): the perpendicular distance from a vertex to the opposite side.

Angle: two rays with the same end point.

Area: the number of unit squares needed to cover a region.

Associative property of addition: When three or more numbers are added, the operations can be performed in any order.
$$(5 + 7) + 12 = 5 + (7 + 12)$$

Associative property of multiplication: When three or more numbers are multiplied, the operations can be performed in any order. $(9 \times 6) \times 2 = 9 \times (6 \times 2)$

Axis (plural, **axes**): either of the intersecting number lines of a graph.   Y-axis or vertical axis

X-axis or horizontal axis

Bar graph: a diagram consisting of bars that represent data.

Base (for a power): the number being multiplied by itself in a power. 2^5 ⟵ base

Base (of a polygon): any side.

Bisect: to separate a geometric figure into two congruent parts.

Bisector: the line that separates a geometric figure into two congruent parts.

Broken-line graph: a graph formed by line segments that join points representing data.

Capacity: the amount a container can hold.

Centre (of a circle or sphere): the point that is the same distance from all the points of a circle or sphere.

Chord (of a circle): a line segment with both end points on a circle.

Circle: a closed curve all of whose points are the same distance from one point, the centre.

Circle graph: a graph in which a circle represents a whole, and portions of the circle represent parts of the whole.

Circumference: the distance around a circle.

Co-interior angles: angles a, c or b, d

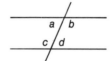

Commission: an amount of money paid by an employer to a salesperson for making a sale. It is often stated as a percent of the selling price.

Common denominator: a common multiple of two or more denominators. A common denominator for $\frac{1}{6}$ and $\frac{1}{4}$ is 12.

Common factor: a number that is a factor of two or more numbers. A common factor of 6 and 18 is 3.

Common multiple: a number that is a multiple of two or more numbers. A common multiple of 2 and 3 is 18.

Commutative property of addition: Two numbers can be added in either order. $8 + 7 = 7 + 8$

Commutative property of multiplication: Two numbers can be multiplied in either order. $5 \times 9 = 9 \times 5$

Compasses (pair of): an instrument used for drawing circles and arcs.

Complementary angles: two angles the sum of whose measures is 90°.

Composite number: a whole number with more than two factors.

Congruent: equal in every respect. Geometric figures such as lines, angles, polygons, that have the same size and shape.

Contained angle: in a triangle the angle between two designated sides.

Contained side: in a triangle the side between two designated angles.

Coordinates: the two numbers in an ordered pair that locates a point on a grid.

Corresponding angles:

angles a, e or b, f or c, g or d, h

$$\frac{a\,/\,b}{c\,/\,d}$$
$$\frac{e\,/\,f}{g\,/\,h}$$

Cube: a polyhedron with six faces, each a square; a regular hexahedron.

Cylinder: a three-dimensional figure having two parallel, congruent, circular faces.

Data: facts or information.

Decagon: a polygon with ten sides.

Decahedron: a polyhedron with ten faces.

Decimal: Numerals such as 0.125, 1.25, and 12.5 are decimals. From the decimal point, places to the left show ones, tens, hundreds, thousands, and so on. Places to the right show tenths, hundredths, thousandths, and so on.

Degree (of an angle): a unit of angle measure.

Degree (of temperature): a unit for measuring temperature. One degree Celsius (1°C) is one-hundredth of the difference in temperature between the boiling point and the freezing point of water.

Denominator: the bottom number in the fraction form of a numeral.
$\frac{3}{4}$ ⟵ denominator

Diagonal of a polygon: a line segment that joins vertices of a polygon, but is not a side.

Diameter: the distance across a circle, measured through the centre; *also*, a line segment having end points on a circle and containing the centre.

Digit: any of the individual symbols used to write numerals. In the base-ten system, the digits are 0, 1, 2, 3, 4, 5, 6, 7, 8, and 9.

Dilatation: a transformation that matches points in two similar shapes like this.

Discount: an amount by which a price is reduced. It is often stated as a fraction or a percent of the price.

Distributive property: A product can be written as the sum of two products. $5 \times (6 + 3) = (5 \times 6) + (5 \times 3)$

Divisible: A number is divisible by another number if dividing by that number gives a remainder of zero.

Division:

$$\begin{array}{r} 9 \leftarrow \text{quotient} \\ \text{divisor} \longrightarrow 5\,\overline{)\,48} \leftarrow \text{dividend} \\ \underline{45} \\ 3 \leftarrow \text{remainder} \end{array}$$

Dodecagon: a polygon with twelve sides.

Dodecahedron: a polyhedron with twelve faces.

Edge: the line segment where two faces of a three-dimensional figure meet.

End point: the point at the end of a line segment or ray.

Equation: a mathematical sentence that uses the symbol =.
$$17 + 2 - 11 = 8$$

Equiangular triangle: a triangle with three congruent angles.

Equilateral triangle: a triangle with three congruent sides.

Equivalent decimals: decimals that name the same number.
6.1, 6.10, 6.100 are equivalent decimals,
but 6.1 is precise to the tenths place,
6.10 is precise to the hundredths place,
6.100 is precise to the thousandths place.

Equivalent fractions: fractions that name the same number.
$\frac{1}{2}$, $\frac{2}{4}$, and $\frac{3}{6}$ are equivalent fractions.

Equivalent ratios: ratios that have the same simplest form ratio.
$\frac{4}{6}$ and $\frac{6}{9}$ are equivalent ratios.

Estimate (noun): an approximation that results from using rounded numbers in a computation; *also*, a reasonable guess of a measurement.

Estimate (verb): to make an estimate.

Even number: a whole number having 2 as a factor.

Expanded form: a form of a numeral written as the sum of products. Each product shows a digit of the numeral times its place value. The expanded form for 7856 is
$(7 \times 1000) + (8 \times 100) + (5 \times 10) + (6 \times 1)$ or
$(7 \times 10^3) + (8 \times 10^2) + (5 \times 10^1) + (6 \times 1)$.

Exponent: a number showing how many times another number is used as a factor.
2^5 ⟵ exponent

Expression: a combination of numerals, variables, and other mathematical symbols. $9, 5 \times 4, 6g, r + 5$

Face: a flat surface of a three-dimensional figure.

Factor (noun): a number used in a multiplication (*see* Multiplication); *also*, for a given whole number, a factor is a whole number that can be multiplied by another whole number to yield the given number. 3 is a factor of 24.

Factor (verb): to express a whole number as a product of its factors.

Factor tree: a diagram used to find the prime factors of a number.

Flow chart: a diagram that shows a sequence of events or instructions.

Fraction: Numerals such as $\frac{2}{3}$, $\frac{2}{2}$, and $\frac{6}{4}$ are fractions. A fraction may represent part of a whole, part of a set, a ratio, or a division.

Frequency: the number of times something occurs.

Graph: a display of data or a relationship.

Greater than (>): describes a relation between two numbers that are not equal. $6 > 4$

Greatest common factor, GCF: the greatest factor common to two or more numbers. GCF of 8, 12, and 24 is 4.

Grid: a pattern of lines or dots.

Height: *see* Altitude

Heptagon: a polygon with seven sides.

Heptahedron: a polyhedron with seven faces.

Hexagon: a polygon with six sides.

Hexahedron: a polyhedron with six faces.

Histogram: a diagram consisting of bars that display the distribution of data.

Horizontal: parallel to the ground; perpendicular to something vertical.

Hypotenuse: the side opposite the right angle in a right-angled triangle.

Icosahedron: a polyhedron with twenty faces.

Image: the figure that results from a transformation.

Improper fraction: a fraction whose numerator is greater than or equal to the denominator. $\frac{9}{5}$, $\frac{6}{6}$

Inequation: a mathematical sentence that uses the symbol $>, <, \geqslant$, or $\leqslant$. $9 > 5$

Integer: Any of the numbers $\ldots, -3, -2, -1, 0, 1, 2, 3, \ldots$

Interest: money paid for the use of money. It is often stated as a percent of the money used.

Intersecting lines: lines with exactly one point in common.

Intersection: the one point common to intersecting lines.

Inverse operations: $+$ and $-$ are inverse operations. $\times$ and $\div$ are inverse operations.

Isosceles trapezoid: a trapezoid with nonparallel sides congruent.

Isosceles triangle: a triangle with two congruent sides.

Kite: a quadrilateral with no sides parallel and two pairs of congruent sides.

Legend (for pictograph): a statement showing the number of units represented by each pictograph symbol.

Less than (<): describes a relation between two numbers that are not equal. $4 < 6$

Line: the set of points in a straight path that continues without end in both directions.

Line graph: a graph formed by a line that contains points representing data.

Line of symmetry: a line that divides a figure into two congruent parts that are reflection images of each other.

line of symmetry

Line segment: a part of a line. It has two end points.

Lowest common denominator, LCD: the lowest common multiple of the denominators of two or more fractions. The lowest common denominator of $\frac{3}{4}$ and $\frac{5}{6}$ is 12.

Lowest common multiple, LCM: the least of the non-zero multiples common to two or more numbers. The lowest common multiple of 4 and 6 is 12.

Lowest-terms fraction: a fraction whose numerator and denominator have no common factor greater than 1.

Mass: the amount of matter in an object.

Mathematical sentence: a combination of numerals, variables, and other mathematical symbols including $=, \neq, <, >, \leqslant$, or $\geqslant$. $3 + 3 = 6, \quad 5 + x < 7, \quad 2 + 6 \neq 9$

Mean: the quotient obtained by dividing the sum of a set of numbers by the number of addends.

Median: the middle value when numbers in a set are arranged in order.

Midpoint: the point that bisects a line segment.

Mixed number: a number greater than 1 expressed as a whole number and a fraction.

Mode: the number that appears most frequently in a set of numbers.

Multiple of a number: the product of that number and a whole number. The multiples of 3 are 0, 3, 6, 9, 12,....

Multiplication: $9 \times 7 = 63$
                                 factors   product

Natural number: any of the numbers 1, 2, 3, 4, 5,....

Negative integer: an integer less than 0.

Net: a pattern for a polyhedron obtained by cutting the polyhedron along some edges and laying it flat.

Nonagon: a polygon with nine sides.

Number line: a line whose points have been matched with a set of numbers.

$$0 \quad 1 \quad 2 \quad 3 \quad 4$$

Numeral: a symbol that represents a number. FIVE, 5, V, 2 + 3; 9 − 4, and ⦀⦀ are numerals.

Numerator: the top number in the fraction form of a numeral.

$$\frac{3}{4} \longleftarrow \text{numerator}$$

Obtuse angle: an angle whose measure is greater than 90° but less than 180°

Obtuse-angled triangle: a triangle that has one obtuse angle.

Octagon: a polygon with eight sides.

Octahedron: a polyhedron with eight faces.

Odd number: a whole number for which 2 is not a factor.

Opposite angles: non-adjacent angles formed by two intersecting lines; *also*, two angles in a quadrilateral that do not share an arm.

Opposite integers: −2 and +2 are opposite integers.

Order of operations: the rules to be followed when evaluating an expression.
Perform operations within parentheses.
Evaluate powers.
Perform multiplications and divisions in order from left to right.
Perform additions and subtractions in order from left to right.

Order of rotational symmetry: the number of times a figure fits onto itself in one full turn.

Ordered pair: a pair for which the order is important. (2,6) and (6,2) are different ordered pairs of numbers.

Origin: the point where the horizontal and vertical axes of a graph meet.

Outcome: a possible result.

Parallel lines: lines in the same plane that do not intersect.

Parallelogram: a quadrilateral with two pairs of parallel sides.

Parentheses: the symbols ( ). When used with operation symbols, parentheses indicate the numbers that are to be combined first.

Pentagon: a polygon with five sides.

Pentahedron: a polyhedron with five faces.

Percent: a ratio that compares an amount to 100.

Perimeter: the distance around a closed figure.

Perpendicular bisector: a line perpendicular to a line segment at its midpoint.

Perpendicular lines: two lines that intersect to form right angles.

π, pi: The Greek letter π often represents the number for the ratio of the circumference of a circle to its diameter. $\pi \doteq 3.14$.

Pictograph: a diagram that uses pictures to display data.

Place value: the value given to the place in which a digit appears in a numeral. In 735, 7 is in the hundreds place, 3 is in the tens place, and 5 is in the ones place.

Plane: a flat surface whose length and width have no limits.

Point: an item that suggests a position. A point has no size and is usually represented by a dot.

Polygon: a closed figure whose sides are line segments.

Polyhedron: a three-dimensional figure with all flat surfaces (faces), each of which has the shape of a polygon.

Positive integers: integers greater than 0.

Power: a product of equal factors.
$3 \times 3 \times 3 \times 3$, or 3^4, or 81, is the fourth power of 3.

Powers of 10: the numbers 10^1, 10^2, 10^3, 10^4,...

Prime factor: a factor that is a prime number.

Prime factorization: the expression of a number as the product of its prime factors.

Prime number: a whole number with exactly two different factors, itself and 1.

Principal: an amount of money on which interest is paid.

Principal square root: The principal square root of 4 is 2 because $2 \times 2 = 4$. $\sqrt{4} = 2$

Prism: a three-dimensional shape with two congruent parallel faces that are polygons.

Probability: a number between 0 and 1, inclusive, that tells how likely it is that a certain event will happen. It is the number of favorable outcomes divided by the number of possible outcomes.

Program: a list of instructions for a computer.

Proper fraction: a fraction whose numerator is less than the denominator.

Proportion: an equation showing that two ratios are equal.

Protractor: an instrument used to measure angles.

Pyramid: a polyhedron having one face a polygon and the other faces all triangles, each of which shares a side with the polygon.

Quadrant: the X-axis and Y-axis divide a plane into four quadrants.

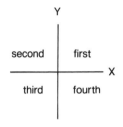

Quadrilateral: a polygon with four sides.

Radius: the distance from the centre of a circle to the circle; *also*, a line segment having the centre for one end point and a point on the circle for the other.

Rate: a comparison of two unlike quantities.
                250 km/2.5 h or 100 km/h

Ratio: a comparison of two like quantities.

Rational number: a number that can be expressed as the quotient of two integers.

Ray: a part of a line. It has one end point and continues without end in one direction.

Reciprocals: two numbers whose product is 1.
4 and $\frac{1}{4}$ are reciprocals. $\frac{3}{2}$ and $\frac{2}{3}$ are reciprocals.

Rectangle: a parallelogram with one right angle.

Reflection: a transformation that matches points in two congruent shapes like this.
reflection line

Reflection image: the figure that results from a reflection. Triangle II is a reflection image of triangle I in the picture above.

Reflection line: a line that defines a reflection. Each point of the shape and its matching point in the image are the same distance from the line but on opposite sides of it.

Reflectional symmetry: a property of a figure that can be divided into two congruent parts that are reflection images of each other.

Regular polygon: a polygon with all sides congruent and all angles congruent.

Regular polyhedron: a polyhedron whose faces are formed by regular congruent polygons.

Repeating decimal: a decimal in which a digit or a group of digits keeps repeating.   0.333...

Rhombus: a parallelogram with four congruent sides.

Right angle: an angle whose measure is 90°.

Right-angled, or right, triangle: a triangle with one right angle.

Rotation: a transformation that matches points in two congruent shapes like this.

rotation centre   rotation angle

Rotation angle: an angle that defines a rotation. Each point of a shape is turned through the same angle about a given point.

Rotation centre: the vertex of a rotation angle.

Rotation image: the figure that results from a rotation. Triangle II is a rotation image of triangle I in the picture above.

Rotational symmetry: property of a shape that fits onto itself after a turn that is less than a full turn.

Rounded number: a number expressed to one of the following: nearest whole number, nearest ten, nearest tenth, nearest hundred, nearest hundredth, and so on. 348 rounded to the nearest ten is 350.

Sales tax: an amount of money paid to a provincial government for goods purchased. It is often stated as a percent of the price of the goods.

Sample: a small group, chosen from a larger group, that is examined in order to make estimates about the larger group.

Scale: the ratio of the distance between two points on a map, model, or diagram to the distance between the actual locations; *also*, the numbers that may be on either axis of a bar or line graph.

Scale drawing: a drawing in which all lengths are the same enlargement or reduction of actual lengths.

Scale factor: the ratio of lengths in an enlargement or reduction to actual lengths.

Scalene triangle: a triangle with no congruent sides.

Scientific notation: a notation for writing a number as a product of a number between 1 and 10 and a power of ten.

Side: a line segment joining two adjacent vertices of a polygon.

Similar figures: figures that have the same shape but not necessarily the same size.

Simplest-form ratio: a ratio using whole numbers that have no common factor greater than 1.

Solid: a three-dimensional figure, whose inside is completely filled.

Solution of equation: a number that gives a true statement when used in place of the variable in an equation.

Solution of inequation: a number that gives a true statement when used in place of the variable in an inequation.

Solve an equation: the process of finding the solution of an equation.

Solve an inequation: the process of finding the solution(s) of an inequation.

Sphere: a three-dimensional figure whose points are all the same distance from one point, the centre.

Square: a rectangle with four congruent sides.

Standard form: the usual form of a numeral. 7856 is in standard form.

Straight angle: an angle whose measure is 180°.

Straightedge: an instrument used for drawing line segments.

Subtraction:

$$12 - 7 = 5$$

minuend   subtrahend   difference

Supplementary angles: two angles the sum of whose measures is 180°.

Surface area: the total area of the outside surface of a three-dimensional shape.

Tally chart: a chart used to record the frequency of an event.

Term: the part of an expression connected by $+$ or $-$. In the expression $5x + 2y$, $5x$ is one term and $2y$ is another. *Also*, in a ratio such as $3:4:5$, 3, 4, and 5 are terms.

Terminating decimal: a decimal with a whole number of decimal places. (*See also* Repeating decimal)   0.25

Tessellation: a tiling pattern made with one shape.

Tetrahedron: a polyhedron with four faces.

Tiling: the process of using congruent shapes to cover a region completely and without overlap.

Tiling pattern: the result of the tiling process.

Translation: a transformation that matches points in two congruent shapes like this.

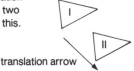

translation arrow

Translation arrow: an arrow that defines a translation. It shows the distance and direction of the translation.

Translation image: the figure that results from a translation. Triangle II is a translation image of triangle I in the picture above.

Transversal: a straight line that intersects two or more lines.

Trapezoid: a quadrilateral with one pair of parallel sides.

Tree diagram: a branching diagram used to show all possible combinations.

Triangle: a polygon with three sides.

Unit: a standard quantity; the metre is a unit of length.

Unit price: the cost of one unit or item. $2.58/kg or 39(¢)/apple.

Unit rate: a rate having 1 in its second term. 90 km/1 h or 90 km/h.

Variable: a letter used to represent an unspecified or unknown number.

Vector: an ordered pair of numbers with an arrow above it. A translation can be described by a vector.

Vertex: the common end point of the two rays of an angle, two sides of a polygon, or three or more edges of a solid.

Vertical: perpendicular to the ground; perpendicular to a horizontal line.

Volume: the amount of space occupied by an object.

Whole number: any of the numbers 0, 1, 2, 3,...

Symbols

+	plus
−	minus
×	times
÷	divided by
=	is equal to, equals
≠	is not equal to
≐	is approximately equal to
>	is greater than
<	is less than
≥	is greater than or equal to
≤	is less than or equal to
π	3.14 (approximately)
. . .	and so on
(1,2)	ordered pair
P′	P prime
:	ratio
%	percent
∠	angle
△	triangle
∟	right angle, perpendicular lines
⋀⋀	parallel lines

Metric Symbols

mm	millimetre	mm^2	square millimetre
cm	centimetre	cm^2	square centimetre
dm	decimetre	m^2	square metre
m	metre	ha	hectare
dam	decametre	km^2	square kilometre
hm	hectometre	mm^3	cubic millimetre
km	kilometre	cm^3	cubic centimetre
		m^3	cubic metre
mL	millilitre	g	gram
L	litre	kg	kilogram
kL	kilolitre	t	tonne
°C	degree Celsius	m/s	metres per second
s	second	km/h	kilometres per hour
min	minute	r/min	revolutions per minute
h	hour	L/min	litres per minute
d	day	W	watt
a	annum or year	kW	kilowatt
		kJ	kilojoule

Table of Related Units

10 mm = 1 cm	10 000 m^2 = 1 ha	60 s = 1 min
10 cm = 1 dm		60 min = 1 h
10 dm = 1 m	1000 mL = 1 L	24 h = 1 d
100 cm = 1 m		7d = 1 week
1000 mm = 1 m	1000 cm^3 = 1 L	365 d = 1 a
10 m = 1 dam	1 cm^3 = 1 mL	52 weeks = 1 a
10 dam = 1 hm		12 months = 1 a
10 hm = 1 km	1000 g = 1 kg	10 a = 1 decade
1000 m = 1 km	1000 kg = 1 t	100 a = 1 century

INDEX

PHOTO CREDITS AND ACKNOWLEDGMENTS
Canapress Photo Service, 24; Fulvio Eccardi/Bruce Coleman Inc., 36; Escher Foundation, Haags Gemeentemuseum, The Hague, 392, 393; Four by Five Photography Inc., 4, 8, 16, 50, 72, 90; F. T. Guthrie and Associates, 288; Dan Hamilton (photo of Randy Samuel), 132; The Image Bank, 20, 52, 62, 70, 240, 340; Jeremy Jones, 10, 157, 168, 188, 198, 200, 206, 216, 223, 224, 232, 234, 249, 272 (photo of Bill Lawrence), 290, 291, 292, 300, 316, 324, 326, 332, 342, 344, 354, 356, 358, 362, 367, 374, 376, 378, 379 (right), 396; Bruce Kemp, 68; Lenscape Incorporated, 63; Masterfile, 178, 306, 325 (bottom); Miller Services Limited, 148, 166, 172, 174, 179, 204, 208, 235, 248, 256, 286, 314, 319, 325 (top); NASA, 54, 56; Ontario Ministry of Agriculture and Food, 402, 403; City of Ottawa, 310; Parks Canada, 78; Brian Pickell, 382, 383 (left); Brian Smale (photo of Dr. Helen Hogg), viii; Toronto Blue Jays, 152; Trustees of the Science Museum (London), 158 (middle); Valan Photos, 350, 394, 395; Harold Whyte Photography, 2, 3, 12, 13, 14, 18, 22, 25, 27, 28, 34, 38, 40, 42, 43, 44, 48, 53, 55, 60, 61, 74, 76, 77, 88, 102, 106, 107, 110, 113, 118, 120, 123, 124, 125, 134, 138, 142, 158 (top), 196, 212, 214, 215, 218, 221, 226, 236, 254, 258, 266, 320, 322, 330, 360, 369, 379 (left, centre), 383 (centre, right), 387, 388, 389. Poster courtesy of Glenn Schulte, © 1983-1984. Verkerke Copyright and Licensing GMBH, 1984, 396.